SCIENCE AND THE FEDERAL PATRON

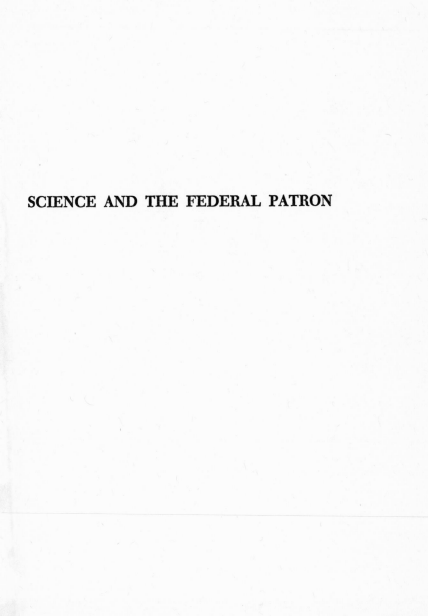

SCIENCE AND THE FEDERAL PATRON

MICHAEL D. REAGAN

NEW YORK
OXFORD UNIVERSITY PRESS
1969

Contents

Acknowledgments

I am grateful for intramural research support provided by the University of California, which made possible the early stages of my work on science and government, and for the substantial support of the Social Science Research Council's Committee on Legal and Governmental Processes, whose grant permitted me the time necessary to write this book.

Professional encouragement is at least as important as funds, and I am happy to express my appreciation for that given me by Dr. Henry David when he was Head of the Office of Science Resources Planning in the National Science Foundation.

An earlier version of some of the material in Chapter 10 appeared as an article in the June, 1967 issue of *Public Administration Review,* and permission to incorporate it is gratefully acknowledged.

I| As Things Are

1 | Science Goes Public

Science is in danger, and so is society—largely because of science and its technological offspring. Never has the public significance of scientific knowledge been greater; yet never has the accessibility of scientific knowledge to the non-scientifically or non-mathematically trained public been less.

"The entire future of a country, not just its military might but its economic strength and welfare," wrote the first Director of the National Science Foundation, the late Dr. Alan T. Waterman, "depend markedly upon its progress in science and technology." [1] One cannot disagree. But neither can one argue with the late Robert Oppenheimer's assertion [2] that

> we so refine what we think, we so change the meaning of words . . . that scientific knowledge today is not an enrichment of the general culture . . . it is not part of the common human understanding. . . .

or with René Dubos's more sharply worded statement that "The world is promised cheap miracles, but no longer participates in the glorious mysteries." [3]

3

It was a schoolboy aphorism of a generation ago that only a few men could understand Einstein's theory of relativity; now it is a truism that an informed, technical understanding of research in *almost any* field of science is beyond the layman— and even beyond scientists themselves who are in other areas of research. In the sense that it is becoming increasingly arcane, mathematical, and abstract, science is today isolated from the rest of society. Mesons, anti-matter, RNA, and DNA —all these and more are mysteries to most of us. Yet we are *more* familiar than previous generations with the *consequences* of modern science. Air and water pollution, biological mutations from radiation or prescription drugs, and The Bomb are intimate companions of our daily life, as are such technological marvels as TV, space probes, computers, jet aircraft, and lasers.

Thus the first paradox of science and society is: the more important it becomes to us, the less we understand it. A second paradox flows from the first: contradictory expectations about the purposes and the workings of science are held by scientists and by the public and its representatives in Washington.

Because of its multiplying uses and consequences, and because we anticipate that in science lie the solutions to many of our problems, if not our very salvation, we are demanding that scientists show us the practical results from their research. We are insisting that the scientific community serve society directly, rather than "merely" satisfy the curiosity of its practitioners concerning the nature of man, his planet, and the universe. Such demands are exemplified by congressional explorations of the research and development (R&D) decision-making process; by calls for special legislative committees or Presidentially appointed commissions on "technology transfer," marine resources, or technology and the urban environment; and by Presidential warnings that expenditures on health research should be matched with attention to improvement of health services.

At the same time, however, scientists are making *their* demands, the sum of which is that society (largely through the Federal Government, as we shall see) support every competent scientist in doing the research that is of greatest scientific interest to him. The scientists rest their case on a variety of grounds, but most strongly on the proposition that undirected scientific research is the investment capital out of which technological applications must emerge; that while the utility of any one piece of research may not be predictable, it is axiomatic that the total effort will pay off in the long run.

An ironic part of this paradox is that this claim arose successfully in the political arena only after World War II, as a kind of cashing in on the practical contributions scientists had made to aircraft, weapons, radar, and The Bomb. Since science had demonstrated dramatically what it could do for government, it became possible to ask that government now do something for science. Not out of altruism, but as insurance that when the bank of scientific discovery had to be drawn upon again, the account would not be overdrawn. The landmark of the scientific community's appeal for public support of research was Vannevar Bush's report to the President, *Science: The Endless Frontier*, which appeared in 1945. Bush, who had directed the war-time Office of Scientific Research and Development, through which the scientists had shown that they could contribute more than the generals and admirals to the technology of war, wrote:

> It has been basic United States policy that Government should foster the opening of new frontiers. It opened the seas to clipper ships and furnished land for pioneers. Although these frontiers have more or less disappeared, the frontier of science remains. . . .

Moreover, since health, well-being, and security are proper concerns of Government, scientific progress is, and must be, of vital interest to Government. Without scientific progress the national health would deteriorate; without scientific progress we could not hope for improvement in our standard of living or for an increased number of jobs for our citizens; and without scientific progress we could not have maintained our liberties against tyranny....

Support of basic research in the public and private colleges, universities, and research institutes must leave the internal control of policy, personnel, and the method and scope of the research to the institutions themselves. This is of the utmost importance.

Because of science's war-time contributions, the Federal Government was persuaded to support undirected research, specifically through the creation of the National Science Foundation, which is directed by statute to "develop . . . a national policy for the promotion of basic research and education in the sciences" and to "initiate and support basic scientific research and programs to strengthen scientific research potential." Yet this was not accomplished without struggles, including, in 1947, Presidential veto of a bill that would have created a science-supporting agency beyond Presidential accountability. When success did come, it was not out of understanding for science, but out of a grudging faith in the assertion that basic research would bring forth more technological miracles. After the Soviets put the first space ship, Sputnik I, in orbit in 1957, funds for science took a sharp upward jump, and by 1963–64 the scientific community seemed to be assuming that a more solid foundation had been laid. A formula was devised that attempted to justify an annual increase of 15 per cent in basic research funds, and some people at least felt betrayed when neither the Bureau of the Budget nor the Congress indicated willingness to accept that formula as an automatic minimum.

What seems to have happened is that just when the scientists had accustomed themselves to ever-increasing support, the total R&D budget (of which basic research accounted for but 10 per cent) broke through the 15-billion-dollar level and the Congress reacted with a rash of investigations into why R&D kept rising, why the funds were not more widely dispersed among the states, and why should it support any specific level of scientific research in any case. Vietnam, poverty, and civil rights pressed more urgently than science on White House attention. The federal budgets for fiscal 1967–68–69 have created renewed alarm among scientists, for the rate of increase in R&D has slowed noticeably (although the Bureau of the Budget points out that the basic research segment has fared better than applied research or development). We are again hearing that society cannot expect to obtain the benefits of technology if the government does not in turn rapidly increase its support of the underlying scientific effort. The number of researchers to be supported, it is pointed out, is increasingly much more rapidly than funds; the costs per researcher are also rising; and discoveries of recent years—in molecular biology, radio astronomy, geology, meteorology, and high-energy physics, to name but a few areas of publicized strength—have opened up opportunities that cry out for further explorations aimed at unlocking the doors of nature. The dialogue between scientists and the government sounds distressingly like that of 1945–50 when the fight for the National Science Foundation was being waged. That this is so suggests that no totally convincing justification for federal support has yet been found. The scientific community's hopes in the early 1960s were premature. The situation this time may be worse, because the agenda of publicly recognized problems of a pressing nature is far longer in 1969 than in 1950, creating far greater competition for federal funds.

With more scientists wanting to pursue more expensive research (a planned, new high-energy physics accelerator will cost $400 million; new radio telescopes may run from $20 to $50 million each) because it is scientifically exciting, at the same time that political leaders are desperately asking that scientific resources (within which the manpower is in even shorter supply than the dollars) be directed on the basis of which problems most urgently require solution, a dangerous tension threatens. The world of science and the world of politics have perhaps never been close, but when their interdependence was less the result could be simply separation rather than tension. The dependence of government programs, both civilian and military, on science needs no elaboration. Perhaps it is less well-known, however, that the dependence is reciprocal, that the Federal Government is now *the* major patron of science, providing two-thirds of all R&D funds expended in the United States in 1968, and 75 per cent of university research. There was a time not so long ago when scientists could be isolated or even alienated from the lay public, and even scoffed at by that public, without having to be greatly concerned. That time is gone: substantively, because one cannot create scientific revolutions without a feeling of responsibility for the social and political consequences; financially, because both scientists and the universities in which they conduct their research are utterly dependent on the federal patron. Today, if political leadership and the scientific community cannot achieve a more rational *modus vivendi* (even though some tension is both inevitable and functional), both science and society will be endangered.

What we know as science dates, as an articulated and institutionalized human activity, from the seventeenth century. In its origins, and until the mid-nineteenth century, science was primarily an avocation, privately supported, and oriented toward practical utilization as much as toward new knowledge in its own right. It is a third paradox of science-society relationships that between 1850 and today science has become professionalized as an occupation rather than a leisure activity, and it is now publicly supported in the United States at a level ($2.3 billion in 1968 for basic research) that taxpayers are likely to think quite generous; yet it has reoriented itself away from utilitarian criteria toward an almost exclusive concern (perhaps more exclusive in rhetoric than in fact) with "science for science's sake."

The scientists may be accurate in asserting that their goals will coincide with the public interest in applications in the long run, but that is not the crucial political fact. The crucial points are that they have not persuaded the public, and that in budgetary politics the short run is generally the winner. The very philosophy of public support is at stake, but only a comparative handful of scientists are active in trying to build the necessary bridges with the rest of society. (In Chapter 2 we will look more closely at the efforts that are being made to supply a convincing rationale for federal patronage.)

The effort to articulate a stable relationship between the interests of science and the interests of government and of the public will be the more difficult because of the heritage of what historian George H. Daniels calls "the pure-science ideal." [4] Perhaps it is akin to free enterprise ideology—the rhetoric of purity becomes greater as the connections with the practical world become in fact stronger. As Daniels sees it, the public defense of science before 1850 exaggerated the usefulness of what scientists did because there was little concrete evidence of utility. By the late nineteenth century, mining technology and the chemical and electrical industries had become dependent on the fruits of science, and Andrew Carnegie admitted that he would rather "lose his buildings and his plants than the services of his scientists." With the utility of science accepted, says Daniels, it became possible for the first time to develop a new ideal for science; science-for-the-sake-of-science could now be safely articulated. (At least, this could work until scientists became almost totally dependent on public funds—but that did not happen until halfway through the next century.)

The accompanying change in the attitude of scientists toward their own role in society is nicely illustrated by Daniels, who quotes Charles Sanders Peirce as explaining that he would not become a professional scientist because a scientist should "be doing that which he most delights to do," but that it would be wrong to pay a man for doing just what he liked. So science was for leisure. Ten years after this, however, in 1869, Benjamin Gould complained that research was the true vocation of the scientist, and he should not have to support himself by other work. Thus science changed from something done largely by amateurs (those doing research not as a livelihood, but for the love of it) into an occupation socially supported, primarily through jobs in private colleges and universities. There was taxpayer support, but only for such projects as geological surveys to locate mineral deposits, astronomical research that would aid navigation for the navy, and agricultural experimentation addressed to specific problem-solving. As the strictly scientific benefits of such work were played out, says Daniels, the scientists increasingly came into conflict with legislators and administrators, for now the scientists wanted support of science *per se*. From that time to this, there has been what Daniels (following Dubos) has called "schizophrenia" in the scientific community

while scientists claim among themselves that their primary interest is in the conceptual aspects of their subject, they

continue to publicly justify basic research by asserting
that it allows leads to "useful" results.

Internal schizophrenia, in turn, has meant conflict in external
relations:

> As long as a group is dependent upon public support it
> must seek some means of contact with the values of the
> enveloping society, and the moment it does this it departs
> in some measure from the ideal purity.

This picture of conflicting interests and ideals, while true,
would be overdrawn if we failed to acknowledge the vast contributions that science has made to the improvement of the
human condition, even if somewhat in spite of its own ideals.
Furthermore, there are counter-currents of some strength, and
these may result in a new synthesis of science with societal
concerns. The objective is not to eliminate the tension, but to
build a tension of understanding and mutual respect between
the scientific and the political communities, to replace one that
consists too much of blind griping and ignorance on both sides.
Paradoxes abound, but they may not all be true contradictions.

FROM PRIVATE TO PUBLIC: THE GROWTH OF SCIENCE

The first reason why the public importance of science has
greatly increased, and why public attention to "science affairs"[5]
should increase proportionately, is the sheer growth of science
as an activity in which men engage their lives. There are some
dramatic expressions of this growth:

> —Of every eight scientists who ever lived, seven are alive
> today.
> —Total R&D expenditures in the United States (public
> and private) approximated $25 billion in 1968, and are

growing at the rate of about one billion annually. In 1940, the figure was less than one-fourth of a billion. The annual expenditure is now more than the total of federal expenditures for science from the Revolutionary War through World War II.

—The first scientific journal, the *Philosophical Transactions* of the Royal Society of London, began publication in 1665. By 1800 there were 100 journals; by 1900, 10,000 journals; today, over 100,000.

No wonder that Derek J. DeSolla Price says: "the growth of science is something very much more active, much vaster in its problems, than any other sort of growth happening in the world today . . . the density of science in our culture is quadrupling during each generation." [6] Price has calculated that a saturation point will have been reached in another generation, that the historic rate of increase in scientific activity will *have to* flatten out. Continuation of the growth rates of the recent past would mean that the R&D budget would exceed the Gross National Product by the end of the century.

It is of course easy for any new phenomenon to show a high percentage rate of growth, if calculation is made from a small base. But science continues at a phenomenal rate even after achieving a large base. Consider this fact: by 1954 there were 237,000 persons counted as R&D personnel (i.e. engaged in professional-level scientific or engineering work); by 1965, this number had grown to 504,000. Put another way, while the labor force as a whole was increasing by 1.5 per cent annually, R&D manpower grew at a 7.1 per cent rate. [7]

We can see just how far science has come by considering that the first professional society of scientists, the Royal Society of London for the Improving of Natural Knowledge, was founded just over 300 years ago in 1662. Arising out of "informal spontaneous gatherings of devotees of experimental science, scholars and amateurs," [8] the Royal Society included businessmen, divines, nobles, scholars, statesmen, potential patrons, and physicians. Some kind of organizational context for scientific activity had then become necessary because the work to be done had outgrown the kitchen as a "laboratory," equipment was becoming too expensive for the non-wealthy scientist to purchase individually, and there was a need for collaborators and assistants. (To the men of the time, this presumably seemed like the equivalent of what is currently being described as the switch from Little Science to Big Science.)

At that time, science was not the discrete, professionalized, specialized activity it has since become. The four-fifths of the original Royal Society membership who were not themselves scientists could share in the discussions and understand the papers read, or at least the meaning of the results. The very word "scientist" did not come into common use until the mid-nineteenth century, and "philosophy" included in its meaning in the early eighteenth century what "science" means today.

The professionalization of science—and in a meaningful way, therefore, the separation of science from society—may be dated in England from 1847, the year in which the Royal Society was reorganized to eliminate from election to membership those who were not actually researchers. As of 1830, only 106 of 662 Fellows had published a paper in the society's journal, and the others were not providing much financial patronage in substitution. The reorganization of 1847 "transformed the Society from an eminent body of men interested in science, containing a minority of research workers, into a body of carefully selected specialists." [9] And specialization increased, too. Only fifteen new members were to be elected each year. With competition intense, one's best chance lay in plowing a narrow field. Interest in the wider aspects of science, including its relations with general society, came to be deprecated in consequence, and in the early part of the twentieth century— as science was really beginning to make an impact on the world around—the Royal Society reached a low point in its attention to the social relations of science.

At the same time there was a shift in the focus of interest from science for social use toward science for science, just as in the United States. In its earlier years, the Royal Society investigated such practical problems as tapestry manufacture, the testing of earth for pottery, the improvement of brewing processes for beer and ale, and the efficient engineering of carriages. Technical knowledge had become a respectable concern with the rise of the commercial and manufacturing bourgeoisie, who had an intense interest in the properties of materials and in product innovations.[10] The movement to cast out the non-scientists from the Royal Society represented a move toward the pure science ideal and away from the conception of science as "useful knowledge."

The growth of science internally, it seems, necessitated a drawing away from practical utilization and from those social aspects of science that, however crucial in human consequences, were peripheral to the pursuit of scientific knowledge *per se*. Growth was not just to be measured in increased numbers, but in changing attitudes. Today, attitudes may be changing again. Just as science had to assert its utility when that was not evident, so now it may be able to make more room for social concern and practical application when its integrity and value as a purely intellectual sphere have been admitted by the supporting public.

The growth of science as such has been sufficient to warrant the assertion that science is now "in the public domain," so to speak. One could not sketch our society's major characteristics today without emphasis upon science and technology. Without overwhelming the reader with facts and figures, we can now elaborate a more specific sense in which science has gone public: in its sources of support, and their magnitude.

(But first, a caveat: all statistics concerning R&D are essentially estimates, partly arbitrary in their categorical definitions; and one series of figures may not be totally comparable with another. Also, figures for years prior to 1953, when the National Science Foundation began systematic data collection, are especially subject to considerable fluctuations.)

The last pre-war year, 1940, provides a convenient base for later comparisons. In that year (and in governmental statistics, "year" usually means "fiscal year": the year ends June 30th), the Federal Government expended something between $74 and $97 million on all research and development. Expenditures by industry, universities, and other sources may possibly have amounted to about as much more. The leading federal supporter of research was the Department of Agriculture, which accounted for at least 30 per cent of the total, the military departments for at least 25 per cent. The Atomic Energy Commission and the National Science Foundation did not exist, and NASA's predecessor, the National Advisory Committee on Aeronautics (NACA), spent but $2.2 million.

For fiscal 1968, the Bureau of the Budget's early estimates were that the national total expenditure on R&D, from all sources, would approximate *$25 billion*. Of this, the federal share would be close to two-thirds, or $17 billion. (NSF estimated $15.5 billion, but that excluded plant facilities.) For details, the latest figures that form part of a consistent series are those of NSF for fiscal 1967. These show the major federal agency sources as follows:

Dept. of Defense (DOD)	$7.682 billion
NASA	4.993
AEC	1.269
Dept. of Health, Education and Welfare (HEW)	1.042
Dept. of Agriculture	0.225
NSF	0.187
Dept. of the Interior	0.131

Agricultural research, although eight times increased over 1940, has faded from about one-third of the federal total to less than one-fiftieth. Defense, space, atomic energy, and (only very recently) health-related research dominate the picture today. Further, if one thinks of the space and atomic energy programs as being largely identified (politically, at least) with national security, then the vast growth in federal R&D funds— a growth of 150 times over the 1940 figure—can be seen as a consequence of wars, cold wars, and continuing international tensions.

As said, federal funds account for two-thirds of all R&D in the United States. Because of war-time military research, the proportion was even higher—70 per cent—in 1945; but the probable pre-war relationship of 50–50 support for R&D between the Federal Government and all other sources (industry, universities, state governments) was approached again around 1955. From then until 1967, the federal share gradually increased again, then stabilized. It seems unlikely that the tax-payer's share will undergo any significant decrease in our time.

Although it is sometimes supposed that Sputnik I, which went into orbit on October 4, 1957, lies behind the R&D budget's explosive expansion, it would be hard to document that supposition except for the particular area of the space sciences, and perhaps for NSF. In the five-year period straddling Sputnik I, 1955–60, federal R&D funds went from $3.490 to $8.720

billion; but an even larger *rate* of increase had been marked up
from 1950's $1.143 billion to the 1955 figure. Without any over-
all planning, the progression of the total has been surprisingly
steady; erraticism appears only in the ups and downs of component parts. Thus, atomic energy's share went down from
$859 million in 1945 (the end of the Manhattan Project) to
$221 in 1950; then it climbed again to $289 in 1955 and to
$761 million in 1960. The space program did take a 450 per
cent jump, 1955–60, but Project Apollo—the program to land
a man on the moon by 1970—gave it an even bigger boost, for
the 1960–65 increase was 1400 per cent, from 329 million to
4.555 billion dollars. Basic research, as represented in NSF,
may have been the major beneficiary of the Sputnik revolution
(although the causation is hard to prove). Its research expenditure increased six-fold in 1955–60, but then less than 300 per
cent in the next five-year interval. What seems to be clear,
basically, is this: while Sputniks, moon shots, and supersonic
transports may cause "perturbations" in the R&D pool, every
area of research, once begun, expands with its own inner logic.
Each breakthrough begets a round of theories and experiments
designed to achieve the next. So new areas of research and
development are added, but few decline, and the total rises
steadily.

To the basic research community, the really important
part of the R&D budget is that devoted to basic research. Ever
since Congress and the press awoke to the fact that federal
expenditures on R&D had broken through the $15 billion
mark, scientists in universities and part of such bodies as the
National Academy of Sciences have been stressing the small
portion of the total devoted to supporting pure science: work
done to advance scientific knowledge, as scientists themselves
judge it may be advanced. The scientists have feared (with
some reason, when one examines attacks on the non-usefulness

of specific projects) that basic research funds would be the
first cut because the least able to demonstrate practical results
in the short run.

In the 1950s and early 1960s, basic research, while fluc-
tuating yearly, averaged 9 per cent of the federal total. Most
recently, its share has risen to 14 or 15 per cent, depending on
which figures one uses. The researchers' fear seems not to have
been well-founded—so far. (That leaves open, however, the
question of whether even 15 per cent of a stabilized budget is
sufficient for the expansion occurring in scientific opportunities
and research manpower and graduate training.) The dollar
amounts for basic research have grown from 400 million dollars
in 1955 to 2.3 billion dollars in fiscal 1968. As with overall R&D,
these federal funds are about two-thirds of the U.S. total.

In support of basic research, however, the public patron
emphasizes somewhat different faces. The Department of Defense is not the principal supporter. For fiscal 1968 the Bureau
of the Budget's expectations were that support would be distributed in this manner:

NASA	$875 million
HEW	375
AEC	321
DOD	270
NSF	226
Agriculture	106

NSF's share, be it noted, is 10 per cent of the basic research
total. Although the basic scientist is not concerned with agency
missions in the work he does, 90 per cent of the funds available
to him derive from mission-oriented agencies.

Support for basic research becomes concrete support for
American universities. Seventy-five per cent of all R&D work in
the universities is performed with federal funds today. The
health of the federal budget, of basic science, and of the universities are all tied together in a single bundle. Particularly in

the natural sciences, research and graduate education are parts of the same thing. So what we find is that NASA, HEW, DOD, etc., are *de facto* agencies of educational support, with greater total impact on the universities than the two federal agencies with an explicit mandate to aid education: NSF and the Office of Education in HEW. In fiscal 1966, NSF estimates that the universities themselves (including funds appropriated by state legislatures for the state-supported institutions) put up $530 million for basic research, while the national taxpayers supplied $1.265 billion. The federal share of university-performed basic research seems to be growing still, although not nearly fast enough to satisfy the researcher "clientele."

Support of the sciences doubtless calls to mind physics, chemistry, and biology—but what of sociology, anthropology, economics, political science, and social psychology? Federal figures are now being gathered on social science support, and a few representatives and senators have recently been exploring ways in which more might be done for and with the social sciences. Federal funds for the social sciences came late, but are increasing rapidly. Since 1955, they have grown from $25.3 million to $127 million in 1965 and $222 million in 1967. Of the latter figure, $58 million is for basic research, the remainder for what is called applied research—though just how to make that distinction is even more slippery than in the case of the natural sciences.

The distribution of agencies supporting social science research is quite different from that in other areas. Of the 1967 basic-applied total of $222, the major components were:

HEW	$90.8 million
Office of Economic Opportunity (OEO)	35.0
Agriculture	27.9
Commerce	18.2
NSF	17.6
DOD	3.9

In the basic research sector, HEW and NSF together account for over 62 per cent of social science support by the Federal Government. DOD, NASA, and AEC are insignificant.

Here then are the characteristics of the science-federal patron relationship that has been described so far. (The reader avid for even more statistics is invited to turn to the Appendix, where several sets of relevant figures are tabularized.)

1) The federal patron was a very minor partner in the scientific enterprise as of 1940. In fewer than 30 years, it has become clearly dominant as a source of R&D funds in the United States. Selected industries, universities, and the scientific and engineering communities are now dependent charges of Washington. Science and technology have lost their autonomous status.

2) Most federal money exploits science (i.e. uses it for non-scientific goals); rather little is appropriated for the primary purpose of developing science. One cannot even say that all of the 14.715 per cent allocated to basic research has a science-generating rather than a science-using motive, since agencies such as DOD and NASA choose their areas of basic research support on the basis of fields most likely to have applicable results. Only NSF's minute share is allocated to those scientific investigations that are most promising in themselves. That means $226 million, or 1.5 per cent, of $17 billion appropriated for the sake of science itself. Military, space, atomic energy, and health programs account for the bulk of both total R&D and of basic research support, and those programs' goals are not the goals of science.

A minor qualification (which could become major) is that in September 1965 President Johnson directed that all R&D agencies consider the strengthening of the universities and the development of additional scientific manpower as additional criteria by which they decide how much to spend, where and how. One institutionalized response, which has met with a mixed reception among university scientists, is the Department of Defense's Project Themis: an attempt to work out arrangements with a number of university research groups to work in areas of mutual interest.

3) It follows from the above that basic research and extra-scientific missions are not entirely separable; that science-using and science-generating (the phrases are those of Stephen Toulmin) spheres of activity are actually in symbiotic relationship. Were it not for the support given basic research *because* agencies hope there will be a utilitarian pay-off (from some of it, eventually), there would be very little money for basic research at all. It may be—in fact, it doubtless is—the case that this creates some special problems for the integrity of science and for the process of allocating funds according to scientifically relevant criteria, but whatever the difficulties, the basic fact cannot be denied. In other words, if scientists consistently applied the "pure science ideal" to the sources from which funds are received, as distinguished from the conditions under which research is done, very little research would be done.

4) Basic research—loosely defined as that which is supported rather than purchased by the government—has been a fairly steady proportion of the R&D total, and its proportion has recently been increasing, but more by the leveling off of the 'D' than by rapid growth of the 'R.' For all the problems individual investigators may run into in pursuing the goal of long-range continuing support, the scientific community has achieved an overall stability of federal support. What it has not achieved is an annual rate of increase that would guarantee support for an expanding number of researchers.

5) Much aid to higher education is bootlegged to the universities in the form of research support. Since the most important part of graduate education in the sciences consists

of research-apprenticeship experience, rather than courses and lectures, the education of science Ph.D.s gets a great lift from funds ostensibly granted to faculty members to obtain research results. Furthermore, the sources of basic research funds indicate that the universities of the United States have strong ties to some quite extra-academic sponsors: the Departments of Defense and Agriculture, the National Institutes of Health in the Department of Health, Education and Welfare, the Atomic Energy Commission and the National Aeronautics and Space Administration. While some of these contain staff members who themselves come from the university world, or have otherwise attuned themselves to academia's peculiarities, only NSF is charged in its organic statute with promoting the universities.

6) Most R&D funds (about 80 per cent of annual R&D appropriations) are spent for work performed outside of the government: profit-making firms, not-for-profits, universities, independent research laboratories. New public-private relationships have thus been forged, and although these began in World War II it is only since about 1960 that serious attention has been devoted to analysis of those relationships and their attendant problems, apart from maverick writings ahead of their time, like Don K. Price's *Government and Science*, published in 1954.[11]

7) The social sciences—social psychology, economics, sociology, anthropology, political science—are clearly the poor relations of science in the federal establishment. Whether the cause be inadequate appreciation in the government for what the social sciences can do, or whether those sciences themselves have inadequate methods for accomplishing their goals, is a matter of current heated dispute. Whether the social science's share of the federal dollar should be larger, and whether any added support should be handled in the same way or through the same hands as that for the natural sciences, are questions we shall face later.

In summary, public financial support has thoroughly pub-
lic-ized science, in the complexity of relationships developed as
well as in dollar aspects. Regarding the latter, it would be hard
to improve upon Caryl Haskins's evaluation: [12]

> When federal support of any American institution
> or activity reaches such levels, it is inevitable that the con-
> trol of that activity or institution, the judgment of its
> directions, the shaping of its courses, will become matters
> of public, and indeed of political, judgment and decision.
> Close and continuing public scrutiny of an enterprise to
> which so large a proportion of the national fortune is dedi-
> cated becomes inevitable—and indeed essential. To its
> traditional patronage, first of private benefactors and then
> of privately managed institutions, science, and to a
> considerable extent technology, have added a new and
> uniquely powerful public patron. This is a major historical
> development of our time.

SOME PUBLIC CONSEQUENCES OF SCIENTIFIC GROWTH

The internal growth of science and its financial dependence upon the taxpayers are in themselves sufficient to justify
the assertion that science has gone public. Yet we cannot stop
there, for the consequences flowing from the growth of science
have further significant public dimensions.

The most apparent of these consequences is that science *
has developed capabilities by which man can in startlingly
large measure re-make (or destroy) his environment, his social
structure, and even himself.

---

* I am here using "science" loosely—as the press and general public
frequently use the term—to refer both to the search for new knowledge
(science proper) and the application of that knowledge in the form of
innovations and inventions (which scientists often refer to separately as
technology). The distinction between research and development would
be roughly parallel, and at this point I am referring to the consequences
of both, which are often loosely compressed under the single heading of
research.

This is not just a matter of potential: many science-based capabilities have already been used, often with unanticipated consequences that turn out to be more significant than those consciously sought. Rachel Carson's exposure [13] (basically true, if overstated or sometimes inaccurate in detail) of the impact of the indiscriminate use of pesticides upon wildlife provided dramatic illustration of the environmental changes we are making with the aid of new biological and chemical knowledge. And her writing has been supplemented by frequent reports of home water faucets emitting detergent suds, because the chemical composition of detergents does not break down as easily as that of soap; of increased levels of dangerous radiation in the atmosphere and in milk, resulting from atomic bomb tests; and the killing of fish and birds from stream pollution and the run-off of insecticides.

Now we are apparently on the threshhold of erasing the old aphorism that "everybody talks about the weather, but nobody does anything," for the atmospheric sciences are approaching the point of going beyond weather prediction to weather modification. The seeding of rain clouds, about which some predictability already exists, may be joined by the breaking up of hurricanes before they can wreak mainland havoc. Already there is evidence that supercooled ground fog can be cleared from large areas, and that both hail and lightning can be suppressed. These and further such developments will clearly have implications that "transcend the boundaries of the physical sciences and embrace important questions in the social and the life sciences, in international relations, in law and governmental regulation, and in the decision-making structure of the federal government." [14] To be more explicit about the international relations possibilities: [15]

> It is clear that a long-range program of weather control and climate modification can have a direct bearing upon relations among nations. It can aid the economic and

social advancement of the less-developed countries, many
of which face problems associated with hostile climates
and serious imbalances in soil and water resources. And,
quite importantly, it can serve to develop common interests among all nations and thus be a stimulus for new
patterns of international cooperation.

I do not think there could be a clearer indication of the public
meaning of research in the atmospheric sciences. If it be said
that this is nothing new, that scientific progress has always
been accompanied by challenges as well as opportunities in its
utilization, then we can reply that there is nevertheless a new
element that requires much greater cooperation between science and the public order than ever before. In Barry Commoner's words: [16]

In the past, the risks taken in the name of scientific progress—boiler explosions on the first riverboats, or the early
experiments with x-rays—were restricted to a small place
and a brief time. But the processes which we now strive to
master are neither local nor brief in their effects. Air pollution covers vast urban areas. Fallout is world-wide. Synthetic chemicals may remain in the soil for years. Radio-
active pollutants now in the biosphere will be found there
for generations.

The public consequences of scientific progress—using the
word "progress" in the neutral sense of additions to knowledge
—are by no means limited to the environment; some are reaching, or will soon reach, man as an individual much more directly. One example has already been etched into the public
consciousness: the effect of the prescription drug Thalidomide
upon unborn babies. The Kefauver amendments to the drug
safety statutes are a direct illustration of the public significance
of scientific advancement in the field of health.

Important as the development of antibiotic and other
drugs has been for the direct improvement (and the some-

times unwanted deterioration) of human health, that area
pales into relative insignificance when one contemplates the
prospect ahead for the deliberate manipulation of our natural
genetic heritage. While the world has been worrying about the
physicists' Bomb, the biologists, chemists, and biochemists
have been making their own "breakthroughs"—developments
only beginning to receive attention in the media that reach us
non-scientists, but of far more awesome human portent even
than The Bomb.

What the molecular biologists and their associates have
done is to isolate some of the materials and processes of the
genetic code; i.e. the sub-cellular "chains" of proteins and
"ladders" of nucleic acids that "program" our children's biological make-up. Research is being done in which mammalian
eggs are manipulated, and the outcome may be to permit
genetic messages to be synthesized chemically and sent as
instructions to the cells to correct congenital malformations or
even to change the intelligence level of a child. Other experiments in the chemistry of the gene may permit us to *choose* a
skin color or other bodily characteristic. Eventually, the same
strand of thought that has advocated sterilization of certain
criminals and some of the insane will doubtless lead also to
demands for alterations of human beings in directions thought
desirable by the advocates. But whose ideals of what constitutes "good" human characteristics will prevail, and by what
social processes will the choices be made? We are presently
in no shape to grapple with such direct, fundamental interven-
tions into individual characteristics as the scientists are rapidly
making possible.

Since the secrecy that surrounded the Manhattan Project
does not surround the biological research out of which these
potentialities are arising, we are, however, in a better position.
If we make use of our opportunities, there is still some time

for thinking through what we should do with what science is going to make possible. Our past history of using whatever is possible as soon as available, and thinking about the consequences later, does not augur well. Some scientists are now publicly worrying about this. For example, Marshall W. Nirenberg of the National Heart Institute: [17]

> The point which deserves special emphasis is that man may be able to program his own cells with synthetic information long before he will be able to assess adequately the long-term consequences of such alterations, long before he will be able to formulate goals, and long before he can resolve the ethical and moral problems which will be raised. When man becomes capable of instructing his own cells, he must refrain from doing so until he has sufficient wisdom to use this knowledge for the benefit of mankind. I state this problem well in advance of the need to resolve it, because decisions concerning the application of this knowledge must ultimately be made by society, and only an informed society can make such decisions wisely.

Although the practical utility of basic research discoveries is often quite unpredictable at the time of initial discovery, in the case of biomedical research the area of application is often clearly and immediately predictable. It is easy to see why the public has such a great interest in what is supported and in what results from it. Man himself is directly at stake.

Another category of science's public-izing consequences lies in the broad area of social structure. Only a few simple examples need be cited. Most apparent is the impact of nuclear weapons upon the nature of warfare and hence of international relations. The balance of power has become the balance of survival. National power is now primarily defined by the competitive ability of different countries in harnessing scientific and engineering brains to problems of weaponry and strategic systems. And national isolation is as dead as the dodo bird.

Air and water pollution, to cite a serious yet less final problem, are increasingly strong factors impelling changes in the structure of intergovernmental relations (i.e. relations among the federal, state, and local governments). When an upstream town pollutes a stream, the downstream communities get the effluence and the odor. The Boston-New York-Washington corridor has been modeled by atmospheric scientists as a single air-pollution problem area in significant degree. Only the Federal Government seems to have the resources—and, more importantly, the will—to act effectively in these matters that spill across jurisdictional boundaries. And effective actions will make hash of the notion of state and local autonomy.

Thirdly, modern science and technology are placing such a premium on innovation that innovation may become the most notable characteristic of our social-economic pattern. This in turn requires a drastic reorientation of the educational system from kindergarten through graduate school: emphasis on receiving established facts has to give way to an emphasis on learning how to learn throughout one's life.

It is not just in our generation that science has affected the way men think and relate to one another. After all, the nineteenth century saw an economic ideology of laissez-faire and dog-eat-dog arise on a basis of social Darwinism. But the pace and universality of scientifically induced change in social relations today are surely creating a new situation for us.

A former Presidential adviser, James R. Killian, Jr.,[18] has called ours the "research-reliant society." Caryl Haskins has referred to the "well-nigh universal acceptance of the scientific view in our society"—although without, he adds, "an equally universal understanding of the actual nature of the scientific process itself." And Jacques Barzun [19] has pointed out that science—or at least a vulgarization of science—has so permeated the general culture that "a winning racehorse is named Correlation and . . . the photograph of the diffraction of electrons by zinc oxide resembles a prevailing mode of painting."

It is a poetic irony that science's permeation of general culture has created a situation in which the public and its representatives, having welcomed almost every technological application of science without thinking until too late about unwanted by-products that result, now expect science can help solve not only problems created by previous uses of science—pesticides, pollution, increased population, for example —but also problems that science has not attacked before or that only now are receiving science's attention—such as the learning process, race relations, or international affairs. There are limits to the magic that research can produce. One congressional committee, holding hearings to encourage larger expenditures and research efforts in the application of science to urban problems, learned that in many civilian problem areas no adequate R&D program proposals exist and that such problems are more often "institutional and economic" than technological. In regard to pollution, for example, the President's Science Adviser, Dr. Donald F. Hornig, says, "Putting limits on what people may discharge [into the air and water] is not an R&D problem." [20]

The range of congressional interest in science and technology is handily expressed in a report prepared by the Library of Congress' Science Policy Research Division. Its summarization of science-related affairs in the 89th Congress alone (January 1965 to December 1966) covers 202 pages. Topics touched on by hearings, in reports, or legislation included:

Antarctic research
Review of the National Science Foundation

Project Hindsight
Economic impacts of science and technology
Marine resources
Traffic safety
Water research
Animal drugs
Jet aircraft noise
Environmental pollution
Patent policy
Technical services for the states
Conflicts between Federal R&D and education
Project Themis
International biological program
Foreign research and the dollar drain
Management of NIH grants and contracts
Education for the scientific revolution

To the legislators, there is no longer need to make the point that national progress depends on progress in science and engineering. Whether they understand that undirected basic research is an essential component of such progress, is another question. Except for the House Subcommittee on Science, Research, and Development, headed by Rep. Emilio Q. Daddario; to a lesser extent its parent Committee on Science and Astronautics, headed by Rep. George P. Miller, which oversees the National Science Foundation; and the Senate Government Operations Committee's Subcommittee on Government Research, headed by Sen. Fred R. Harris, the great bulk of legislative attention has been given to the application —rather than to the support—of science. And even the Daddario subcommittee has sponsored amendments that are leading that bastion of "pure" research, the National Science Foundation, into some applied research efforts as well. Today, every congressman wants to use science.

While not misplaced, such faith may be exaggerated. Surely some dimensions of our "pressing social problems" result more from past history, misunderstanding, and just plain human cussedness than from failure to perform enough research. One thing we might usefully research, in fact, is the extent to which research *cannot* save us: the limits of science in social problem-solving.

Congress is also making increasing demands for greater support of *social* science research, in the obvious hope that human nature and human social patterns are as open to understanding as the physical universe. Until recently, social scientists still operated privately, no matter how public their subject matter. Now they, too, are about to join in force the parade to the national treasury; that is, they too are about to be publicized. And as this happens the reaction of taxpayers to support of research will become greatly intensified, for the social scientists will be investigating phenomena—men—who can bite back. If public understanding of physics and biology leaves something to be desired, understanding of what social research means leaves everything to be desired. But the proper public handling of social science is a question we will touch upon at greater length later. For now, we need only note that if too great hope is raised as to what extent or with what speed social scientists can contribute significantly to social solutions, a disastrous let-down is bound to ensue. Earlier public indifference to science, both physical and social, seems unfortunately to have taken the form today of the opposite extreme —blind faith.

Scientists are becoming, quite properly, worried about the problem of protecting the spirit and integrity of science as a high activity of the human mind, while using science for ends that are those of society rather than of science. To their further credit, some of them, at least, are now more inclined than at the heyday of the "pure science ideal" to address themselves to the uses of science and the problems arising out of such use. In fact, some organizations of scientists are taking the initiative in accepting social responsibility. The National Academy of Sciences, for example, has had since 1962 a Committee on Science and Public Policy (COSPUP), which has sponsored an important set of reports of the needs and resources of scientific fields and has cooperated closely with the Daddario subcommittee of the House of Representatives in attempting to clarify the public support-scientific community relationship regarding both basic research and applied science.[21] The American Association for the Advancement of Science has a Committee on Science in the Promotion of Human Welfare. Thanks to Prof. Barry Commoner [22] (chairman of the latter committee from 1959–65), the city of St. Louis has a group called the Committee for Environmental Information, which publishes a journal of quality, *Scientist and Citizen*. And of course there is the 2200-member Federation of American Scientists, which began as the atomic physicists' base for *The Bulletin of the Atomic Scientists*, and today remains an important arena for public discussion of science affairs. Furthermore, more particularized professional associations, such as the chemists and the pharmacologists, have been establishing public affairs committees.

I am not sure that the evidence, if one could obtain more than individual impressions in such a matter, would support the contention of Alan Waterman [23] that "I suppose it is fair to say that scientists as a class have deeper concern about the present state of the world than most groups," but there is a growing concern among scientists that the public understand both the problems that society must anticipate as we enter the ages of space travel and genetic manipulation as well as the needs of science itself if it is to be healthy in its own right and in a position to make its maximum contributions to human

welfare. This concern obviously comes none too soon. The
need for dialogue between scientists and their societal patrons
increases as the ramifications of science expand.

In the age of public science, then, both the further development of science and the social application of science are
public policy problems demanding the closest thought of scientists, analysts of government, and the interested public. In
the chapters that follow, the focus will be on federal support of
science, with attention to the uses made of science only insofar
as these have a feedback effect on support questions. Since
1945–50, science has been an *establishment* in Don K. Price's [24]
apt description: "a social institution that is given permanent
public support and status apart from current shifts in political
power"; or, more pungently in an earlier writing [25] of his, "the
only set of institutions for which tax funds are appropriated
almost on faith, and under concordats which protect the
autonomy, if not the cloistered calm, of the laboratory."

While Price's characterization fitted the picture up to 1962,
from 1963 onward congressional investigations and explorations, and writings of both scientists and outside observers
(including, notably, Price himself), have considerably reduced
the extent to which funds are appropriated "on faith." Now,
how to support science, how much to support it, by what
means, and with what kind of representation from the scientific
community—these are all public policy questions being asked
insistently. It is our hope to contribute toward a more "satisfactory equilibrium between scientists and their patrons,"
which has been called "the basis of public policy in science," [26]
by analyzing such questions.

2| Justifications and Criteria for Support

In pathbreaking papers in 1963 and 1964, Alvin M. Weinberg, Director of the Oak Ridge National Laboratory and one of the most articulate spokesmen in the scientific community today, wrote:

> Society does not *a priori* owe the scientist, even the good scientist, support any more than it owes support to the artist or to the writer or to the musician . . . scientists cannot expect society to support science because scientists find it an enchanting diversion.[1]

And:

> society expects science somehow to serve certain social goals outside science itself. It applies criteria from without science—broadly, criteria concerned with human values— when it assesses the proper role of science as a whole relative to other activities.[2]

Why, then, should public support be given to basic science? On the question of *which science fields* to support, Weinberg proposed both internal criteria—Is the field ready for exploitation? Are the scientists in that field really competent? —and external criteria—technological merit; contribution to

34

other fields of science; and social merit, or the relevance of the field "to human welfare and the values of man." On the question of how to justify public expenditures on *science as a whole,* he has suggested an ingenious three-step process by which applied research would be charged to (justified by) the socially approved tasks to which it contributes (e.g. research on rocket fuels to the space program); mission-related basic research would be charged to the applied research program to which it is hoped to contribute; and the purest science—that for which no application can be foreseen at all—would be justified as an overhead charge "on the entire scientific-technological enterprise," because in a general way it is expected to make an eventual contribution (e.g. when a graduate student trained in pure high-energy physics becomes an engineer on a nuclear-desalting plant project). Weinberg would *like* to see the purest science (which he defines in one place as "the science which cannot be justified by any reason except that it satisfies human curiosity") supported on an analogous basis, and at a proportionate rate, to the support given the creative arts, to which pure science is closely related in motivation and characteristics. However, he fears to put forward this reason politically at this stage of the game, since there is not nearly the public appreciation for pure science discoveries that there is for the arts, even the more *avant-garde* arts.

In those seminal papers, Weinberg established a framework of discussion within which much of the later literature on the criteria problem has been written. But all of the discussions have been abstract: they have considered what the authors thought ought to be considered. Let us ask instead, at this point, what arguments *in fact* have scientists been making for public support? Why do they tell us the Federal Government ought to support science in general? Particular fields? Do they provide any clues to a priority framework?

WHY SUPPORT BASIC SCIENCE?: THE ARGUMENTS

Delving into a substantial volume of congressional hearings[3] held since 1963 on general questions of research and federal support, plus assorted books, reports, and articles in such journals as *Science* and *Minerva,* I have found twenty-odd distinguishable but overlapping reasons given by science spokesmen for substantial federal support. Without too much arbitrary squeezing, these can be arranged in five categories:

1. Intellectual and cultural values of science.
2. The utility of basic research as the foundation of all technological development.
3. Research as an essential component of graduate education.
4. The high costs of scientific research, and the unlikelihood of adequate private financing.
5. The political values of science, especially in international affairs.

Despite Weinberg's reservations regarding the acceptability of *science-as-culture* as a justification, most spokesmen —particularly those from the university sector of science—do stress this theme. In one of the most articulate general statements setting forth a variety of justifications, Leland Haworth, Director of the National Science Foundation, asserts that basic research "has a very great intellectual and cultural value . . . the same kind of cultural value that music or paintings or things of that sort have."[4] Roger Revelle relates the goals of science to those of the public at large by stating that "greater understanding of the universe about us and of ourselves is itself a national goal."[5] Similarly, Harvey Brooks (one of the most prolific—and best—of the academic spokesmen of science, Dean of Harvard's Division of Engineering and Applied Physics) sees basic research as "one of the characteristic expressions of the highest aspirations of modern man," and asserts the existence of "a degree of public acceptance" partly composed of "identification with the adventure of exploration into the unknown." [6]

Brooks defends support for science on cultural grounds with an argument differentiating it from art or music, however, on the basis that science, because it "is always in principle subject to independent validation or verification," "has a public character that is still lacking in other forms of knowledge." [7]

Directly *contra* Weinberg, physicist and *New Yorker* magazine writer Jeremy Bernstein puts the cultural satisfaction of science forward as the best ground for securing public support. On the premise that "if taxpayers are unwilling to spend larger and larger sums on pure science, it will stagnate," he presents his case in this manner:

> In the long run one cannot trick people into supporting scientific projects by fostering the notion that they inevitably lead to rapid and highly visible technological advances. Someone who had backed, say, Einstein's discovery of the equivalence of mass and energy in 1905, would have had to wait until the 1940's to see its first technological application, with the invention of the self-sustaining nuclear reactors. And someone who in 1915 had backed Einstein's greatest discovery—the general theory of relativity, which has replaced Newton's theory of gravity—would have nothing practical to show for his investment today, and probably never will have.
>
> While discoveries in pure science often turn out to carry remarkable technological implications, I believe that the only really sound ground for the public support of pure science is the return it offers in intellectual satisfaction—"seek the source and not the shapes," as the Vedic phrase has it—and such satisfaction is impossible without understanding. In fact, scientists are now discovering, to

their extreme discomfiture, that government support of pure science is beginning to be withheld in favor of vast expenditures on space projects, which have little or no pure science content but which are readily understood by the public. If this trend is not reversed—and it can only be reversed by public understanding—pure science will certainly wither and possibly die.[8]

Clearly, to the scientists themselves, science commands society's support as an activity intrinsically at the apex of social values. But that may work when an affluent society has more than enough money to meet its urgent needs. What if such crises as war, the re-discovery of poverty, and the re-building of the urban environment press hard on the governmental budget—should science then give way temporarily?

The *New York Times* said it should in an editorial in which it complained that a fiscal 1968 item of $10 million in the AEC's budget, to begin work on a 200 BEV electron accelerator at Weston, Illinois (a high-energy physics facility that will eventually cost $300 million to build and $50 to $100 million a year to operate), was irrelevant to "any real present national problem," and called the accelerator an "interesting but unnecessary scientific luxury." Since the *Times* has generally been a staunch supporter of undirected research, this came as something of a shock to the scientific community. Victor F. Weisskopf, noted physicist and writer of an excellent book about science for the layman, took up the cudgels, when he said in a letter to *Science:*

> In times of stress it is of utmost importance never to forget the aims of our civilization and the ideas which made our epoch uniquely distinguished and great. Certainly basic science plays an essential part in this. . . . The total expenses for basic science in the United States, including the planned giant particle accelerator, amount to

less than one-third of a percent of the gross national product. . . .

The troubles of today are, to a large extent, caused by our insufficient efforts to create a society in which more people can partake in a life which is worthwhile, interesting and significant. These efforts would become senseless if we begin to sacrifice some of the most active parts of our cultural life. In these difficult days, we must, more than ever, continue to support all that is positive and valuable in our civilization.[9]

This argument is, given my own scale of values, fully persuasive. The trouble is, however, that when the scientists justify basic research the public tends to think not of the $2 billion it uses but of the $17 billion total for R&D, which is a good deal more than one-third of a per cent of GNP. On the other hand, when Congress cuts R&D funds, it is more likely to do so in the less expensive (but less useful and so more vulnerable) basic research sector than in the highly expensive developmental end of the spectrum—rockets, supersonic planes, etc.

Now that Congress has decided to support the arts and humanities (through the National Foundation on the Arts and the Humanities), it should be easier for science to claim cultural support, because it need no longer justify a unique position in this respect. It still seems unlikely, however, that this will provide the major line of reasoning for purposes of political persuasion, at least not to the tune of $2 billion, while at the same time the arts and humanities get $15 million; and it is not in fact the one most often stressed. That honor may go to the claim for basic research as the foundation of technological (and so economic) progress and growth.

The nub of the *utilitarian justification* is expressed in this quotation from congressional testimony of then-Presidential Science Adviser Jerome B. Wiesner:

> While the scientist and the engineer follows his career . . .
> because he enjoys it as a creative activity, and a pleasant
> way to spend a man's life as a constructive member of
> society I don't believe this is why the country is prepared
> to expand these vast sums of money, because we don't
> support art, music, or other creative, enjoyable activities
> to the same extent. We do so because we have learned
> that science makes it more and more possible to do the
> things we want to do.
>
> We have learned that technology allows us to extend
> our human facilities in all kinds of ways.[10]

This justification has two approaches, covering the same
ground but from opposite directions. In one, emphasis is on
basic research as "investment capital" from which technological
developments will be derived. The other starts from the
"hardware" and processes that the government needs to fulfill
its objectives (as in space, defense, and urban transportation),
and then points out that these tasks and social goals cannot be
sustained without a healthy basic science foundation. It emphasizes the technologically useful developments directly, and
the basic science that makes them possible becomes the derivative. Both end up in the same place: a major justification for
public expenditure on basic science is the expectation of a
pay-off.

To develop a base for technology and to serve governmental and societal needs are, of course, entirely external criteria for support. These ends may be served by the findings
of researchers regardless of the researchers' motivations. It is
parenthetically worth noting, therefore, that the argument from
utility is made strongly and often by men who in other respects
jealously guard the preserves of basic science as an area where
the important thing is the desire to increase knowledge for its
own sake. Perhaps the two elements can be put together in the
same way that classical economics assumes public benefit to

be the unintended by-product of individual self-interest: the
scientist, by satisfying his own curiosity about nature, gives
society what it wants—the means for further technological
and economic progress.

A concrete example of basic research as the foundation
of technology may be helpful here. Discussing the topic of
supersonic flight, Dale R. Corson says:

> The underlying science includes the physics and chemistry
> of compressible gases as well as the physics, chemistry,
> and metallurgy of high-temperature, high-strength ma-
> terials. In the case of compressible gases much of the
> science has been known for several decades. In the case of
> materials much of the science has been done more recently
> and much remains to be done in the future.
>
> The science has been done, by and large, in univer-
> sity laboratories by people with no concern for, and no
> competence in, the practical problems of high-velocity
> flight. Such science constitutes a great reservoir of insight
> and understanding, produced by a relatively small group
> of people, a reservoir ready to be drawn on, no one knows
> quite how or under what circumstances. All we can be
> sure of is the requirement for a reservoir as large as pos-
> sible. Supersonic flight could be achieved more readily if
> the reservoir of materials science were greater.[11]

Although this seems to characterize the general line of
argument, there are variations worth noting. Paul M. Gross
has made the case in rather specific terms, asserting that "basic
research has been leading with increasing rapidity to applied
research that has been of widespread benefit to the American
people," [12] citing improved public health and federal medical
research expenditures, military strength as a "direct outgrowth"
of scientific responsiveness, and safety of civil aviation as the
product of research that has made improved navigation and

traffic control possible. Further, Gross cites multi-million dollar savings to the cattle raisers of Florida through basic research on sterilization of the screw-worm fly, an example, he says, picked "more or less at random."

Leland Haworth made a more cautious claim of the same type to the Daddario committee. After stating that basic research "is the foundation on which rests all of our technological advances," he goes on to discuss a misunderstanding for which he thinks the scientists are themselves partly responsible:

> . . . . it is usually in the broad sense that it [basic research] is the base.
>
> It isn't usually the case that from one set of basic research facts, or the results of one experiment, you go on to something practical. It is usually a mosaic made up of a great many experiments; your house doesn't rest on one brick, it rests on a whole array of bricks that must be put together to support what one wants it to do.
>
> Very often there is confusion, because a certain piece of basic research will be talked about and someone will say, "Well, how can that piece of basic research possibly ever have any application."
>
> Well, one shouldn't try to find an application for that particular thing, but he should try to find application for the total understanding that grows out of that and many other experiments.
>
> I think we scientists have been careless in not saying these things. I think we have also fallen in a trap in that when someone says, "Well, give me a case of basic research leading to application," we tend to pick out one of the very rare cases where a single experiment did have a big impact—like nuclear fission, for example. That has been a favorite one. . . .
>
> Even then there was a whole series of experiments that preceded and followed that one discovery of fission; without all the rest the fission experiment alone couldn't have accomplished the results. . . .

Among a multitude of statements expressing the investment capital aspect of basic research, the following are typical:

1. Paul Gross asserts the need "to review and extend our
fundamental stock of scientific knowledge";

2. Samuel Lenher speaks of legitimizing federal support
because we "are feeding supply into the reservoir of knowledge
that can be used for eventual technical application to increase
our economic and industrial strength in the future in this
changing world," and

3. economist Carl Kaysen asserts that the fundamental
justification is that federal expenditures on basic research "are
capital investments in the stock of knowledge which pay off in
increased outputs of goods and services that our society
strongly desires." [13]

The derivative nature, in practice, of federal support for
basic research is clearly indicated by Harvey Brooks, who
points out that in many areas, such as public health and national defense, "for the most part, basic research support has
tended to derive from these special missions rather than from
any overt policy concerning the desirability of social support
for research." He extrapolates from this that many problems
emerging from urbanization and industrialization (such as
education, air pollution, pesticides, natural resources, and
urban transportation and transport safety) will require federal
support for the research needed to attack them, even if the
operational responsibilities ultimately lie in other jurisdictions.[14]

A related variant of this position holds that use of the basic
"pool" of basic research by the mission-oriented agencies
creates an obligation on their part to make reciprocal contributions toward replenishment of that pool. AEC and NASA
fellowship programs are justified on this basis, for example,
the AEC having taken the lead. Frederick Seitz, President of

the National Academy of Sciences, has argued in this connection that

> The leadership of NASA must remember that they will depend significantly upon the universities at large for the quality of the product of the staff which they use in their own effort. I believe that in view of the long future life of NASA, it can profitably provide support on a broad basis to individual scientists in academic institutions whose research contributes to the mission of NASA.[15]

Yet another strand may be added to the web of argument at this point: the contention that applied research and development programs are strengthened by close association with basic research. This argument is made, for example, by Seaborg:

> Because all of these development programs of the AEC are continually pushing the frontiers of technology, the AEC has always been convinced that substantial participation in basic research is essential. If the AEC failed to participate in basic research in this age, it would first find itself unable to communicate with the expanding forefront of science, and then find itself unable to evolve any radical new systems upon which technological advancement—and even the survival of free men—depend.[16]

If one switches from generalities to the more specific area of biomedical research, a new tone emerges. Here, what is basic and what is applied would seem particularly hard to separate. Yet, to the self-styled basic researchers, there is a very clear separation between biomedical research and the utilization of that research for medical care of patients. And here one finds the researchers very much aggravated, rather than pleased, when research and its use are explicitly linked together.

The occasion for this finding consists of a series of Presidential statements in 1966 and 1967, the purport of which was to emphasize that whenever medical research has a potential pay-off, it should be made actual. Said President Johnson:

> A great deal of basic research has been done. . . . But I think the time has come to zero in on the targets by trying to get our knowledge fully applied. . . .
>
> I am keenly interested to learn not only what knowledge this [$800 million yearly of NIH funds] buys but what are the payoffs in terms of healthy lives for our citizens.[17]

Interpreting and extending the President's statements, the deputy director of the Office of Science and Technology, Ivan L. Bennett, Jr., said that governmental support of biomedical research has been popular and generous, but not as basic research:

> This is not because the American public has any particular desire for, interest in, or understanding of science for the sake of science. It is because of the carefully nurtured belief that medical research will contribute directly to improved medical care and better health.[18]

Bennett quoted several science reporters' and editorialists' reactions to the tone of Presidential pronouncements placing some emphasis on use of research:

> —"A 20-year honeymoon for science is drawing to a close."
> —"There is a tendency among some scientists to equate the refusal of a grant with the persecution of Galileo."
> —"A widespread impression that the scientific community has grown rich and rotten on government subsidy."

Clearly, some basic scientists and their spokesmen see an insistence on utilization of basic research results as a threat in itself: because funds for use might be subtracted from funds for further research. They do not deny the connection—in biomedical research, one couldn't—but they fear the "payoff." This seems not quite cricket, sympathetic as I am to basic research goals, in view of the funds made possible for basic research out of belief in eventual pay-offs. Should one gouge the hand that feeds one?

So the basic research community is ambivalent about stressing the technological justification: it is there, but should not be stressed at the expense of basic research itself. An attempt to build a bridge is often made by reference to the time scale of the basic research-payoff relationship. Bennett said, in the address quoted, that President Johnson "is interested in 'payoffs' but not merely in *quick* payoffs." So long as the government is interested in indirect, long-range pay-offs, the basic researchers have not too much to worry about. But their position is exposed, in any case, when they show such fright—rather than pleasure—that the President wants to ensure that patients benefit from medical research!

The idea of long-range pay-off leads us into the next category of justification: science funds as an essential ingredient of science (particularly graduate) *education*—for this is the longest-range pay-off of all.

The educational justification has for a long time been an important line of argument; it is perhaps the dominant one now. Further, it represents a specific justification for Federal Government support, while many other lines of argument assert a need and simply *assume* that the Federal Government is the appropriate institution to meet it. The so-called Seaborg Report (named atfer its committee chairman) is an articulate source of this ideology:

.... graduate education and the process of basic research *belong together* at every possible level. . . . From the point of view of the graduate student, the teaching and the research of his professor are, at the crucial point which defines the whole, united. . . . As learning and teaching require research, so research, in the end, cannot be sustained without teaching. . . . No other agency [than the federal government] in our society is responsible for the national security, and . . . for the general welfare, and all major fields without exception can be expected to contribute to the general welfare. No other agency, finally, has the financial strength to provide the necessary support —and incentive—for work in expensive new undertakings. . . . No matter how many diverse elements of our society may join in their support(and the more the better), basic research and graduate education are in the end, by their very nature, a problem for the nation as a whole, and so for the national government. There is not one physics for California and another for Texas. . . . Both basic research and graduate education must be supported in terms of the welfare of society as a whole. It is in this large sense that the role of the Federal Government is inevitably central. . . . *Either it will find the policies—and the resources— which permit our universities to flourish and their duties to be adequately discharged—or no one will.*[19]

The insistence of this report on the *national* character and relevance of science and science education provides a concrete basis for the justification of *federal funds*, and is closely related to the economic argument that lack of market incentives for private support of basic research provides a specific reason for governmental support.

Perhaps the best sign that the government itself endorses this line of argument consists of a memo from President Johnson to the heads of departments and agencies, September 14, 1965; said the President:

Of the $15 billion which the Federal Government is spending in research and development activities this year, $1.3, or about 9 percent, is spent in universities. The $1.3 billion, which includes only Federal research grants and contracts, accounts for about two-thirds of the total research expenditures of our American colleges and universities. Over 25,000 graduate students in engineering, mathematics, physical and life sciences are supported indirectly by employment under these research grants and contracts. Plainly the Federal expenditures have a major effect on the development of our higher educational system.

The strength of the research and development programs of the major agencies, and hence their ability to meet national needs, depends heavily upon the total strength of our university system. Research supported to further agency missions should be administered not only with a view to producing specific results, but also with a view to strengthening academic institutions and increasing the number of institutions capable of performing research of high quality.

He went on to direct that agencies encourage the "maintenance of outstanding quality in science and science education" where it exists; assist in developing more front-rank institutions; and provide opportunities for institutions not already heavily engaged in federally sponsored research to become so.[20]

When I began my inquiries into justifications for federal support, scientists seemed to be stressing the "overhead" concept: that basic research should get some percentage of total R&D or of GNP. The latter continues to rise, but the former has been leveling off. Since basic research demands are not leveling off, there has been a tendency for the grounds of argument to shift, the emphasis most recently being on the science-graduate student link, and on the increasing numbers of graduate students.

The trend of the argument was both illustrated and helped along during the summer of 1967 by a spate of articles in *Science,* the weekly magazine of the American Association for the Advancement of Science. In August and early September of that year appeared four articles expounding the same essential theme: increased financial support of graduate science education in the universities was essential, and support of education necessarily also meant support of research.

Lee A. DuBridge, President of California Institute of Technology, emphasized that 85 per cent of federal funds in the universities come from mission-oriented agencies rather than from NSF, and that such funds should not be looked upon as "handouts" or "benefactions" to the universities, but simply as payment for public service rendered by universities and their faculties and students in doing research that furthered agency missions. Although the system of research "purchasing" has had the by-product effect of supporting graduate education and the basic research that faculty wanted to do, duBridge is concerned that a larger proportion of university research funds be received from NSF, which can "be depended on to look to the long-range future . . . depended upon to recognize the cultural as well as the practical values of basic science." [21] So he would justify some basic research and graduate education funds on cultural grounds, but most of it on the basis of services rendered, and hence not in need of justification at all so far as thinking of the money as a "gift" from the government is concerned. That is, basic research funds from DOD would be justified as part of defense expenditure, and funds from NIH as health expenditure—and neither as educational or science-supporting money in a direct sense.

George Pake, vice chancellor of Washington University, wrote on the financial crisis of the private universities especially, but some of his points are of equal validity, whether the

institution concerned is private or public. One of these is that
we are still "institution building," as it were: that although the
United States had achieved pre-eminence in many areas of
science, we are still in process of developing an adequate educational structure to serve our needs for the future. His point
is worth quoting at length:

> the U.S. educational system is still engaged in a transi-
> tion from the situation of the 1920's and 1930's, when
> serious scholars of science in the U.S. often had to antici-
> pate the necessity for carrying on graduate studies or post-
> doctoral studies abroad before they would be prepared
> for careers in this country. Since World War II, we have
> been steadily engaged in a process of establishing quality
> research and graduate study on U.S. campuses, so that we
> might have a fully self-sufficient educational system that
> leads the world. This effort to establish research and
> graduate study in the United States is still far from com-
> plete. To make it complete, there will have to be further
> investments in graduate research facilities, in reducing
> teaching loads in some institutions, and in increasing
> faculty-to-student ratios. So long as substantial portions of
> the higher educational system remain immature, we must
> expect that the growth rate for the funds supporting grad-
> uate education and research will need to be far larger
> than suggested by the simple numerical increase in overall
> numbers of students at all levels.[22]

Although I believe many academics would agree with
Pake's argument, and all with his conclusion regarding a need
for greater funds, it is in fact the total number of graduate
students that forms the more frequent justification for academic research support. Thus the chairman of the National
Science Board, Philip Handler, wrote that "a central parameter
for estimating the magnitude of the academic research-graduate
education component must be the dimensions of the graduate

student population." Handler's feeling resembles that of the Seaborg Report, quoted earlier:

> our nation should continue to capitalize on the mutually beneficial relations of graduate education and research. The support of university-based research in the natural and social sciences simultaneously and *indivisibly* serves diverse purposes which are of equivalent value to society. The funds so utilized make possible the education of those who will be tomorrow's teachers, investigators, and administrators; they expand the frontiers of man's understanding of himself, his society, and of the universe, while providing scientific bases both for tomorrow's technology and, hopefully, for tomorrow's social forms; and the very endeavor itself establishes the tone and quality of life, not only for those immediately at the university or in the region about it, but for the nation at large.[23]

Kenneth S. Pitzer, then-president of Rice University, on the other hand, dares to question whether science may not be approaching a point of diminishing returns, in so far as increasing support for the purpose of obtaining more research results is concerned. He sees three components in his doubt: (1) "further growth brings less able people into research"—everyone of real creativity already has support; (2) further increases in the published literature of science would only place a burden on the communication of the important findings; and (3) as science grows, overspecialization develops, and this works against the making of major discoveries. Is there any viable argument, then, for further growth in the academic science budget? Pitzer says, yes:

> Educational opportunity is given great importance in our society, not only for the welfare of the society generally, but also because we value the individual most of all. In accordance with this principle, we believe that

gifted individuals should be able to pursue their education
to the most advanced level if they wish. An increasing
number of brilliant and creative students are choosing to
seek the Ph.D. with the research experience that it
implies. This research opportunity should be provided,
at least in fields of modest cost, by the necessary expansion of academic research.

In short, Pitzer seems to be turning what was an argument for
research into an argument for education funds, in fields where
education happens to require research.

He adds another important strand to the argument by
relating the educational justification to the technology-and-
utilization theme:

One of the best methods of encouraging useful developments based upon new scientific discoveries is to
bring students who have participated in the scientific work
into the development laboratories. In any event, the staff
recruits for development, as well as for management of
technologically advanced activities, need to be familiar
with the latest science and with the nature of research.
And the best way to accomplish this is through research
activity in the universities in which these recruits receive
their most advanced education. Thus, *one can build a
much stronger case for additional research which is associated with graduate education than for the research
alone.*[24]

The same connection is forcefully made by the late
Lloyd V. Berkner, who stressed the connections between the
need of our economy for technologically innovative industries
and the growth of higher education-academic research institutions in every part of the country. The educational aspect is
stressed in this passage from *The Scientific Age:*

for each Ph.D. we can employ five to ten engineers, and
for each engineer we can use ten to fifteen skilled workers.
The creation of new industry, new products and devices,
new methods and applications from the new technology
arises out of the creative and imaginative insights of
scientific and technological leaders who have access to the
very limits of knowledge. Without that flair for innovation at the top, men of lesser skills will be deprived of the
opportunity they would otherwise find. Therefore we cannot discuss the development of the new economy without
discussing the educational needs of the men and women
who must provide the top brainpower to effectuate our
national research program. . . . Indeed, in the future we
may have to count a hundred or more unemployed for
each Ph.D. we fail to educate.[25]

Education, it would seem, is—like science—supported
both for its intrinsic cultural value and for its technological-
economic utility. In the American tradition, the latter orientation has, of course, been dominant.

The next set of arguments relates to the *high cost of
carrying out science,* and to the related question, the argument
that most specifically provides a rationale for public support
of basic research, of the adequacy of market incentives for
private support of basic research.

Federal support is increasingly justified by referring to
the skyrocketing costs of sophisticated equipment. While high-
energy physics may provide the spectacular illustration, the
problem is general. An electron microscope may cost $40,000
(as against $1,000 for a good light microscope), and perhaps
one of every four laboratory biologists could use one in his
daily work. The NAS Committee on Science and Public Policy
put the high costs of equipment down as a major problem for
university research, and justified expenditure on it by citing
some of the recent developments that have been possible only

because the expensive equipment was available. For example, deeper understanding of molecular structure and behavior has depended upon "new and costly techniques, such as nuclear magnetic resonance, electron spin resonance, and microwave spectra"; and the molecular study of the gene has required "electron microscopes, ultracentrifuges, mass spectrometers," etc. The Committee says, "No university can hope to acquire much of such equipment without assistance." [26]

Lawrence R. Blinks effectively combines the pervasiveness of science in our society with its increasing cost to make a strong argument for governmental support:

> It is a fact that science now molds our daily lives to a degree unimaginable 50 years ago. And it is also a fact that if we were to shut down our laboratories and burn our scientific libraries, our society would not survive very long under its present form. . . . science, which has been felt so far mainly in technology and medicine, is now spreading to all human affairs. The second characteristic is that as science progresses the cost of each new bit of information increases as it becomes more difficult to obtain. Exploring the surface of the earth, for example, is relatively cheap compared to the exploration of its interior. These two trends explain why governments are increasingly called upon to support science: both its scope and cost now vastly exceed the resources of a private institution or group.[27]

If, on the one hand, basic research is becoming very expensive, Seitz reverses the coin to argue that it is still so much cheaper than developmental costs that it should be used extensively to increase the rate of predictable successes in development:

> . . . . the success and the cost of developmental programs usually depend enormously on the amount of sound basic

knowledge that is available from fundamental research. It is easy to give numerous examples in which developmental programs have proved to be enormously extravagant or outright failures because those carrying on the developmental program did not have adequate basic knowledge to guide them. Differences in costs of developmental programs can range over a factor of 10 or 100, depending on the extent to which basic scientific knowledge is available.[28]

Probably the most telling, direct-cost argument for federal support is that derived from the economic problem of market incentives. As an economist states,

there is good theoretical reason for expecting that, left to itself, the market would not only tend to allocate too few resources to research in general, but would also tend to bias the allocation against basic scientific research as contrasted with applied scientific research, and toward research in scientific areas related to the technology of industries dominated by large multiproduct operations. This expectation seems to be substantially confirmed by the facts. . . .[29]

Kaysen puts it that the "market mechanism operates on the principle that he who pays the cost gets the benefits, and vice versa, and relies on an anticipation of benefits that is certain enough to justify the outlays required to realize them."[30] The benefits derivable from basic research, however, are both unpredictable as regards any particular project supported and difficult to retain for the exclusive benefit of a particular firm or individual. Rather, the benefits of basic research are (and should be) distributed to the community at large, thus further justifying community expenditure in return.

In theory, it could be argued that internal university funds and grants from private foundations represent alternative methods of filling the gap left by the operation of market forces. In fact, the high costs of equipment and the tremendous difference between current levels of university-foundation funds and what would be required if the Federal Government were to withdraw from the field lead most observers to argue that these theoretical alternatives are "only theoretical"—in the pejorative sense of the phrase. The cost argument therefore has both a positive and a negative aspect: that the entire public benefits and should pay the cost through taxes; and that there is no feasible alternative source of funds for the level of research felt to be necessary.

Finally, there is a category of argument that can only loosely be called *political* justification, much of it turning on the contribution of science to national security and, more broadly, international relations. Leadership in science, it is argued, has contributed to American world leadership in several ways, most obviously, through contributions to defense technology, and additionally, to our economic strength, including the ability to finance foreign aid.

Beyond these tangibles, U. S. leadership rests upon "voluntary recognition by other nations of our culture as a healthy and successful one, worth emulating." It is not just our technology that we hope others will emulate, however. Hendrik Bode suggests that leadership in basic science is vital to international leadership because "in the underdeveloped countries, intellectual communication with science on a global scale may be better than it is with technology, if only because science is so internationalized." He continues:

> The struggle of cultures is, of course, one that the country must wage on a broad front. . . . Expenditures in science and technology may be indirectly effective for our position of international leadership, in addition to their more direct values. Thus, such expenditure can properly be

compared in value with sums spent for information agencies, direct aid, or other similar means of strengthening our international position.[31]

Last, but far from least in the scale of values, is the claim that science contributes to the *maintenance of a free and democratic society*. That there is a connection between political freedom and the spirit of free inquiry engendered by scientific study is frequently asserted in writings by scientists. For our purposes, the following quotation from Verhoogen serves well to illustrate the theme:

> Is it accidental that the 18th century produced at the same time the first great burst of basic science and the first great step toward free democratic societies? Is it mere coincidence that the American Constitution and the French Declaration of Human Rights are contemporaneous with the great mathematics, physicists, chemists, geologists, on whose work all of our modern science still rests? Many have considered the relationship between a free society and the scientific spirit to be fundamental. A democratic society, it is said, is one that is uniquely favorable to the scientific spirit; conversely, a society is more likely to prosper and remain free if it fosters in all its citizens the spirit of free inquiry, the desire to know, the search for new and better ideas, and the curiosity that are basic ingredients of science. Even though science has occasionally been misused, and scientists have supported undemocratic philosophies, it remains true that allowing the scientific mind free play is a means of strengthening the individual freedom of mind without which a democracy may find it hard to survive.[32]

And on that high note we conclude this review of the arguments for support of research in general, noting that support of research has also meant, in practice, support of education, of students, and of university faculties. Research is an

abstraction; it is necessarily people whose activities are supported.

SPECIFIC FIELD JUSTIFICATIONS

Having looked at the reasons scientists give when justifying the public patronage of science as an undifferentiated whole, we must now examine the nature of the arguments made when specific disciplines or areas of research are being discussed.

It turns out that there are noticeable inter-field differences, the most obvious being that some fields can more plausibly assert practical utility than others. Thus chemists, biologists, biomedical scientists, and plant scientists all assert a strong claim in "pay-off" terms, and the chemists would make this an integral element in determining who-gets-what through science support:

> the fundamental basis for allocating federal funds for research must be the potential for scientific discoveries in the field, *and* the probability of the application of these discoveries to the nation's needs. (Italics added.) [33]

In Galbraith-like phrases, the NAS report on chemistry asserts that "nearly every article of commerce is coated, colored, cleaned, protected, stabilized, or otherwise modified, by synthetic chemicals." Not surprisingly, the chemists call chemistry "an extraordinarily useful science." [34]

Similarly, in the related NAS report on needs and opportunities in the plant sciences, we learn that "in the study of plants (perhaps more than in other sciences) fundamental science and practical application are closely interrelated," and fifteen recent developments of practical significance are then enumerated.[35]

High-energy physics (also called elementary particle physics: the high-energy accelerators are used to study the particles) and radio astronomy stand in stark contrast. Here the persuasive grounds offered for support are cultural; i.e. that we may learn more about the nature of matter and the origins of the universe, whether we can do anything with that knowledge or not. (Although of course the argument is made that we may be surprised, that technological pay-offs may develop—as is so often the case with basic research, etc.)

Thus the NAS Panel on Astronomical Facilities began its analysis of needs with the premise that astronomy is "a branch of the physical sciences engaged in basic research of the purest sort, traditionally motivated by the desire to know and understand." [36] Similarly, devotees of elementary particle physics call their investigations "an expression of the highest spirit of our culture," [37] and even a critic of the sums expended on this exotic field of research credits its practitioners with a considerable philosophic contribution in the discovery of the antiproton. [38]

Somehow, however, neither astronomers nor physicists are content to be cultural contributors—or perhaps they fear the taxpaying public won't be content—for they both make valiant efforts to attribute utility as well as knowledge to their fields. Even if the scientific findings of the accelerator investigations are not utilized as such, the instrumentation needs of this field are an important stimulus to improved technology; engineers are well-trained by their work on accelerators in company with "physicists of the highest qualifications"; and "biology and medicine will have to turn to the techniques of high-energy physics in order to study the submolecular world in greater detail." [39] The utility of astronomy is said to lie in the work it can do in relation to the space program's needs, but often at far lower cost than through space-based observations. An orbiting astronomical lab, it is stated, would cost $60 million for each instrument launched, designed to last one year; a comparable ground instrument would cost $0.3 million and last 50 years. Ground-based astronomy, in other words, can save us money.[40]

Finally, when one looks at the space program and its justification as a science expenditure, one immediately discerns that if it is justified at all it is on grounds of adventure or international prestige or military security—but not on grounds of scientific contributions worth $5 billion annually in comparison with other fields.

Probably no program is more strongly identified with "science" in popular presentations than is the space program. The Manned Space Center at Houston is surely closer to being the focal point of popular thought about science than are the offices of OST or NSF. Equally, however, no program is *less* at the heart of science in the views of some scientists and critics. Perhaps the vehement feelings that have developed about the space program are attributable to "over-selling" of its scientific components, or to jealousy on the part of less financially favored fields. Whatever the reasons, the subject of space goals justification has become emotionally charged, and has led some eminent men of science and technology into an unusual show of their extra-scientific thoughts. A convenient compendium of such thoughts is found in a set of congressional hearings, *Scientists' Testimony on Space Goals*, from which the quotations in the paragraphs that follow have been taken.

Although one does find justifications for the space program, even for the manned lunar landing phase, on scientific grounds—including the assertion by biologist Colin S. Pittendrigh that exobiology's study of the origins of life and the possibility of life on Mars presents the greatest opportunity since Darwin for "an impact on our overall view of nature"—

the major thrusts are upon the explorer syndrome, the needs of the American character, and national prestige.

Harold C. Urey, for example, states that he switched from opposition to support of the space program because it would be a "striking bit of discovery" of a kind that men have always wanted to do, and he asserts that "the prestige of the country" has to be taken into account in evaluating the program. To Urey, "science is not the principal objective of the program." To Simon Ramo, a scientific industrialist, we are engaged in a "Science Olympics"; we should not "under-estimate or be ashamed of an interest in science that is partly for prestige purposes." He also ties prestige to the potential of military applications, which inheres in "all research into the unknown." Lee A. DuBridge seems to endorse prestige as a legitimate value, yet he confesses ignorance regarding the amount of prestige to be "bought" with one or five billion dollars, and whether the same sums would produce the most prestige if applied to space ventures or to "education or medicine or military power or foreign aid." His own answer is one of technological expediency:

> Of course, there are lots of other things we would like to do as well as explore space. We would like to cure cancer, but we do not know how. We would like to abolish hunger throughout the world, but we do not know how. Technologically we surely could do it, but the economic, social and political barriers baffle us. But we do know how to go into space, and in this real and practical world we must go ahead with things we know how to do, and to capitalize on the technical discoveries that have already been made.

Illuminating, I think, an element of disdain on the part of some scientists for their fellow men, we find several assertions that the national character (even the "moral fibre," by implication) *needs* the space program's excitement. Thus Berkner, arguing against diversion of space funds to work on "man's immediate welfare," asserted that

> in satisfying man's primitive aspirations to conquer the unconquered, we spur him to greater effort . . . poverty is far more likely to disappear when men work vigorously under strong motivation. . . . Our goals in space provide to our Nation that spirit and momentum that avoids our collapse into the easygoing ways that tolerate social abuse.

In the same vein, Martin Schwarzschild, astronomer, says that if we do not carry out the space program the likely alternative is to "just play more bridge or poker," and H. H. Hess, geologist, puts the alternatives in this form: "Shall we settle comfortably before our television screens or shall we sweat, struggle and deprive ourselves of some comforts to accomplish this mission?" And he adds the political argument that a manned lunar landing is an "inspiring goal" for the man on the street, providing an appeal for the public that is essential if the public is to support adequate appropriations for less glamorous aspects of space exploration.

These facile assumptions about the impact of space spectaculars upon national character and social processes are in turn premised on the appeal of the explorer syndrome, which is cited as justification by Seitz and Urey. The latter characterizes the space program as "fundamentally a great adventure for all of us" and as, in a way, "our cathedral." Seitz sees the space program as a "continuation of the pattern of search and migration that has motivated man throughout his history."

A somewhat dissenting view from these celebrations of man's exploring instincts is expressed by Polykarp Kusch, a physicist who is concerned about the costs of the space program. After stating that "the response to the urge to climb mountains justifies, in a sense, the exploration of space," and that he would not deny man the opportunity to try to walk on the moon, he demurs from the *priority pace* of the moon program on the ground, partly, that there are more pressing needs.

As a general criterion for any major national effort, Kusch would ask about "its effect on the lives of people, on their standard of living, their health, and the opportunities they may find for leading satisfactory lives." In this frame of reference, he thinks that "the space effort will contribute very little to lives of people except perhaps pride in achievement." Water and air pollution, mental illness and oceanography are offered by Kusch as alternative major possibilities with greater contribution to people's lives.

Those are the major strands of argument offered by scientists testifying on behalf of the space program's large budget. Additional arguments include that of the space program's contribution to our technological capabilities in general, and the small share of GNP that space programs cost (yet only space advocates have to use GNP as the point of comparison to make their own pet program seem small).

What emerges from these instructive hearings is that scientists, too, are subject to emotional commitments and non-scientific motivations. The space program offers a good illustration, too, of the importance of one's sense of *human* priorities (i.e. scale of values) in determining one's position on "scientific" issues where these have a more obvious end-product than basic research implications. The specifically *scientific* conscience of the scientists is seen in an occasional statement that assumes the primary importance of the advancement of knowledge. For example, the Space Science Board of NAS asserted in December 1964, that, "the primary purpose of space exploration is the acquisition of knowledge relating to the solar system." Such statements, however, are less numerous by far

than those in which the scientists play "national psychologist"
or "international political strategist" roles.

Exactly because there has been a political controversy
over the space program and its budgetary claims (with scientists, it should be said, among the leading critics as well as
among the leading supporters), the *priority* accorded the program has become an explicit issue. The priority criteria expressed in the hearings covered, however, are *not* scientific
but deal with contributions to technology, national character,
and national security. *Justifications* are offered on scientific
grounds, but these do not, any more than in the more obviously "basic" areas, constitute priority reasons. The apparent
conclusion is that it is easier to discuss, if not to prove, priorities in terms of social-political-economic utility than in terms
of criteria intrinsic to science.

ANALYZING THE ARGUMENTS

My initial objective was to explore the priority arguments
offered as bases for allocating scientific resources, but very few
explicit priority criteria are offered, either on behalf of specific
fields or as general criteria. Rather, one mostly finds autonomous sets of justifications for expenditures in each field alone,
with occasional indications of higher and lower priorities
within that field. Implicitly, one understands that each statement of the opportunities and needs of a given field are seen
by its supporters as constituting also a statement of priority. It
thus turns out that scientists' justifications for federal support
do not give policy-makers bases for deciding *which* fields to
support more than others.

One loose, and perhaps not entirely consciously developed,
set of criteria may be discerned in arguments asserting the
technological and social utility of basic research. There are two

variants of the argument, differing in that one strand emphasizes direct utilitarian developments as such, while the other stresses the "investment capital" aspect of basic science. The latter strand makes the argument that within any given field of endeavor liberal allocation of resources to basic research will assure a solid base before a development work is begun, for basic research is much less expensive than development work.

In any case, it is clear that for purposes of arguing federal support scientists are willing to play upon the public's appreciation for technological marvels. One cannot cynically assume this is all there is to the argument, however, for statements such as that by Kusch (already quoted) indicate a legitimate and sincere concern that scientific efforts be related as closely as possible to human needs, so long as those needs are fundamental and relatively unmet.

There would seem to be an implicit argument that those research projects and those areas of science which can demonstrate especially large proportionate contributions to the educational process should receive extra support. (Only Pitzer makes this priority explicit, however.) To the extent that this argument might be accepted, it would seem logically to require a considerable reorientation of the grounds upon which project funding awards are currently made. The emphasis would place less weight on the prospect of scientific findings of importance and more weight on the extent of graduate student participation, and on the relationship of the senior investigator's research to his teaching function. Institutionally, this further suggests that those portions of the National Science Foundation, for example, oriented respectively to research project awards and to support of graduate student education cannot be treated as autonomous entities; rather they must be closely related, if not fused.

If one attempts to relate the arguments reported here to

Weinberg's criteria, social and technological merit seem to emerge in higher standing—or at least more frequent mention —than either scientific merit (as defined by Weinberg) or his internal criteria, namely the readiness of a field for exploitation and the competence of the scientists in the field. One suspects that the relative underplaying scientists make of their competence can be explained in large part by their natural desire to live and let live with one another—at least in public pronouncements. That is, one can easily enough assert that one's own field is ready for exploitation, but it is socially difficult for anyone within the scientific community to say that another man's field is not. It would be even more surprising if scientists in any field were prepared to state publicly a belief that those in another field—let alone in their own—were incompetent. One would undoubtedly find more stress on these criteria in anonymous and private statements than in public ones. Relatively little guidance for comparative allocations can be obtained in this area through public comparisons, however.

Arguments are rarely based entirely upon *scientific* criteria. Arguments for *development projects* in particular are based on external factors and make little use of scientific criteria. Conversely, in those fields where scientific knowledge does not have obvious applications, there is more attention paid to, and more weight placed upon, the advances to be gained in such knowledge itself as the reason for supporting the field. This suggests that Weinberg's criteria framework may try to make too broad comparisons: it may be that the arguments for development projects will inevitably be made in terms of social utility, while those for support of science as a set of academic disciplines will instead emphasize internal criteria, plus one additional criteria that Weinberg includes under the external heading but that I would call internal: namely, relevance to neighboring fields of science. On the other hand, this line of thinking might pose too artificial a separation between the support of science and the support of social end-products, when attainment of the latter depends upon generalized advances in the former.

In the end, it is a bit surprising that scientists themselves use social utility as an argument as much as they do. Without psychoanalyzing their motives, it is at least plausible to suppose that this may have as much to do with their ideas of an appropriate "sell" as with their "real" scale of values and the reasons they would give if discussing the matter just within the scientific community itself.[41]

Of the five types of general justification, those based upon the intellectual and cultural values of science and those based upon political values are the most difficult to make operational, the hardest to prove or to measure. Yet they may be the most value-laden reasons one could ultimately give for public support of science.

The high cost of science is a demonstrable and dramatic fact today; coupled with a belief that a large dose of science is necessary for achieving technological objectives, from exploration of outer space and development of satellite communications to new forms of urban mass transportation, it makes a compelling argument for a sizeable public investment in science. It does not, however, answer what to Congress may be the crucial question: how much is enough? Perhaps this cannot be answered on an overall basis at all; perhaps it must be the sum of the amounts of research required to achieve all specific goals, plus some amount of undirected basic research.

That there is a connection between science and technology is indisputable. Whether it works as easily and automatically as some scientists' statements seem to imply is another matter. Is it likely that some fields of science will have greater technological spin-offs than others? And is this not relevant to priorities if one is using technological pay-off as the original justification? One wonders just how far scientists would be willing to follow the logic of the technological claim for support, for it does seem clear that when two projects compete for support, the one that can be utilized most readily would have to be preferred—and that is, with equal clarity, not what the defenders of basic research want to see.

The contribution of basic research to graduate education, and hence to increased scientific manpower, is one of the more tangible relationships. One can estimate the manpower needs of, say, five years hence (with what degree of reliability I am not certain), and one can estimate the number of graduate students various departments collectively expect to enroll. But the process may be a circular staircase: funds provided on the basis of such estimates may in fact be the leading factor in producing that number of students. And is the apparent assumption valid: whatever number of students expected is the appropriate number to support in each field?

Next, we should note that the criteria used to justify general support *could* also be argued for choices between fields. For example, if contributions to economic growth and national security are given great weight, then would it not be logical to assign priorities among such fields as engineering, mathematics, biology, and economics? If cultural progress and knowledge of our universe are the justifying values, perhaps high-energy physics, molecular biology, and astronomical and oceanographic studies should take precedence.

Very few indications are given in the materials covered as to which of the five general types of argument would be given priority, even though many scientists would support the entire package as a combined set of justifications. With reference to political realities, although this may be without any reference whatsoever to scientific or philosophical values, the technological and social utility of a given area of science may turn out to have highest priority value. A close contender, however, would be the contribution of research expenditures to education, particularly to the extent that support of education is in turn seen as instrumental in technological and economic growth. The political value of scientific research—perhaps even more so of technological spectaculars—is certainly at times also accorded high priority, as in the manned lunar space program.

Within each category of argument, furthermore, there are different levels of concrete predictability or measurability of relevant factors. Thus the technological-social utility of molecular biology consists of fairly tangible predictions about areas of application, for example in potential replacement of defective parts of a person's genetic code. The utility of high-energy physics, on the other hand, turns fundamentally on a rather intangible general prediction that all basic science eventually proves useful.

Similarly the various groups of scientists who have put forth statements of needs and opportunities for their respective fields differ in the types of supporting evidence they bring to bear. The Westheimer report on chemistry, for example, uses a number of ingenious quantitative surveys to measure "proposal pressure" and levels of support among various fields, and to substantiate its claim to a high degree of technological utility by citation counts of basic science research connected with applications. Even if one discounts the exact validity of some of the statistics, it would be hard to deny that this report moves further than any other in attempting to find objectively quantifiable measures for its claim.

In addition, there are a number of arguments common to each field, even while each field stresses its unique situation, its special opportunities and problems. Among the common ingredients are: graduate students—the number existing, prospective, and desired; increasing costs of instrumentation; and the contribution of research expenditures (in educational institutions) to graduate education. Instrumentation costs and the numbers of graduate students in each field are relatively tangible and measurable factors, and could be fed into a quantitative analysis of science resources needs.

At least as important as the common elements are the special situations. For instance, in astronomy, the manpower-equipment ratio is a crucial one; in chemistry, the absence of any agency with a special interest in the discipline, to provide it a governmental "home," so that it assertedly does not have a "fair share" of funds and also the unusually large numbers of chemists active in industry rather than in academia—these are all special factors; in the earth sciences and oceanography there is an emphasis on resource-use benefits and upon human welfare gains; in high-energy physics there is the special situation that no other source of support than the Federal Government exists for something so esoteric; and the space program raises questions of international politics more sharply than do other fields. The variations among fields stand out as much (at least) as the similarities. The similarities may provide a base for support for all of them, but the special situations will then have to be brought into the framework of decision very quickly.

We may conclude, then, that the recent efforts of scientists to articulate bases for federal support of science have been fruitful in laying out suggestive hypotheses, questions, and categories for a choice-making checklist but have not gone very far toward providing an operationally usable framework for decision-making. Too much of what the scientists have said comes down to sophisticated special pleading for university-based research, or for specific disciplines. It is evident that the scientific community has not yet faced up to the problem of priority in allocation of funds to support science. It is apparently still in a state of wistful longing for the "good old days" of 1950–64 when competing claims were handled by increasing funds sufficiently to satisfy all claimants simultaneously.

3| Scientists and the Structure of Government

"The criteria [for allocation of science funds] are considerably less important than who applies them," writes Harvey Brooks, and he continues with the assertion that "the fundamental problem of resource allocation within basic research is who makes the important decisions and how they are made." [1] If his statement were broadened to include all of the R&D spectrum, not just basic research, I would still agree with the point. And since (as we have seen in the previous chapter) the criteria are still being disputed, it doubly makes sense to look now at the institutional structure of science policy formation.

CENTRAL PLANNING: THE EXECUTIVE ROLE

Although there have been science-oriented bureaus in the Federal Government since the early days of the Republic, it was not until the creation of the National Science Foundation in 1950 that there appeared an agency charged with what could be called a "central planning" function. NSF, although set up as an independent agency rather than under direct White House control, was originally directed by statute

to develop and encourage the pursuit of a national policy
for the promotion of basic research and education in the
sciences; and,
to evaluate scientific research programs undertaken by
agencies of the Federal Government.

Responsibility for these and other functions of the Foundation was assigned to the Foundation's Director, and to a National Science Board, whose approval was required before the
Director could take final action on contracts, grants, and fellowship programs. The evaluation of research programs in
other agencies was never seriously attempted, and in 1962 this
function was transferred to a newer policy unit, the Office of
Science and Technology. Along with this transfer went "so
much of the [national policy function] as will enable the
Director [of OST] to advise and assist the President in achieving coordinated Federal policies for the promotion of basic
research and education in the sciences."

What NSF did do was to establish a policy for itself, and
a program of grants to university faculty members to further
academic research. Since no other agency was specifically
charged with promotion of basic research, the Foundation's
policy for itself was as close as we came in the 1950s to a national policy. And it was, and is, a very successful policy from
the viewpoint of academic researchers interested in pursuing
science projects independent of any applied mission. But NSF
never has provided the centripetal force needed for an overall
view of the science-technology field.

The National Science Board is a peculiar entity. Composed of 24 members appointed by the President with the
advice and consent of the Senate, it is a part-time organization
of scientists and educators not otherwise connected with the
Foundation. (University administrators have, in fact, been the
dominant group.) Meeting about once a month, it concentrates

on developing major programs and on analyzing the strains between the agency and its institutional clients, the universities. It is the legal, policy-determining peak of the Foundation, yet as a part-time aggregation of notables it is in no practical position to "run" the agency. It is, in effect, a board of overseers or trustees. And despite the breadth of its name, National Science Board, it has been in fact simply a National Science Foundation Board. That is, it has not been able (any more than the Director) to get itself treated as policy-maker for the entire federal establishment. So long as it is part-time and elects its own chairman (thus being unusually independent of the President), it is rather unlikely to be treated differently.

In 1951 a Science Advisory Committee was established by Executive Order and located in the Office of Defense Mobilization, with the function of giving advice "in matters relating to scientific and technological developments of significance to national security and on the utilization of science resources to assure their availability in the event of mobilization." [2] This committee consisted of 15 part-time members, and with a specific orientation to science in national security, it was also too narrow to perform much of a general policy role.

It was with Sputnik I that we found the stimulus to awaken centripetalism. In the fall of 1957, President Eisenhower upgraded the Science Advisory Committee and moved it into the White House establishment, under the title of President's Science Advisory Committee (PSAC). At the same time, he created a new White House position, that of Special Assistant to the President for Science and Technology. Under James R. Killian, George B. Kistiakowsky, Jerome Wiesner, and Donald F. Hornig, this has become a true focal point for science in government. The Special Assistant acts as chairman of PSAC (by election and custom rather than by law), performs liaison between it and the President, and also acts as a personal science adviser. He even has two other hats: as Director of the Office of Science and Technology (OST), which was created in 1962 as a part of the Executive Office of the President; and as chairman of the Federal Council for Science and Technology (FCST), an inter-agency coordinating committee composed of agency representatives at the assistant secretary level. (This superseded in 1959 a lower level interdepartmental committee that had been set up in 1947.) Of the Special Assistant's role, personal and through OST, we have a description in the words of Donald Hornig, who says it is

> to bring to the president a previously-lacking perspective, since science now provides so many of the new initiatives that are available to the government. First, to look ahead for him, to see what is possible, to bring him new ideas which have been critically evaluated. Secondly, to bring to his attention the relevant scientific and technological considerations which affect our domestic and foreign policies, even when they are not in themselves scientific or technical. Thirdly, to weigh and to analyze the flow of proposals which reach the White House from throughout the government and from outside the government, and to be sure that what is proposed by enthusiastic advocates makes scientific and technical sense.
>
> Fourthly, it is to bring before him the range of alternatives which are possible; this is important because the traditions, the habits, and the ongoing programs of the agencies of government frequently automatically commit them to certain courses of action, to the exclusion of potential alternatives. Fifthly, it is to view the entire fifteen billion dollar research and development enterprise of the government from the president's vantage point and as a whole, so that its elements can be seen in national perspective and not as a collection of isolated programs. And lastly, it is to evaluate, coordinate, and help set up sound management for the entire effort, and to help adapt governmental structures to the new demands which are placed on them by the new activities.[3]

A National Aeronautics and Space Council was created in 1958, as part of the act setting up the National Aeronautics and Space Administration. NASC is headed by the Vice-President and includes the chief administrators of NASA, DOD, and other agencies with major involvements in space. Its function is to oversee both the civilian and military aspects of space programs, to act as inter-agency coordinator, and to consider on a continuing basis future plans for space exploration. It is thus a centralizing program review body, but for a specific field only. NASC meets formally six to ten times a year, and holds many informal conferences with agency officials to iron out specific problems.

Another single-field locus of centripetal force is the National Council on Marine Resources and Engineering Development, created in 1966 as an expression of congressional feeling that oceanography deserved more high-level attention than it was receiving at the hands of executive agencies concerned. The Marine Council, headed by the Vice-President, has these functions: to assist the President with a survey of marine science activities; to reconcile differences among agencies operating oceanographic programs; and to make long-range studies of benefits the nation may derive from oceanic exploration and exploitation. The Council is unusual in that its mandate expires when a companion body, the Commission on Marine Science, Engineering, and Resources, makes its recommendations toward an overall national oceanographic planning system and program. This report is to be made by July of 1969, if the original schedule is adhered to.

Another significant step in the White House level institutionalizing of science was the Reorganization Act No. 2 of 1962, by which President Kennedy brought into being the aforementioned Office of Science and Technology and made the Special Assistant its director. OST is charged with science policy development and with evaluation of research programs

throughout the government; it also plays a significant part in
the development of science agency budgets, through close and
constant liaison with its Executive Office neighbor, the Bureau
of the Budget. (The latter role may have been enhanced, or at
least its path made smoother, by the fact that the Executive
Assistant Director of BOB, William D. Carey, has a very strong
personal interest in science policy.)

PSAC, FCST, OST, NSB, and the Special Assistant constitute an impressive mechanism for bringing scientists and
their views into high policy councils, both for policies directed
at scientific development and for those aimed at effective
utilization of science in programs oriented toward other social
goals—such as defense, health, or space. Each of these therefore warrants some additional remarks, to fill in the reader's
picture of how science policies are made and by whom, at the
Presidential level.

We should first note that only NSB has direct operational
responsibilities—in its statutory requirements of determining
NSF policies and passing on contracts recommended by the
Director of NSF; even so, its more significant functions have
been the representation of the academic science community
and the forming of a locus for discussion of more fruitful
modes of federal support. The Special Assistant and the other
groups are all entirely advisory. Although NSB never has been
and is not now what its name would imply—OST and the
special assistant come closer to fulfilling the broader role of
policy ideas for the full spectrum of science—it may yet become, in effect, the National *University Basic* Science Board.
Certainly its focus of major interest has been in that direction,
with little attention to other aspects of science policy, and particularly *not* in the direction of policies for the utilization of
science. A chairman of the NSB, Philip Handler, has said that
the group eschewed the wider role indicated by its name

because the budget of NSF constituted so small a fraction not only of total federally supported research and development but also of academic science, and because of the embarrassment inherent in the fact that the other science-supporting agencies are at the same hierarchical level in the government as is NSF.

And although Handler [4] thinks it is time for a change, that remains to be seen.

The Federal Council for Science and Technology is an inter-agency coordinating committee. Technically it is part of the White House Office, while in fact it operates as a part of OST in the Executive Office of the President. Because so many programs—oceanography, atmospheric sciences, graduate fellowship support, etc.—today are of an inter-agency character, it is necessary to provide some mechanism by which each agency will be assured of knowing what related agencies are doing, and to attempt some planning for, and integration of, federal programs. These tasks OST has partly delegated to FCST and its subordinate committees. Coordination has many levels of meaning and effectiveness; one breakdown lists five levels and asserts that most FCST committees fulfill only the first:

1. Inter-agency exchange of information on current plans. By this, areas of duplication—and also programmatic gaps—may be identified.

2. Development and understanding of common goals. This may involve staff studies setting forth policy alternatives together with an evaluation of their consequences.

3. Communication among agencies of their future plans.

4. Mutual planning ahead: development of government-wide objectives, comparison of these targets with individual agency plans, and agreements to fill gaps and/or eliminate duplications.

5. Assignment of programs to optimize effectiveness of the total effort.[5]

One of FCST's committees, the Interagency Committee on Oceanography, has received "conspicuous accolades" for its coordinative efforts on behalf of an area of science in which more than a dozen agencies are active. It has drawn up a ten-year plan and has issued yearly planning documents. But even ICO is limited in its effectiveness, for neither it nor the parent FCST has authority to direct participating agencies to participate at desired levels or in desired ways—i.e. ways and levels desired from a national program, rather than from an individual agency, outlook. An FCST committee may draw up a plan, but its plans are at best a beginning, a bargaining or rallying point. They do not *settle* inter-agency differences. Granting these limitations in FCST's role, it is still said to be useful for information exchange, discussion, and for stimulating common views, both on substantive programs and on managerial problems of science involving a number of agencies.

Although it is difficult to isolate OST's specific role from its involvements with other science planning units, a few of its functions are identifiable. Overall, OST might be characterized as the institutionalization of the Special Assistant's more personalistic role. One member of OST staff has described its functions in this way:

OST staff endeavor to identify priority issues related to public or science policy; phrase questions intended to illuminate choices; collect facts; staff advisory groups assembled to furnish counsel and recommendations on specific issues; interpret these results in a framework of day-to-day operations requirements, or of legislative, budgetary, or institutional considerations; prepare recommendations for Presidential action; then serve to follow through effective implementation of these actions.[6]

Another listing of OST functions has been given by the Director, Dr. Donald F. Hornig:

1. Analyze questions of scientific and technical judgment that enter into the formulation of non-technical policies and programs. For example, arms control is basically a political matter, yet appropriate policies cannot be made without judgments regarding the directions of weapons development and the means that might be used for inspection under an arms control treaty.

2. Aid BOB and the President in ensuring that R&D allocations made by separate departments and agencies reinforce national goals as set by the President and Congress.

3. Develop and monitor organizational arrangements for R&D programs.

4. Evaluate the substance of agency R&D programs. An example was the OST-sponsored study of Biomedical Science and its Administration, the so-called Wooldridge Report of February 1965.

5. Coordinate R&D programs. The FCST and its subcommittees are the operational arm of coordination.

6. Provide leadership in stimulating agency cooperation in pursuit of national goals involving science and technology. PSAC and its panels are frequently a source of new ideas and programmatic leadership.

7. Publish reports to aid the President, Congress, and the public with authoritative facts, analyses of issues, and a basis for discussion of scientific and technological problems.[7]

These are essentially the things the Special Assistant had earlier done as an individual. With OST, he now has a staff of approximately 20 professionals through which his own efforts can be extended. Like the Special Assistant himself, OST began its operations with most of its attention focused on national security uses of science; more recently, it has devoted its efforts to a wide range of problems associated with governmental support for and uses of R&D, including areas of civilian application. OST staff contribute importantly to FCST operations, both with background studies and with individuals to head FCST committees. OST also serves as staff for PSAC and its panels. In addition to these coordinative and "back-up" roles, OST has two additional significant functions. One is to be alert to the needs of science and to new developments that may affect science policies. Another is to be the Administration's spokesman for science before the Congress.

Legislators wanted an Administration spokesman, because so long as the Special Assistant was an individual in the White House staff, the doctrine of executive privilege made it difficult for Congress to gain information and advice. With OST established by legislation, rather than Executive Order, and its Director subject to Senate confirmation, which is not true of White House special assistants, the Congress has an opportunity to request more advice and information about science plans and programs at the Presidential level. Congressional appearances of the OST Director (Wiesner, then Hornig) in 1962–66 were focused on such topics as civilian technology, energy resources, general R&D policy discussions, health research role of NSF, oceanography, patents, pesticides, supersonic transport, water pollution, and weather modification.

As mentioned, OST also provides staff work for PSAC panels. OST has some 300 consultants to call upon for more specialized counsel than its own staff can provide on the wide range of science policy matters. That same list of consultants is also drawn upon for making up PSAC panels.

Given its Office of Defense Mobilization origins, PSAC, once brought to the White House level, naturally continued in its early years to focus on national security matters—from missile systems to the nuclear test ban treaty. In fact, it appears that PSAC was the major protagonist for moves toward pacifying the nuclear arms race. In the past few years, however, PSAC has considerably broadened its field of vision to include a much larger proportion of subjects connected with domestic uses of science and the support of science in the universities. One of the most widely noted of PSAC reports, for example, is the Seaborg Report, *Scientific Progress, the Universities, and the Federal Government,* which was issued on November 15, 1960. Other publicly issued PSAC reports (many dealing with national security have gone into the limbo of classified documents) include: *Introduction to Outer Space* (the first report of PSAC), *Strengthening American Science, Food Additives, Meeting Manpower Needs in Science and Technology, Use of Pesticides, Innovation and Experiment in Education, Restoring the Quality of Our Environment, Effective Use of the Sea,* and *The Space Program in the Post-Apollo Period.* While FCST has sometimes addressed itself to quite similar problems, PSAC provides an outside view from which to evaluate and provide alternatives to the inside views of FCST committees. OST and the Bureau of the Budget are thus afforded opportunities to compare and contrast views, seeking to develop the most rational federal policies.

PSAC's membership (17 persons, plus the Special Assistant as chairman) consists of distinguished scientists, mostly from academic life. It operates generally through panels for specific subjects, each panel usually having one or two PSAC members, plus several non-member scientists (many from industry) coopted to the panels for their particular expertise. It is thus a flexible system, arranged to be able to draw on the entire scientific community, but without letting PSAC become too large to function effectively.

PSAC has sometimes been criticized for excessive secrecy

(more in the early days than recently); for being overloaded with academics and insufficiently loaded with scientists and engineers from industry; for excluding social scientists and using few life scientists; and for being an East-West Coast clique. Recent appointments to PSAC, however, have largely dissipated the last concern, and a social scientist was finally appointed in 1968.

PSAC is the highest-level advisory body for national policy regarding science and technology, but it is far from being the only advisory body. As we have already seen, there are also a Space Council and a Marine Council to provide programmatic advice in those two areas. Further, there is the National Science Board, which we have mentioned, and a Defense Science Board, which we have not examined. Apart from the Presidential level advisory and coordinating bodies, perhaps the best known science advisory groups are the review panels of NSF and the study sections and divisional advisory committees of NIH.[8] These operate at the level of particular programs and individual projects rather than at the level of grand policy, and constitute the "peer group" system by which the scientific merits of projects and programs are decided (*de jure*, it's advice; *de facto*, it's decision-making) by the scientists themselves, usually operating in a disciplinary framework; i.e. NSF funds for chemistry are allocated through the advice of a chemistry panel—only it's usually not that broad. More often, it is a matter of a sub-panel for a sub-disciplinary field, say, polymer chemistry.

In whatever way it is set up, the advisory system has to operate both on strictly technical levels and on levels where technical and policy-political inputs must be fused together.

An important external source of advice, one whose committees and panels are not appointed by agencies but by itself, is the National Academy of Sciences. Chartered by Congress in 1863 for the specific purpose of providing advice when some unit of the national government asked for it, NAS is both an honorific, quasi-private organization—next to the Nobel prize, membership in NAS carries with it the greatest prestige for a scientist—and a working organization. Through its associated research arm, the National Research Council, NAS is able to provide advice in the same way that PSAC does: by drawing on both its own members and on other specialists for a given topic. (Some men hold dual positions of influence by being members of NAS and of PSAC.)

The advisory function of NAS was for a long time almost dormant. Like the rest of the society, however, the NAS has found that government-science relationships have been developing rapidly in recent years. NAS's response, in part, has been to set up a Committee on Science and Public Policy (COSPUP). Begun in 1962, COSPUP has already made its mark on science policy. At the request of the House (Daddario) Subcommittee on Science, Research, and Development it has developed and published two overall reports [9] that have definitely affected science policy attitudes, both among scientists and within government. It has also, through sub-panels, issued a series of reports on the needs and resources of various scientific fields. Some of these reports, like that on chemistry,[10] have been able to make an effective case for additional federal support, and OST and NSF have acted to provide that additional funding. One thing that COSPUP has not done, however, —nor has any other group—is to make inter-field comparative assessments of priorities, although this is what the government agencies are most anxious to have.[11] Weinberg's comment on the COSPUP disciplinary reports may be appropriate here:

> Despite the value of these formal reports, I think it is important that the informal debate on scientific priorities continue. Formal reports delineating the achievement and

promise of various fields all tend to be isomorphic. It
makes little differenece whether the field is astronomy,
physics, or computers: its achievements have been outstanding, its promise superb, and its needs and tastes very
expensive. Nor is this surprising. Each report is prepared
by dedicated members of a particular scientific community
whose passions and aspirations, as well as knowledge,
center on a single field. The very reasonable theory underlying the preparation of these reports is that each field
should put its very best foot forward. Judgments among
the fields would then be made by a higher body, like the
President's Science Advisory Committee (PSAC) that
represents many different scientific fields.[12]

PSAC, however, has not been inclined to take on the com-
parative priorities task any more than COSPUP has. Still the
COSPUP reports do contribute grist to the mills operated by
PSAC, OST, FCST, and NSF.

To this point, we have largely described Presidential-level
science policy structures. The picture would be significantly
incomplete, however, if one left out the departments and
agencies and the developments occurring within them. Ours
is a pluralistic system for science decisions, despite the overall
evaluation function performed at the level of OST and the
Bureau of the Budget. That is, most decisions are made by the
agencies and confirmed or amended at the top, rather than
being imposed from the top initially.

All 12 cabinet departments are at least partially engaged
in scientific activities, some deeply, some only in marginal
ways (e.g. the Post Office), or only through certain sub-units
(e.g. the National Bureau of Standards in the Department of
Commerce). Additionally, a 1962 review of science activities
in the national government listed 27 independent (i.e. not in
cabinet departments) agencies engaged in science. Until recently, science planning in agencies was at the bureau level.

Now several of the departments and major agencies have a full-time scientific officer at the level of the secretary or agency administrator's staff. His functions include integration of sub-unit science programs and liaison with other agencies and with Presidential science staff. Thus there has been some degree of centralization within the agency structure, as well as at the Presidential level—and some increase in staff capacity for making technical judgments. Also, two independent agencies are themselves entirely organized around specific technologies rather than public purposes; these are the Atomic Energy Commission and the National Aeronautics and Space Administration.

The making of science policy and science program decisions is thus largely a matter of pluralistic agency initiatives, upon which some coordination and wider perspective is brought to bear by the Presidential-level advisory-review mechanisms we have described. Yet another centrifugal element is introduced by the phenomenon of contracting-out; i.e. the system by which the research funded through federal agencies is performed by industrial firms, universities, and not-for-profit research organizations. For several years now, approximately 80 per cent of federally financed R&D has actually been conducted in this way. Regarding particularly the huge programs of development under DOD and NASA sponsorship, a Presidentially appointed inter-agency committee in 1962 raised questions about whether the contractors might not sometimes be running away with policy decisions, because the contracting agencies and departments did not appear to have sufficiently strong staffs to monitor the contractors effectively.[13] In other words, there has been some concern lest contracting-out amount to pluralism run riot. Even though better controls over contracting have developed as the system has matured since 1962, one must say that the business firms and universities performing federal research are a definite part of the policy-making machinery for R&D. These organizations, in addition to performing tasks put to them by federal agencies, are also quite adept at proposing research they would like to do and/or suggest ought to be done. The system as a whole, then, is private as well as public, thanks both to external advice and to the research performers.

By and large, the scientific community has been insistent upon pluralism in the government's R&D programs. The centripetal idea of a Department of Science has been broached several times in recent years, always to be rejected—with some vehemence—by the self-appointed spokesmen of the scientific community. A fairly typical defense of the existing system is that made by L. V. Berkner:

> 1. Each department and agency is kept close to the advances of American science most intimately affecting it and is progressively influenced by that participation in scientific activity. Such participation counteracts the inevitable tendency toward obsolescence in government so evident where its agencies are insulated from science. The influence of science throughout our government is now very strong and productive of youthful, virile attitudes that are in striking contrast to the dead bureaucracies so often seen abroad.
>
> 2. Since each department and agency functions primarily in its own areas of interest, its leadership is automatically equipped with an inherent, "built-in" comprehension of the research it must administer. This ensures efficient administration and effective evaluation of research results.
>
> 3. Because the form of administration and regulation of research grants and contracts varies somewhat from agency to agency, American science has had the opportunity to experiment with different types of administration. As a result, steady improvement has occurred,

and bureaucratic authoritarianism in one agency can make little headway in competition with contrasting methods in other agencies.

4. Diversity in the administration of research grants tends to reduce the hazards of scientific orthodoxy because the administrative point of view varies among agencies, and the broader aspects of science have greater opportunity to be recognized for their worth. This gives us great national scientific strength.[14]

According to Berkner, the Presidential level accretions of recent years represent "a typical American response to the desire to retain the advantages of pluralism and at the same time establish a control mechanism to keep it from getting out of hand." [15]

Even if one grants Berkner's points, as a matter of emphasis rather than black-or-white choice, there still is a growing need for more science planning than scientists have been willing to admit.

The science policy agencies described so far have been those specifically oriented to science. It is now the time to bring into the picture the role of BOB. We have it on the testimony of BOB's Executive Assistant Director that "budget decisions affecting science are among the hardest to make." The starting point, as in other budget areas, consists of the proposals, programs, and budget requests of the R&D supporting and using agencies and departments. The agencies make their respective cases for research and BOB then tries to

review the major points of justification for science budgets, interpose challenges where the justifications display a high fog index, and focus on considerations of need, timing, and costs. We do not hesitate to question the merit or usefulness of high-cost R&D proposals. But, in general terms, the final stages of budgetary review come down to a selective process which identifies critical questions from the perspective of the total program and budget of the President.[16]

To aid in making its judgments, BOB has three devices: (1) external reviews of science fields by such groups as PSAC and NAS; (2) the preparation of a special analysis of all federally sponsored R&D activities (though this is partly an after-the-fact exercise that rationalizes what has been done); and (3) the assistance of OST and the Special Assistant.

OST has joined with BOB, for example, in making selected reviews of multi-agency research in such areas as high-energy physics, oceanography, and atmospheric science. BOB has preferred to rely on OST rather than build up its own staff for technical judgments.

Looked at from the viewpoint of a PSAC member who has worked closely with both BOB and OST, BOB staff, although they cannot make independent technical judgments, do "develop a sure instinct for significant issues and for what decisions depend mainly on professional judgment and what mainly on informed interpretation of national goals." [17] Of the OST-BOB relationship, the same observer writes:

> The O.S.T. is not a separate budget bureau for science, but, through its detailed knowledge of technical programmes in agencies, it is in a unique position to assist the bureau in formulating issues, asking the right questions and evaluating the degree to which the detailed technical activities in a programme support its asserted goals. The relationship between the bureau and O.S.T. is a dialogue in which neither party takes for granted the judgments of the other, but each has something important to contribute to the discussion.

Although many scientists might find it hard to understand, both BOB and OST have always recognized that issues involving technical matters at the Presidential level are never "purely" or "simply" technical. There is always a policy-political element, and this the agencies and BOB can contribute to the technical aspects brought in by OST.[18]

The essence of budgetary planning in the United States, we may conclude, is an attempt to achieve balance—on the basis partly of factual evidence and partly (perhaps the larger part) of informed, experienced judgment—among the competing, or sometimes complementary, programs advocated initially by the line agencies. Thus there is no master plan imposed from above, but neither are all the scientific choices left entirely to the sheer play of agency politics.

CONGRESS FACES SCIENCE

Unlike the executive branch, the Congress has no single hierarchy, formally or factually, but only a series of little (committee and subcommittee) hierarchies. It thus happens that what the President, his staff, and the agencies put together with much travail is often turn asunder at the other end of Pennsylvania Avenue. If the executive branch can be characterized as pluralistic, the appropriate term for the legislature is chaotic, or so it often seems.

While many committees of Congress have long dealt with science-oriented agencies (e.g. the Senate Commerce Committee with the Weather Bureau and the National Bureau of Standards; the House Merchant Marine and Fisheries Committee with the Coast and Geodetic Survey), the Joint Committee on Atomic Energy, created in 1946, was the first committee entirely oriented toward some portion of science and technology. In that instance, a very powerful legislative body has developed, one that has played an initiating and control-ling role in relation to the Atomic Energy Commission's program on numerous occasions. JCAE is, however, the only joint committee dealing exclusively with science, and it is unique in its degree of influence over the corresponding executive agency.

Since 1958 (which means since Sputnik I and the legislation creating the National Aeronautics and Space Administration), a number of committees and subcommittees focusing on science and technology have developed. The Senate Committee on Aeronautical and Space Sciences and the House Committee on Science and Astronautics were both established in that year. Although it is generally true that the Senate takes a broader view than the House, in this case it is the House committee that has by far the more expansive title and factual scope, while the Senate committee is restricted to space programs. There is no full Senate committee with jurisdiction over science generally. The House committee, in addition to jurisdiction over NASA, also handles the National Science Foundation, science scholarships, scientific research and development across the board, and the National Bureau of Standards.

What full committees have not done with regard to the full spectrum of research and development, or with basic research not tied to a practical mission, has been increasingly done by subcommittees. These include the House Science Committee's Subcommittee (Daddario) on Science, Research, and Development; the House Government Operations Committee's Research and Technical Programs (Reuss) Subcommittee, and its Intergovernmental Relations (Fountain) Subcommittee, which has in recent years zeroed in on management problems in the National Institutes of Health; and the Senate Government Operations Committee's Subcommittee (Harris) on Government Research. (The Reuss and Harris

subcommittees were both created in 1965.) In addition,
R&D's budgetary breakthrough in 1963–64 led to the creation
of a temporary Select (Elliott) Committee on Government
Research. In 1963 and 1964, the Daddario and Elliott committees held perhaps the most extensive hearings to date on the
government's roles in supporting research, including government-university relationships involved in science-supporting
programs.

Each committee tends to carve out some special fields of
interest for itself, so that, despite the increasing number of
committees in the science field, there is not necessarily a great
deal of duplication of effort. For example, Senator Harris has
been particularly interested in biomedical research and in the
federal role *vis-à-vis* the social sciences, while Representative
Reuss concentrated, at least initially, on the impact of federal
research funds upon university teaching and upon the re-
direction of R&D efforts toward civilian technology problems.

Despite the existence of these newer legislative units organized around science affairs specifically, the bulk of legislative supervision still comes from a variety of substantive
standing committees and from the appropriations subcommittees. (The substantive significance of appropriations committees is well recognized in NSF: it was the House Appropriations Subcommittee on Independent Offices that killed
Project Mohole—the plan to drill under the ocean through the
crust of the earth to the mantle—in 1966 by withholding
further funds.) Not all of the jurisdictional assignments make
much sense to the outside observer; for example, OST reports
not to the House Science Committee, but to the Military
Operations Subcommittee of the House Government Operations Committee, while oceanography—to the extent that it
has a congressional home at all—is under the surveillance

of a subcommittee of the House Committee on Merchant Marine and Fisheries. There is a connection there, of course, but not the most important one.

Legislative control is most fragmented in the field of oceanography. Granting that oceanographic work is done in at least eight different executive agencies, still the FCST is able to come up with one agreed-upon overall program each year. But this program does not go to Congress as a single entity. Instead, it arrives on the Hill in partial packages attached to the budget of each separate operating unit. And, according to one survey of coordinative problems, the parts are then parceled out to 13 subcommittees of seven House committees, one joint committee, and nine subcommittees of six Senate committees.[19]

A number of representatives and some senators have become concerned in recent years over rationalizing the legislative structure dealing with science and over how to acquire the technical information and advice that make them better able to compete on equal ground with presentations from executive agencies "selling" their programs. Although proposals have been made for a congressional office of science and technology to render staff assistance, and for a Joint Committee on Science and Technology,[20] the major step taken to date is the creation in 1965 of the Science Policy Research Division (SPRD) in the Legislative Reference Service of the Library of Congress. SPRD has already issued a number of useful reports, educational for the executive and for outside observers, as well as for members of Congress.[21] Congress has made no progress in creating its own advisory staff of scientists, and indeed it would be difficult for it to do, because it would then have to duplicate the extensive resources, both within the Administration and advisory, possessed by the executive branch. Since no congressional staff could be large enough to contain all specialties, the committees have made do, so far, with ad hoc panels of witnesses, appropriate to particular subject matters.

There are, however, three more formalized avenues by which Congress receives the thinking of scientists, two of which are connected with the House Committee on Science and Astronautics. One is that committee's standing Panel on Science and Technology, a small group of men eminent in the universities and in industry who meet with the committee for several days annually to discuss some broad, cross-cutting problems without reference to specific pending legislation. Another is a relationship being developed with the National Academy of Sciences, particularly its Committee on Science and Public Policy. (It will be interesting to observe, if this relationship broadens, whether executive agencies' use of NAS is affected by its service to the competing branch on the Hill!) And then we should not forget that the President's Science Adviser, wearing the hat of OST Director, now provides a top-level executive source of information and advice—though legislators would, understandably, prefer to have their own equivalent source.

In staff recruitment, OST looks for people who have some technical understanding, of course. But it also is looking for policy understanding and a sensitivity to technological-public policy relationships even more than narrow expertise as such. Similarly, attempts to staff Congress with sources of scientific advice may miss the mark if too great an emphasis is placed on technical expertise, at the expense of broad understanding of science and technology, coupled with an understanding of political processes. Questions of technology that reach the congressional or the Presidential level are never merely technological. Managerial problems of funding, manpower, schedules, program objectives, by-product effects on other programs,

etc., loom larger, generally, than the strictly technical questions. Because of this, it is not clear that a scientific staff as such
would greatly assist the legislators—so long as committee staffs,
perhaps with the aid of OST and NAS, learn how to find the
appropriate witnesses as each problem area arises.[22]

So far, scientists and engineers have rarely chosen to enter
electoral politics. The Congress, therefore, cannot count on
finding among its own members many men of scientific sophistication, although there have been a few. Perhaps this pattern
will begin to change, as scientists are brought into the public
arena more often. Until it does, the Congress will necessarily
be at some disadvantage relative to the executive branch,
which numbers a high proportion of graduate scientists and
engineers among its professional civil service, as well as in
selected positions of political appointment, such as departmental assistant secretaries for science and technology. On
the other hand, legislators not trained as scientists may nevertheless develop a "connoisseurship" sensitivity through study
and constant exposure to policy issues affecting or affected by
science. This is what has happened in the previously arcane
field of economics, through the work of the Joint Economic
Committee, and in at least one area of science—atomic energy
—through the Joint Committee on Atomic Energy. Up to this
point, however, there is a considerable difference between
Congress and the executive regarding the roles of scientists in
national policy, both for the sake of science and for the use of
science. Congress has access to scientists, and scientists have
the access of frequent witnesses to the ears of the legislators.
But the scientists are not *in the Congress* in the same way that
they are *in* the executive. In the latter case, they are participant
decision-makers at several levels; in the former, they are
ad hoc suppliants and pleaders of particular cases.

CHARACTERISTICS OF THE SYSTEM

What then are the major characteristics of the system whose parts we have described?

First, centrifugal, pluralistic elements appear to remain dominant over centripetal forces, and our capacity for science planning is therefore limited. Despite the proliferation of centralizing, coordinating bodies and devices since 1957, the basic mode of operation of the system is one in which individual agencies push individual programs, and BOB-OST-FCST try to smooth out the rough edges, to make a meaningful whole. The overview does not come first, and rarely is dominant.

Second, to the extent that there is an overview at all, it takes place in the later stages of the budgetary process, with OST and BOB working closely together. Were it not for central budgetary review, it is doubtful that there would be any program integration at all. OST by itself would lack the leverage needed.

Third, representation of science and technology, research and development through major advisory groups is heavily weighted on the side of the academic natural sciences. Of 65 PSAC members during 1957–66, only 14 were scientists with industrial affiliations. Of these 14, four were from Bell Telephone Laboratories. The space and defense industries, major users of science for national purposes, had almost no representation on this highest level advisory committee; nor did they fare much better as members of particular PSAC panels.[23] The same is true of representatives of civilian technology industries. The NSB story is much the same. As of June 30, 1966, only seven of its 24 members were not primarily administrators, either of universities or of corporations. The remainder are largely men who once were scientists, but have moved into administration.[24] Since NSB deals only with basic research and education, it is not inappropriate that only three of its members are from industry; but it may not be representative at all of relevant rank-and-file faculty sentiment, since most of its members are now administrators—and university administrators do not always see eye-to-eye with the faculty. NAS committees seem to follow a similar pattern in general, although the panel for the 1967 COSPUP report, *Applied Science and Technological Progress,* was exceptional in including seven industrial representatives out of 20 members.

Further, government laboratories (which perform 20 per cent of federal R&D) and the life sciences have had almost no representation on the highest level bodies; nor have the social sciences (for all the talk about the need to develop and use them) been represented; nor has the general public, through men notably involved in public affairs, whatever their vocational affiliations. In short, if the academic physical scientists feel they are not getting what they should, it is surely not because they lack a strong voice in governmental advisory councils: their voice is in fact dominant, almost exclusive.

Fourth, if the major criteria for federal funding of science are as reported in the previous chapter, there are some gaps in the fit of the science structure to those criteria. The cultural values of science are well-represented, it is true, but: (1) the educational role of science support is handled without direct representation of the Office of Education on major advisory bodies (although informal liaison does take place with increasing frequency between NSF and OE); (2) the coupling of science to technology is a problem about which the academic advisers are not likely to be aroused or are especially competent to consider, despite the claim that science support can rest on the contributions of basic research to technological progress; and (3) the economic and social impacts and significance of science and technology are talked about (as in problems of pollution, governmental organization, utilization of research, and support for social research) without benefit of economists, sociologists, or political scientists, with very few exceptions. If there are (as I believe to be the case) major differences between the social sciences and the natural sciences, and in the appropriate ways of using them for national purposes, few elements in the present system are in a position to make informed judgments about the consequences of those differences.

Fifth, the executive and legislative machinery for science and technology is not closely integrated. Congressional committee jurisdictions, both substantive and appropriations, are not in correspondence with whatever programmatic unity the executive branch is able to achieve. Only two subcommittees look at science across the board, and even they do not have R&D programs shown to them as a whole each year. That is to say, there is nothing in Congress to provide a focal point equivalent to that of the Joint Economic Committee for economic policies and programs.

Finally, and looking at a more favorable side of the coin, the existing structure has considerably improved the capacity of the government to consider government-in-science questions, and to a lesser degree, questions of science-in-government, as compared with pre-1957 or pre-1962. The mechanisms needed —at least some of them—are now present; their composition of interests may need to be changed, but there is no reason why that cannot be accomplished. In one area only is there missing even a mechanism waiting to be improved: that is the area of science-technology transfer.

THE BREADTH OF ADVICE

It has often been remarked that the higher the policy level, the less strictly technical are the factors that have to be taken into account; and, conversely, the lower the level the safer it is (and the more necessary) to let the scientists themselves have the exclusive say. On this supposition, NSF review panels and NIH study sections (the outsider peer groups that rate particular research proposals) have been "pure science" bodies; i.e. they have consisted only of scientists and only of those in the field whose proposals were being rated. A few years ago Alvin Weinberg suggested that panels should include representatives from neighboring disciplines, to aid in evaluating the degree to which particular pieces of research might contribute to the development of the neighboring fields, and to provide a broader perspective. It is not apparent that his suggestion was taken up.

One step up from the panels stand NSF's divisional committees and NIH's advisory councils, one for each Institute. NSF's committees appear to be almost as narrowly structured as its panels—perhaps because the basic research orientation of the agency is not thought to call for any injection of outside considerations; but NIH's advisory councils are somewhat broader. Established by statute, each has 12 members who "shall be leaders in the field of fundamental sciences, medical sciences, education or public affairs and 6 of such 12 shall be selected from leading medical or scientific authorities who are outstanding in the study, diagnosis, or treatment of the disease or diseases to which the activities of the Institute are directed." Thus, half of an NIH Advisory Council may bring non-specialist perspectives to bear, with the result that at least the structural possibility of relating basic research to societal objectives exists here, whereas NSF's system tends toward the purity of total isolation.

There is an issue of scientific ideology involved here, about which two rather sharply divergent views exist. On the one hand, we have the position articulated by Michael Polanyi, and probably taken by the majority of working scientists:

"society must cultivate science on its own terms and for its own intrinsic purpose, if science is to make any progress at all." Hence, the only appropriate direction of scientific activity consists of the "spontaneous coordination of independent initiatives." [25] It follows that an invisible hand like that in Adam Smith's economics is to be relied upon to maximize scientific results, and that non-scientists (or even those from another field than the one being considered at a particular moment) are not to be consulted or even considered. A milder version of this theme is widely disseminated. For example, Leland Haworth's statement that it is NSF's position "that the scientists of the nation are best equipped to determine what is in the best interests of science." [26] I wonder if this is necessarily any more the whole truth than would be the analagous assertion that the nation's generals are best equipped to determine what is in the best interests of the national security. There is a grain of truth in each, if the area of application is appropriately circumscribed, but taken at face value these propositions would constitute an overstated autonomy. The health of science is tied up with the health of the universities, for example, yet is every physicist and chemist an expert on universities, their operations and needs?

In contrast stands the viewpoint that stresses science's interconnections with the larger society. A quotation from Donald F. Hornig, the President's Special Assistant, articulates this position well: writing of how we are to nourish basic science and "encourage the exploitation of the knowledge available to us," he says:

> We must ask how a democracy nurtures basic science in a way that is also healthy for its other vital interests, such as education. Should basic science be pursued for science's sake alone? I doubt it. . . . Or should the emphasis be colored by national need, as conceived by the agencies

of the government and by the Congress? Even within an
area where comparisons are possible, we can ask whether
it may not be shortsighted to make research grants on
what has been called the merit system alone. What about
the long pull? What about the development of our educational institutions to the development of educational opportunity for all our young people? And what of the
relation to the regional development of educational opportunity for all our young people? And what of the relation
to the regional development of our country? These are all
goals of the government, and the possibility of achieving
them is part of the reason why science is supported. But
questions like these cannot be answered by formal processes or debates conducted by experts. The questions
are inherently political, and the answers must be, too.[27]

This gives quite a different connotative flavor from the
Polanyi or Haworth view. Yet they may not be so far apart in
recognizing that support of science inevitably involves other
considerations as well; that one cannot effectively consider
science as existing "in itself, for itself." Let Hornig spell this
out a step farther, for there are structural implications in the
two views:

I think that our tying of science and technology to the
political goals, the social goals, the economic goals of our
government and our society has been one of the major
reasons that it has been possible to persuade the American
taxpayer to fund science on the scale that he has, which
is greater than in any other country in the world. I myself
think—I know some of my colleagues disagree with me—
that to isolate science as an abstract formal activity would
take away much of the vitality which results from the
involvement of science with the political goals of the government.[28]

Hornig's view would suggest that advisory bodies should
not be constituted only of scientists from the field concerned,

and that the criteria of choice should include an injection of social purpose, which is only likely to happen if the advisory and decisional structures include representatives of societal purposes as well as scientists. Engineers, for example, could often serve as a bridge between basic science and governmental or societal programs—yet they are rarely included.

Since the whole science advisory and policy-making structure has grown in piecemeal fashion, and since society's sense of the crucial nature of science is still developing and changing, it comes as no shock that some further rationalizing and re-arranging of organizational patterns should seem necessary. As we work toward improvements, it may be necessary to clarify more than has so far been done the rather separate roles and corresponding structures needed. One is a structure of advice for making overall policy for science development, while another is a structure for making individual grants to persons or institutions within the overall policy. The latter function needs less emphasis on non-specialists than the former, although there should, I strongly believe, be some non-specialist, or at least neighboring-discipline, representation on all advisory committees (e.g. a physicist on a panel of chemists).

Similarly, the policy machinery for establishment of programs to support science may not fit the needs for policy development in exploiting science for economic-technological purposes. We are perhaps better equipped at present to support science—partly because until recently we assumed that its exploitation would take care of itself, and we are only now realizing that this is not necessarily so. Congress is once again somewhat ahead of the administrators in this realization of a science problem. Can PSAC, for example, serve equally well both the science-supporting and the science-using advisory roles? Not, I think, without major changes in its representational pattern.

One other refinement needed is the institutionalization of a "needler." More than one commentator has noted that advice for some programs is stacked with proponents and interested parties: the NAS space sciences panel, for example. At least a few dissident scientists (they can be identified sometimes from the pages of *Science* or the *Bulletin of the Atomic Scientists*) should always be included in committees and in congressional testimony as a challenge to proponents of things as they are. This does not happen often enough.

THE SCIENTIFIC AND THE POLITICAL ESTATES

In sketching science-government structure relationships, we have so far concentrated largely on formal institutions. Another dimension can be added, however, by comparing the operating characteristics of scientists with those of politicians and the government. In these differing characteristics lies a permanent tension requiring certain conscious balances in the science-government structure if the cooperative aims of the two are to be maximized.

In his 1965 book, *The Scientific Estate,* Don K. Price develops the concept of four estates—the scientific, the professional, the administrative, and the political—lying along a continuum which has truth and knowledge at one end, power and action at the other. At the truth end we find abstraction from the fullness of reality and from social purpose (the basic researcher is interested in physical nature, not in the human uses to which his knowledge might be put); and at the power end, we find societal purposes. The constitutional need of our time, says Price, is to work out the relationships among these estates (particularly between the polar ends—science and politics), and he describes some of the ways in which existing relationships already form a system of "checks and balances." [29]

Price sees the professionals (those who combine knowledge of science with attention to social purposes, like engineers and medical professionals) as constituting "intermediaries between abstract knowledge and political action." And if one looks at some of the characterizations of the style of physical scientists in relation to the normal modes of politics, one quickly concludes that an intermediary is essential.

Robert C. Wood, for example, has written of the natural scientists (primarily the physical scientists) as an "apolitical elite" which is successful in politics exactly because it does *not* adapt itself to normal political modes of operation, but rather carries over to public affairs the attitudes that have been so successful in the pursuit of scientific knowledge.[30] Not only, says Wood, does the public see scientists as "miracle workers"; the scientists see themselves as nature's agents, or in C. P. Snow's famous (or infamous) phrase, they feel that they have "the future in their bones." They will bring truth, logic, and objectivity to the messy area of politics, and bring order out of chaos. The scientist, Wood continues, is an inherent and indomitable optimist regarding the possibility of solving problems. "Quick, far-reaching solutions" are what he expects to contribute to the policy process. He deprecates obstacles and impediments, whereas the diplomat's perspective, in contrast, is to doubt that there is any solution to his problem, except to learn to live with it. And from his university base the scientist can make forays into the political arena, cutting through red tape and ignoring channels, then withdraw again when his raid has accomplished its objective. Particularly in the politics of executive branch decision-making, as distinguished from the more open, ritualized politics of the legislative branch, the scientist's skills in marshalling a logical argument through quiet memoranda and oral advice give him a base for considerable influence.

Another writer mentions the "naive utopianism" of scientists, their disposition to achieve a simple solution, and their belief that the scientific method will find answers in politics as it finds results in experiments.[31] Yet another examines the postwar record and concludes that the prophecies of the scientists in national security affairs have not been better than those of politicians or generals—yet the scientists continue to act as if they had prescience.[32] The mode of thought of the scientists, this writer believes, is not one that can easily accommodate itself to conflict situations, for those are not what he deals with in nature; yet conflict situations are at the heart of political choice-making.

If the presuppositions and intellectual style of scientists do not fit easily into the political framework generally, we sometimes also find it suggested that we may need to build into different kinds of problem-solving structures different kinds of scientists. This is an intriguing, but not yet much investigated area: the different thought style of each science. As an example of what is meant, here is Christopher Wright's contrast of the physical and biological scientists:

> The characteristic emphasis on clear definitive achievements is not, of course, equally pronounced in all scientific disciplines. The physical scientist tends to be concerned with scale and the magnitude of quantities that can be mathematically modeled. His world can involve both extremely small and extremely large phenomena and extremely short and extremely long periods of time. In contrast, the life scientist is necessarily bound to the scale of living organisms and the social environment. He is constantly reminded of the problems of balance and adjustment and of environment, ecology, and the concept of the organic whole. The extension of one or the other of these contrasting modes of thought to the realm of science affairs helps determine the problems which are identified

or overlooked and proposes solutions to them. One outlook encourages attention to a single objective and neglect of side effects because they are deemed relatively unimportant or impossible to calculate. The other outlook is more sensitive to the possibility that apparent side effects may turn out to be crucial to the main mission.[33]

Exactly how these factors of style should or can be structured into a balanced science-government system of decision-making is not yet easy to see. Perhaps the most important factor is that both scientists and officials realize sympathetically that each has his own professional bias, and make allowances for it. If we are lucky, the perspectives of politicians and administrators will complement, rather than contradict, the perspectives of the scientists.

4| De Facto Science Policy

A few years ago, Wallace S. Sayre wrote that talk of a national science policy as a "unified, comprehensive, coherent, rational statement of goals and methods for science" had "an essentially fictitious quality."[1] Partial policies there might be, but consensus among scientists and between them and other policy-interested, politically active groups on an overriding single policy was not to be expected. A special congressional committee studying R&D programs concurred, its report stating that the development of a "single, complete, well-organized, specifically stated policy" was "not characteristic of the Federal Government" in any area.[2]

Certainly no science policy fitting these rigorous definitions has yet developed. Equally, in that sense, one could not say that we have an economic policy or a foreign policy—yet we do have meaningful policies. What policy we have may be fragmented, partially incoherent and inconsistent, and largely implicit rather than explicit, but it does exist. And the parts do add up to something: some goals in fact have priority over others; some structure of roles has developed among the many agencies dealing with science; and there is a dominant, if not a universally agreed-upon or necessarily permanent, set of operating assumptions that serves to guide particular actions. An impressionistic sketching of those partial policies and assumptions will give us a picture of the nation's *de facto* science policy today.

Overall, we can discern a clearly accepted premise that science has a high public value, one that justifies substantial taxpayer support. While the term "science" in this context includes both science *and* technology, research *and* development, there does appear to be an understanding (however reluctant in some quarters, particularly among some congressmen) that support must extend to basic research if only to ensure continued technological strength, and if only accepted on faith from the scientific community's repeated assertions. While there is a difference between executive enthusiasm (where scientific advisers have made their greatest headway) and legislative reluctance, it is their combined acceptance that has increased the basic science budget of the national government to the $2 billion annual level. (It may also be true, however, that this level has been attained only because the Congress never votes on it as a unit; rather, the segments of basic research are mostly hidden in agency budgets directed primarily toward other purposes. Only NSF's share has to bear the brunt of being examined on its own merits—and NSF has been successful enough to bring its budget close to the one-half billion mark.)

Clearly, it is the practicability of a technological pay-off that sustains basic research in the legislative wars. As representative Chet Holifield of the Joint Committee on Atomic Energy has remarked, "a primary justification for the support of basic research is the fact that our basic research can be translated into practical achievement." [3] Whatever other justifications may be offered by, or appeal to, scientists, this is the one that is operative in the political arena. At the same time, however,

Holifield expressed a realization that "no definite technological achievement can be predicted" for a field such as high-energy physics. In such areas, Congress appears to be willing to go along with the scientists to the extent that they present clearly stated programs whose expenses do not take away very much from the hardware-oriented developments that lie closer to the legislators' hearts. Acceptance is undoubtedly aided by embodiment of 90 per cent of all basic research in the budgets of mission-oriented agencies: high-energy physics would have a hard time getting the funds it has for major accelerators if the Congress voted on those alone, apart from the high-status field of atomic energy with its connotations of national security and electric power.

If the science budget is leveling off, and the word "doctor" is no longer spoken in hushed tones at congressional hearings, it is nevertheless still the case that national policy is heavily committed to the cause of salvation by R&D. The multiple congressional hearings on the R&D budget since 1963 do not portend a reversal of support policy; they do portend a higher level of realism and sophistication on the part of the legislature, and an insistence that the executive branch put into the best possible shape its machinery for handling science, to eliminate "wasteful duplication" and to accommodate other perennial congressional bugaboos.

CONTRACTING-OUT

Given a policy of supporting R&D, the next question is: Where is the work to be done? There is a rather clear policy answer to this: outside the government. A rather constant four-fifths of all federally financed R&D is performed in business firms, universities, and other non-profit institutions. The policy seems to be to perform within the government's own laboratories only enough research to retain a sufficient competence of government people to provide supervision of what is contracted-out. Actually, it's not quite that simple. Also involved are the traditions of individual agencies (old line agencies, such as the Interior and Agriculture departments do more of their own research); the experience of World War II when work had to be farmed out so that it could be started quickly where the scientists were; the desire to avoid civil service regulations by setting up *quasi-public contractors* (such as RAND and the Aerospace Corporation); and the desire to build up an external clientele that can in turn provide political support for the contracting agency and its programs.

As a corollary to the contracting-out policy, the instruments of the R&D contract and grant have been developed. While these overlap, the grant in general is to be used to *support* research that the researchers want to do, while the contract serves to *purchase* research that the government wants to have done. From the receiving institutions' perspective, however, both instruments bring financial support. In theory, though apparently not so much in practice, the two instruments also differ in the modes and amounts of accountability and reporting to the sponsor that are required. Executive agency policies seem to require more accountability than the universities or business would like, but less than some congressional critics would like to see. There is, at any rate, a clear policy that even in basic research, where the work financed does not necessarily have any clearly measurable "product," some kind of accountability (at least of an investigator's time and effort) must be imposed. The funds are not to be left in a hollow stump in the middle of the night, as some researchers would like.[4]

RELIANCE ON OUTSIDE ADVICE

Government agencies also rely heavily upon outside advisers, in the development of programs to support or to utilize science and in the specific allocation of research support grants. From study sections to PSAC and NAS panels, the government does not trust the unaided judgment of its own people, but prefers to act only after obtaining external advice.

There are several bases for this policy. One is the ineluctable fact that science-and-technology (S&T) as an area of governmental action is uniquely technical and specialized, and the government cannot have within its fold every single specialty that may be required at one time or another. For another, scientists prefer other institutional atmospheres to that of the civil service, so government frequently has to take them where they are, using their brains on a per diem basis. A somewhat different reason for administration-by-advice in this field is the ideology of the scientists themselves. It is an article of faith among articulate scientists that only scientists, not administrative officials, can make sensible judgments concerning science. Ignoring, as we already have seen, the fact that science affairs include more than science, they have successfully insisted that government refer its major science policy questions to outside review by members of the scientific community. It is because of the scientists that so much outside advice is used. They want to have influence, but do not care for administrative discipline; an advisory role fits their objectives perfectly. And government has accepted the scientists' policy of hit-and-run participation as its own.

The National Science Board exemplifies an extreme of policy by advice. As originally designed, in the legislation vetoed by President Truman in 1947, the board of NSF

DE FACTO SCIENCE POLICY

would run the agency and select its director, who would be appointed by the President, but NSB was still allowed the unique status of being a part-time board of non-governmental educators, scientists, and ex-scientists who were to advise the government on basic science policy and—even more than advise—control the actions of "their" agency by the requirement that all final actions on grants taken by the Foundation be approved by the Board. And although the members of the Board, as is the NSF director, are appointed by the President, NSB elects its own chairman. To that extent, the organic statute of NSF places the policy-making authority for the agency in the hands of what is essentially an outside, part-time advisory body.

PSAC advises on the uses of science in non-science policy areas—pesticides, population, pollution, test bans, space objectives—as well as on policies of science development. It is thus an advisory group of scientists who have extended their reach to general societal problems, wherever these have a recognized or potential technical dimension to them. Since almost nothing exists today without at least a potential technical dimension, this means that PSAC has become almost a general policy "think tank" for the whole of public policy. One could say, then, that it is now government policy to explore the scientific aspects of everything, through the use of science advisers.

The line between advice and decision is not always easy to see. Advisers (and the better and more trustworthy they are, the more likely this is to happen) have a way of reducing the options open to the person advised. When a very prestigious group advises publicly that this be done rather than that, it is a strong executive who can blithely go ahead and do that—especially when he would be widely seen as imposing an unin-

formed judgment upon what is likely to be seen as a "technical" question.[5] The influence of scientific advisory groups is
magnified by a peculiarity of the Congress:

> Looking at a particular field of policy, a Congres-
> sional committee sees the scientific professionals within
> the executive branch [or those outside it, I think] as right-
> thinking men, dedicated to high technical standards and
> the accomplishment of their particular missions. It sees
> their political and administrative superiors . . . as political
> meddlers.[6]

We have noted earlier that the advisory apparatus for science is largely in the hands of representatives from the university community. Add to this the fact that the larger segment of basic research is performed in the universities (which
leads to an equation of basic research with university research)
and we have a situation in which basic research policy has
been largely delegated to the universities—or, more accurately,
to men whose institutional base is the universities. Except for
the Bureau of the Budget's role in devising devilish and de-
vious (as seen by the researchers) forms of accountability on
research grants, there is little regarding basic research that is
done outside the hands of the research-performing community.
The line between advice and decision is particularly hard to
see where university-oriented policies are concerned.

Given mutually reinforcing policies wherein research is
performed outside the government, and wherein the government is advised regarding that research by the same outsiders
as those performing the work or similar outsiders, it may be a
wonder that government has not entirely lost control of R&D.
BOB, OST, and FCST must then play a more important role
than has yet been realized, for they represent the major factor
safeguarding the government from an R&D runaway.

What is true at the level of policy development is even more firmly fixed at the level of specific grants for basic research: here the scientists, with the help of NSF and NIH, have firmly established the principle in federal policy that grant awards are best determined by allowing scientists from the field in which the proposal comes to pass upon its merits. It is of course technically possible for the basic research agencies not to follow the advice they are given; but one rarely hears of this happening—and of course there would be little utility in having peer-group panels if their advice were not followed most of the time. So advice is probably even more conclusive of action at this level than at the policy-making level.

DECENTRALIZATION

In some ways the most basic factor of all in relation to procedure is the policy of decentralization in scientific decision-making. Decentralization began as an accidental fact: the armed forces departments had research programs, AEC had a research program, the Public Health Service had one. Then came NSF, long after most of the mission-agency programs (the major exception is NASA in 1958) had been started. With R&D in departmental bits and pieces, in such a way that little could be done about organizing it differently, it was easy to rationalize what existed. An ideology of decentralization thereupon emerged (just as I suspect an ideology of centralization would have developed to fit the pre-existing facts, if the initial development had been in that direction). Intramurally, mission-oriented agencies insist that only by doing or sponsoring research on their own can they keep adequately abreast of work pertinent to their missions. Externally, the scientific community has feared that centralization would put an end to the game of playing one agency against another—or, to put it more kindly, the game of playing upon different agency perspectives —in the effort to obtain grants. What NSF rejects, NIH may be willing to fund, or vice versa, runs this line of thought. While I am dubious about whether what exists is necessary or simply customary, this is not the time to examine the merits. The point is that decentralization is presently a conscious policy, and a basic one.

Some second thoughts are emerging, however. Particularly as billions have been piled on top of billions, the feeling has developed, both in the executive branch and in Congress, that some control from the top may be necessary, too. OST, PSAC, FCST and the Special Assistant reflect this feeling, and they contribute to an overlay of centripetally oriented thinking. Specifically, it is coming to be seen as an anomaly rather than an advantage that the only agency charged specifically with promoting the health of basic science, NSF, handles only 10 per cent of the basic research funded by the government. Various spokesmen have recently been calling for an NSF budget of 30 to 70 per cent of total basic research, to magnify its importance by drawing it together, and to increase NSF's intramural leverage as a spokesman for the scientific community. A 10-per-cent spokesman stands little chance of dominating the field. Only by accounting for a significantly larger share could NSF play the "balance wheel" role now being advocated for it. (This is an issue we will look at in more detail later.)

THE EDUCATION-RESEARCH SYNDROME

At least from the viewpoint of the basic science community, the policy most strongly defended, and whose extension is strongly urged, is that of tying research and university education together more openly and more tightly. Thus, as noted earlier, some scientists would now defend basic research funds largely on the grounds of their contribution to graduate education, rather than to scientific knowledge. For some years now, basic research funds have been defended as contributing in a by-product manner to the health of the universities. Now it seems that the logic is pushing us toward the reverse position: that basic science findings may be defended as the by-product consequence of supporting graduate education! In either case, the policy assumption is that a condition of tight symbiosis exists between research and university development, such that programs directed toward one of these institutional sets must be shaped to take adequate account of the needs of the other.

Partly, this attitude arises from the sleight of hand by which "basic research community" has increasingly come to mean "university research community." I say sleight of hand because the universities are by no means in fact the sole performer (even though the largest one) of basic research—much as the scientific advisers from the universities would like us to think that they are. By fiscal 1966 estimates, for example, of a total basic research expenditure of $3.233 billion from all sources, the universities used $1.899 billion, leaving $1.334 to be used in government laboratories, industrial firms, and non-profit institutions other than universities. That remainder is 40 per cent, not a negligible proportion. It would be surprising if these institutions felt that basic research was equivalent to university research, or if they were willing to accept a policy that made the search for knowledge a by-product of the financing of education.

Despite this qualification of the symbiosis, it has 60 per cent truth in it. And although an occasional voice is now heard to remark that a science-education consolidation in federal agencies would make sense, an explicit policy has only been revealed so far in a Presidential memorandum, cited earlier, directing all agencies to take note of the university dimensions of their research programs, and to maximize the ways in which these programs contribute to the educational and research capacities of the educational institutions. Science policy also becomes partly educational policy.

In the article mentioned at the beginning of this chapter, Sayre suggested that one important aspect of any policy area consisted of the interest group relationships that made up the ecology of policy. For some time, scientists have bemoaned the fact that science lacks a political base, a set of supporters in the outside world. The bemoaners were simply too short-sighted, for there is indeed such a base. It consists of the universities, the colleges, even the elementary and high schools—for all of these are heavily dependent on the Federal Government's science and science-education programs. This constituency may not yet be effectively organized for pursuit of its governmental goals, but it does exist and on occasion—as when changes are made in grant reporting requirements—has used its muscle. One of the most widely noticed bits of science politicking occurred between 1963 and 1967 in the Midwest universities' successful efforts to gain an accelerator, to match the high-energy physics equipment located in Massachusetts and California. In that instance, a group of universities worked with congressmen and governors in fairly knowledgeable fashion to make the AEC and even the President well aware of their demands. Further, Don K. Price has noted that legislators are taking on segments of R&D as devices for making themselves known as they once took on the defense of major industries in their geographic jurisdictions. Some senators and representatives, moreover, are already wired into the university-science agency syndrome—Representative Emilio Q. Daddario of Connecticut being perhaps the prototype. Now that NSF has a program specifically designed to aid liberal arts colleges, we may expect these to become as much a part of the science constituency as the larger universities have been. Furthermore, the scientists themselves, even apart from their institutional affiliations, constitute a recognized constituency of the executive branch, as is indicated by the amount of thought and attention (which is a great deal—more than most scientists would recognize) given to their expressed needs by OST and even by BOB.

Alongside the basic science constituency, and somewhat overshadowing it in size and developed political muscle, stand the aerospace and electronics industries—those that make up the somewhat mysterious entity of the "military-industrial complex." They constitute a formidable R&D constituency, even if not the cabal that some have been concerned about, and on at least some policy questions may make common cause with the basic researchers.

These (and other) clients of federal science policy have not been as much studied, nor their policy activities as publicized, as have the traditional relationships between farm groups and the Department of Agriculture, or chambers of commerce and the Department of Commerce. Yet they are of essentially the same character. Given the size of the R&D total—which far exceeds the amounts considered politically crucial by business and farm groups in "their" agencies, we can safely assume that constituency pressures will gradually become as manifest in the science policy area as in any other. As that occurs, we will find being picked out, program by program, a set of criteria determining what parts of R&D will be done by industry on its own, done by industry or the universities with federal funds, or done by government within government. A sectoral shakedown will take place, and then we will have another room built in the structure of science policy.

MODES OF SUPPORT

Within basic research, a policy of support for science and science education has had to be particularized into policies concerning modes of support. One might, for example, have a policy that all support is to be in the form of financing faculty projects, or that all of it be given to institutions to divide among their members. What we have in fact is a policy of multiple modes: support is given through project grants, facilities and equipment grants, institutional grants, curriculum development efforts, and teacher training institutes.

Project grants were clearly uppermost in the early years of NSF and NIH, when almost the entire emphasis was on financing the best scientists in whatever they wanted to do. The role played even by these grants in aiding the universities as well as their faculty members was, if recognized, certainly not emphasized. And because the best scientists were the ones supported, there was a high degree of concentration. Similarly, the first fellowship programs utilized national competitions, the winning students being able to take their fellowships wherever they wanted—which also resulted in considerable concentration.

Policy has been changing in recent years, as the institutional side-effects have become clearer (and probably as the agencies have realized that they would have smaller administrative burdens if institutions were given the money and allowed to make some of the more particular decisions on their own). Fellowships, or traineeships, are now also awarded in part through grants to universities which in turn select the winners from among their own applicants or enrolled students. An institutional grant, fixed as a percentage of project grant support obtained by the same university, is now awarded to provide some science funds that can be used much more flexibly than those tied to specific projects.

The most important recent change is the effort by NSF to raise almost-first-rate institutions to the front rank—to create 20 or more additional "centers of excellence" equivalent to those already constituting the top 20. Thus grants up to a few million have been given in all areas of the country, and NSF now has a program of equivalent support for four-year colleges, and even one for streamlining specific departments in institutions not ready as a whole to move up to the top.

As these paragraphs suggest, procedures—such as institutional grants as a way of aiding universities—also embody substantive policies such as raising 20 institutions to the first rank. And in doing that, NSF has followed another substantive Presidential directive: to make the widest possible geographic distribution of research funds compatible with effective utilization.

Geographic distribution, or redistribution, as a focus of government science policy began with congressional concern. At least to satisfy Congress, and perhaps also because they see some substantive merit in the idea, the executive agencies have begun to make real efforts to achieve a broader distribution of funds. This is partly a matter of "broadening the base" and stimulating improvements widely, so that students need not travel across half the country to reach an adequate graduate school. It is also very much a matter of acceding to the "Route 128 syndrome."

Route 128 is the highway around Boston and Cambridge, Massachusetts, on which have erupted a host of R&D business firms, some of them spin-offs from academic research at M.I.T.

and Harvard. The "Route 128 syndrome," therefore, means that having research-oriented universities in a given metropolitan area is a fine way to ensure the growth of modern industries. It is a domestic idea for regional economic development, in other words. Whether it will always work, or whether university-economic development relationships are more complex and dependent on other, so far unidentified, factors, is open to dispute, technically; in the minds of governors, mayors, and congressional delegations, however, it has become an article of faith that it will work. At least, they all want it tried in their areas. So we now have a science-economy (or scienomic, in the apt phrase of one observer) [7] strand of science policy. In this area, programs of DOD and NASA will obviously have great impact, not just those of NSF. But all will be tied together in concept because of congressional and Presidential pressures to strengthen universities, throughout the country, by means of the R&D budget.

The basic science representatives have been less than wildly enthusiastic about broadened geographic distribution. This is partly because they take a short-run view emphasizing that science be done where it can presently best be done, without paying much attention to the problem of developing a broadened base. It is also partly because, even if they agree with the end, they fear that the funds for more equal distribution will come not by adding to budgets, but by subtracting from the haves in order to give to the have-nots. And they may not be wrong in this fear, for Congress is quite capable of insisting on the broadening policy while not adding much to agency budgets.

Seventeen billion dollars makes a good-sized "pork barrel," and political realism would have dictated that tight concentration of R&D financing could not long continue once legislators realized its size and developmental significance. Allocations policy must now perform a balancing act, with existing merit at one end of the see-saw and developmental potential at the other end. The latter end is aided, too, by the shift in focus toward the educational values of science support. As the educational by-product increases in importance, the research-result values must begin to share in the limelight in which they have previously bathed alone.

THE SOCIAL SCIENCES

One could say without much exaggeration that the scope of science policy was until quite recently identified with the physical and biological sciences, and mathematics and engineering, to the exclusion of social science and social research. Although NSF included the social sciences in its data-gathering about R&D funds, no one in NSF or elsewhere paid much more than fleeting attention to them. Only since 1966 has NSF included in its grant programs all of the social sciences. Now (perhaps partly to diminish any potential support for the concept of a separate social science foundation), NSF is making strong avowals of its interest, and backing up the avowals with requests for more funds in this category. By and large, to support science meant, for years, to support things other than social science. That is now changing, and current policy (still stronger in rhetoric than in practice though it may be) is to give the social sciences a "fair shake." A number of spokesmen from the natural sciences have even been telling congressional committees that social research should receive some priority today, as our problems require as much social as technical "engineering."

Whether it makes sense to lump it all together, or to treat social research as a different animal, is presently being debated. Under whatever rubric however, a policy of conscious and conscientious support for the efforts of social scientists, both basic and applied, is rapidly developing. The danger now, in fact, is that legislative enthusiasm may outrun the ability of the social scientists to perform the miracles being asked of them in such fields as race relations, slum rebuilding, and population control.

PRIORITIES

Out of all the components that a rounded science policy must contain if it is to deserve to be called a policy, one of the most important is some set of priority guidelines. It is in this respect that we least possess a policy—in the sense of a conscious rationale. As we saw in Chapter Two, scientists offer many reasons for supporting science in general and their respective fields in particular; but few are willing to stick their necks out by engaging in comparative evaluation of fields.

This does not mean that there are no priorities, in the sense of fields or programs that receive more funds than others, or that are more likely to win budgetary contests. In these senses, a glance at agency sources of R&D funds (see Appendix) indicates some of the obvious priority choices that have been made, more out of expediency and political appeal than out of scientific merit. Or, to put it another way, out of external criteria rather than internal ones.

Most succinctly, financial priority goes to research applicable to war, to space exploration, to atomic energy, and to health. Among these, war (or, to put it more delicately, national security) is easily the top priority item. Not only is DOD's the largest single agency R&D budget; we also have to consider that the NASA and AEC budgets are at least in part identified in the public mind with war. Were there no connection, politically, there would not be such large budgets in these agencies. Health is the only area not connected with national security that has an R&D budget exceeding one billion dollars, and at that it is only a little more than one-seventh of DOD's alone. The funding is a symptom of a political intangible: that priority must go, in publicly supported research, to the areas that the public and its representatives are most concerned about—rather than what concerns, say, the National Academy of Sciences.

If one turns from total R&D to fiscal priorities in basic science alone, things do not change as much as one might expect. NASA replaces DOD at the top, and health moves up to second place, but these, plus atomic energy, all come ahead of NSF. This would not be the case if undirected basic research were considered as important as applications in federal decision-making.

Given the way that the federal budget is constructed, it would be difficult to find any priorities in the stricter sense: items that have consciously been pushed ahead of others in comparative reviews. In basic science, perhaps the closest thing is the way in which FCST and NSF, through analysis of proposal pressures and review of field surveys (the needs and resources reports of NAS, for example), have recently been able to isolate particular fields for special effort in the budget. Chemistry, for example, was singled out in fiscal 1967 in this way.

In Big Science, it is federal policy that each proposal for an accelerator, a radio astronomy facility, or the like—i.e. research facilities that cost many millions or hundreds of millions of dollars—receive intense scrutiny and that priorities are set. In this area, it is obvious that the total budget would not be increased enough to avoid conscious choice. And when several expensive programs or facilities are suggested within a field, special panels may be assigned to aid in establishing priorities. This happened in 1967, for example, with regard to radio astronomy instruments.

Although Big Science and little science are not consciously put into competition with one another, so far as I know, there probably is a competitive effect. I would hazard a guess that little science (small grants to individual investigators) suffers somewhat in that a single Big Science facility may use up the funds that would otherwise support hundreds, possibly even thousands, of individual investigators. This is not to say that they would so be used, but I suspect there is a dampening effect, for a few Big Science items can make the basic science budget look very large, although actually very few individuals and institutions may be supported under each item. For example, $10 million to start the Weston accelerator would mean support for the research of 200 scientists at a rate of $50,000 per scientist. In preparing the fiscal 1967 budget, it probably was not considered in that way. But if the $10 million were not actually used by AEC, it was unlikely to be given to NSF. So there was no explicit trade-off. But there may be such trade-offs when we finally devise a method for determining priorities.

In the competition among the Big Science areas, the governing factors seem to be scientific ripeness of a field (oceanography, molecular biology) and congressional-political receptivity. The latter is clearly enhanced by any element of "glamor." Where a program achieves a working consensus among people and groups excited by it, it has a chance of priority treatment—which is just to say that in science policy as in all other areas of political allocation of resources, a strong, well-organized and well-articulated group interest can make all the difference in the world. Not all scientists yet realize this —or at least are yet ready to accept it as a fact of life.

A more explicit federal science policy will then await both an intellectually plausible framework for setting priorities, and an acceptance by scientists of the fact that to win in politics you must be willing to act politically.

II| Challenges and Change

5| Challenges to Things as They Are

According to the old French proverb, the more things change, the more they remain the same. Perhaps the reverse is also true: the more things appear to be the same, the more they are in reality changing.

Certainly this is true of the Federal Government's dealings with science. On the surface, the scenery looks much the same today as it did in 1962 when OST was added to the machinery. Some of the arguments do stay the same: universities are still fighting the same ground of overhead costs as they have been doing for years; and while still complaining that federal grants cost them money, they continue to seek more of them. Yet changes are occurring, and even bigger ones are in prospect.

Taking a Toynbee-esqe view of change as the product of "challenge and response," we here take up a series of challenges and some of the responses being discussed or already implemented.

THE CHALLENGE OF GROWTH AND THE NEED FOR PLANNING

In 1963 the author of an unpublished report on science planning in the United States wrote that a "central purpose of long-range planning is to provide a framework within which individual agencies can do their own planning more intelligently." Our ability to plan, in this sense of providing an overall framework, apparently has not developed as far as one might like, for in 1967 the President's science adviser, Dr. Hornig, told an appropriations subcommittee that

> One of the central jobs we have from the President's side is to get this $17 billion under control, because there are agencies responsible for each little piece of it, all of whom promote their own part of it. Someone has got to look at the one against the other and make some recommendations as to what looks good and what looks less good, and so on.[1]

Because the United States dips into any kind of planning hesitantly, one toe at a time, the closest thing we have to a science plan so far is the President's annual budget: it is the cooperative-competitive relationship between the President's Special Assistant for Science and Technology and the Director of the Bureau of the Budget, and their respective staffs, that comes closest to producing a plan for science.

As noted earlier, the concept of decentralization—philosophized as an essential part of the national tradition of pluralism—rules the roost, and government-wide overviews are, so far, largely glosses imposed after the fact. A realization that this is not enough, that the importance of R&D's impact on several aspects of national life cannot be ignored or assumed to be automatically worked out to the best advantage, is beginning to develop. Several of the reasons for an increased planning need have been set forth by Harvey Brooks:

1. The "sheer magnitude of the Federal Government's technical activities and their rapid rate of growth."

2. The unique position of the Federal Government as the

dominant customer for R&D. Fifty per cent of the nation's scientists and engineers are supported from federal R&D expenditures, and government R&D exercises important leverage on regional growth. Congress and the public are therefore bound to be concerned with the direction of R&D.

3. The "increasing interdependence of the whole structure of science and technology."

4. The growth of "big science," i.e. "pure science carried on with complex and expensive equipment, and with a large supporting technological effort."

5. The increasing role of the government as supporter of graduate education in science.

6. The "emergence of international programs and the use of scientific cooperation as a tool of international relations."

7. The "emergence into public attention of a series of major social problems for which technical inputs are believed to be essential"; e.g. pollution and urban transportation.[2]

In addition to these factors, since planning usually means looking as far ahead as possible, it is relevant that science increasingly requires a long lead time for the development of resources—facilities and trained manpower, both—with which the work is to be done, and that these resources (e.g. an oceanographic vessel, and accelerator, or a scientist who has just received his Ph.D.) will be in use for many years after their emergence.

For all of these reasons, then, some long-range centralized planning is on the cards for the future. Minor attempts are already being made, out of which the major accomplishment to date seems to be to have clarified the problems that have to be faced before planning can be effective.[3] Brooks has himself headed an FCST Committee on Long-Range Planning (an interesting example of an inter-agency governmental committee headed by a non-governmental person).

Perhaps the strongest factor of all in impelling us toward science planning is Congress' insistence upon knowing what is being done with R&D's $17 billion, and on seeing that it is used effectively. Although "planning" as an abstraction has as little appeal to Congress as to the scientists (even less, probably, since the legislators are more often ideologically inclined), the legislators nevertheless want planning in the concrete, as a matter of economy, efficiency, and effectiveness. They have a professional fear of "wasting the taxpayers' money" and tend to identify planning with anti-waste activity. So political pressures are added to the more intrinsic reasons for developing science and technology plans.

The earlier tradition of science and scientists was a privatized and individualized one, and to suggest science planning still means to many a stupid attempt to plan what is unplannable: basic research is unpredictable and no one—particularly no administrator away from the bench—can direct who should do what research. At the level of the individual researcher, particularly when engaged in academic research not connected with any mission at all, this is certainly true. But the scientists worrying about this have ignored the fact that there are other stages and other types of planning. While we cannot plan the individual's efforts, we can—and had better, if facilities are to be available as needed—plan some of the resource development that makes the individual choices possible. And we can plan some of the relationships between science and other sectors.

Note, for example, that Brooks's list of reasons for planning include such matters as the effect social problems are likely to have upon the careers of scientists and engineers, upon universities, and upon regional economic growth. None of these is entirely a science problem as such; they are all societal problems in which the development and use of science provide important parameters. What they need, desperately, is some basis other than hunch, if effective use is to be made of the resources we are developing. And being more than science problems, they call for a planning process and a set of institutional arrangements that will provide all the appropriate contributions (what social scientists today like to call "inputs") from all affected sectors. OST and PSAC do not fulfil this need, for they lack adequate representation from outside the scientific establishment. They can cover one area, congressional hearings another.

Within the realm that science planning as such can occupy, there should be a major effort to develop common assumptions and some overall goals to serve as guidelines for agency planning. So far, we have largely worked in the reverse fashion, with agency programs coming first and BOB-OST interjections of common goals only afterward. Some of those engaged in efforts at science planning apparently feel it cannot be done any other way. Thus an FCST commentary on planning efforts proclaims that

> The starting point in long-range planning for the Federal Government is planning within the agencies. What the Federal Government does is the sum of what they do.[4]

While there is truth in this, one hopes it is only part of the truth—that what the government does is not *merely* the literal sum of agency plans. For if it were that, the Special Assistant and his associates would not even be trying to "get this $17 billion under control."

Admittedly, the term "planning" has a variety of denotations and connotations, and the processes and limits of planning will vary with the amenability of different types of subject matter. For example, we can plan to have a new accelerator ready for use in x years, and be quite definite about it. But if we "plan" to double the number of social scientists in x years, we are expressing a hope, and perhaps inaugurating a financial stimulus through fellowships—but we are not dealing with as controllable a subject. Admittedly, also, planning in the area of science-social problems resembles planning for manpower more than it does planning the use of bricks and mortar. Yet even if a plan were in fact a guideline of preferred results rather than a fixed program, it would be an advance over what we have today. As in economic policy, American science planning will be of the looser variety, but the days of treating R&D as unplannable and lacking in any need for top-side rationalization are clearly drawing to a close.

Although we have not gone at the planning business deeply enough or long enough yet to be able to speak with confidence about just what should be included and what categories of planning will prove useful, we can suggest at least some of the factors to be considered.

At the most broad and basic level, any effective framework for science planning will have to face the problem of how to mix three quite different variables: (1) the scientific merits of various fields—how ripe they are for making significant advances in scientific knowledge, significant here meaning from the viewpoint of science itself; (2) the specific practical uses that the society would like to make of scientific knowledge— mass transportation, supersonic flight, weather modification, planetary exploration, food from the oceans, or the treatment of urban disorganization and alienation; and (3) by-product consequences of the R&D effort—support of graduate education, broader geographic distribution of scientific activities, or greater public understanding of the origins and nature of our universe. Because each of these categories requires a different set of criteria for basic decisions, and each has to be related to the others, one can see immediately that the institutional

CHALLENGES TO THINGS AS THEY ARE

structure of science planning will itself have to be comprised of a variety of stages, levels, and inter-institutional groupings.

At another level, science planning will have to deal with such questions as the respective roles of universities, government laboratories, non-profit institutes, and profit-seeking business firms in performing research and development activities of different kinds. And it will have to review and determine the appropriate mix of modes of R&D support in relationship to the particular needs of each kind of institution.

At yet another stage, dealing with the most internal questions of science, planners will have to face such questions as: Why this field at x-dollars per year? Why this field at x-dollars while that field is funded at y-dollars? Why this project rather than that one within a specific field? Why a specific total for R&D: As the sum of all parts? as a percentage of Gross National Product? as a function of the existing and desired levels of manpower? Some of these call for overall consideration; others (especially choice of specific projects) are matters for the specialists to handle once the overall pattern has determined the allocation for a specific field.

These questions lead us from planning in its overall aspects to the setting of priorities in specific cases.

PRIORITIES: THE CHALLENGE OF LIMITS

While each discipline within basic science is willing to examine its own needs and opportunities and make its own claim on the federal treasury, no group of scientists has yet come to the fore to take on the difficult (some think impossible) task of comparing one field's needs and ripeness with another. Alvin Weinberg's willingness to devise criteria and apply them concretely is a rare example that simply proves the rule. As Daniel S. Greenberg has said, in remarking that the question of Project Mohole's priority never arose, "The ideology of basic science was such that all unanswered scientific questions were equal; the only inequality lay in the ability of the various researchers to tap into the federal treasury." [5]

Furthermore, it is not just basic disciplines that have to be compared but a whole range of needs and institutions affected by R&D budgets. Are the universities that do 60 per cent of basic research to be given priority over the government and non-profit laboratories that do the other 40 per cent? Among development projects, is an atomic energy-desalinization plant to take priority over (or under) a supersonic transport, or a soft landing on Mars over an anti-missile missile? Is manpower development more or less important than hardware developments? How about optimal research results *versus* broader institutional involvement in research? These, and hundreds of questions more, await a priorities framework. The framework is partly an institutional question of planning, as we have seen; it is equally a matter of devising intellectually and politically defensible criteria by which whatever group making the choices will be guided.

Some observers feel that explicitly formulated, generally acceptable comparative criteria are beyond our capabilities and will be for some time. In that case, one turns to the institutions that make the choices and says that if these are well-structured, then we will just have to trust to their judgments. That may in fact be what we do—it is partly what we do now —but it will not suffice for the long run. The questions are too pressing, the stakes too high, for either scientists or their political overseers and patrons to be satisfied until the criteria problem is squarely faced and some consensus reached.

Why are the questions too pressing? One reason lies in the budgetary situation, another lies in the apparent pattern of scientific advance.

Scientists and political figures are most conscious of the budgetary situation. So long as the R&D budget was in the steeply inclining upward stage of a growth curve, most of these problems were minimized, if not entirely obviated, by growth: policy was not so much a matter of choice as of addition: add to last year's figures whatever new amounts were called for this year. Federal money was a heady wine in the 1950s and up to 1963–64. Since then, if the wine has not soured, it is at least not flowing as freely. Not that there has been a decline—which some of the more shrill cries of protest would lead one to believe—but the rate of growth has slowed substantially, while the number of problems and researchers eager to tackle them still grows at the pace to which the scientific community had happily become accustomed. Therefore, there may actually be a decline in the amount available *per scientist* despite some rise in the overall dollar figure. In any case, budgetary tightness is upon us, begun perhaps by congressional alarm as the R&D total approached the 15-billion-dollar mark, and accentuated by the general stringency occasioned by Vietnam war costs.

As if this were not enough, there seems to be a problem intrinsic to science: each major or minor breakthrough that the scientists succeed in making leads to a larger number of new scientific questions to be answered: the opportunities for new knowledge expand as the previous set of opportunities is fulfilled. Furthermore, new research tools and technologies open up the way for experiments previously not researchable. A dramatic example is provided by Project Mohole, the abortive (aborted by congressional appropriations fiat) effort to drill through the earth's crust to the mantle, under the ocean. Mohole cost some $30 millions before it was called off; it would have cost over $100 million if it had been carried through. It would not have been tried at all, however, unless the technology of deep-sea drilling had not taken a big jump forward to make feasible the positioning of a ship for drilling from an ocean perch and unless new drilling bits and materials for the drilling pipe had been developed. Other examples of the same phenomenon would include the laser and the computer: because of them, we need money for experiments that could not otherwise be conducted.

One can hardly feel sad that research opportunities are being enlarged, but there is reason for concern over the adequacy of our intellectual and institutional bases for making the hard choices that now loom before us—choices between basic research and technological development, choices within each of these realms.

Within basic science of the kind performed by individuals the intrinsic criteria of scientific merit—ripeness of the field and competence of the people in it—almost undoubtedly are the appropriate ones, but we have institutionalized only the choices within each field (the panel system), not the choices of fields as such. The panel system is a mechanism by which panels of academic scientists in a given field evaluate the proposals made by other scientists in the same field, and then advise the funding agency which proposals to approve. Proposal pressures (the number of proposals approved compared with the funds available) provide one key, and this comparison has apparently helped chemistry to argue successfully for an increase in its share of NSF funds. Major breakthroughs, as in molecular biology, perhaps provide another intellectually defensible way of determining which field should get a priority: money should be available to exploit the major breakthroughs. And, since NSF funds only a small proportion even of basic research, there is another priority-determining criterion that is in fact used—though I am not certain that the spokesmen of academic science would explicitly endorse it. I refer to the support of basic research by mission-oriented agencies on the criterion of what will be most likely to advance their missions. Assistant Secretary of the Air Force Alexander H. Flax explains that in supporting most of the nation's fundamental research, the mission-oriented agencies

> provide, in effect, a means of orienting the research efforts in this country and of emphasizing some fields more than others. Now by this I do not mean that a physicist doing research in plasma physics under the sponsorship of the Department of Defense will be in any way constrained to orient his research toward some specific conception of a weapons system of a communications system which might possibly result from his work on plasmas. On the other hand, all other things being equal, the Air Force is more likely to be supporting work on plasmas having characteristics like those in the ionosphere or around the re-entry vehicles as opposed to those to be found on distant stars. At the same time, we are aware that it may, in some future decades, be a plasma like that on some distant star which is relevant to some defense problem.[6]

In Flax's view, it is NSF's task to assure "that no promising area of research is overlooked merely because the vision of the mission-oriented agencies is too short." Our challenge is to see if these procedures and criteria can be improved upon.

One thing that might help, for example, would be the development of a concept of diminishing returns in science: can we identify areas that are about to become "played out," in which no further large gains can be seen from existing approaches? If we could phase out (or scale down) some research areas as they reach that state, it would be easier to phase in newly emerging fields and projects.

An intellectual basis for a concept of diminishing returns would seem to exist in the fact that some limits are absolute, so that as they are approached, we would know we had reached the end of the line. Caryl Haskins writes that "there are indeed limits in nature which lie wholly outside man's making, and . . . , rather than feeling responsible for these limits and frustrated about them, we should actually welcome them as opportunities to release our energies in new directions." He then points to high-energy physics, asking whether further increases in energy levels to 200 BEVs or possibly to 1000 BEVs will be as fruitful as the earlier moves from 20 million to half a billion to 30 billion electron volts. Every seven years, he points out, the energy level has been increased by a factor of ten. He doubts that we can keep this up. Similarly, in the technological field of travel speeds: the train was a big jump over the horse, the plane over the train. The supersonic plane represents another large jump, but perhaps a less crucial one than that from propeller craft to existing jets. And there is an absolute limit ahead of 18,000 miles per hour—orbiting speed, which is not likely to be of (literally) earthly value. As examples of played-out fields, he mentions the determination of atomic weights and the identification of new stable isotopes. But then he suggests that two opportunities of greater promise are likely to arise for every single opportunity that fades out.[7] If this is a good guess, then it becomes even more important not to pour funds into dying areas; we should identify them *before* rigor mortis has set in, and begin to shift resources away toward more promising new areas.

If we could couple the identification of areas of diminishing returns with solid analyses of the major gaps in our knowledge (and on an inter-field basis, to include gaps in biology, say, that could be aided by some development in physics), perhaps we would be on our way to the creation of a rational priorities system, intellectually if not institutionally.

THE CHALLENGE OF BIG SCIENCE
AND INSTITUTIONAL SUPPORT

The prototype science around which most discussions of science policy by academically based scientists have revolved is what is often called "little science." It is done on the campus by a single researcher (or a small, informal group) with his (or their) graduate assistants. It is closely tied in with teaching —is, in fact, a part of graduate teaching—and its federally financed projects are funded as the result of individual application (endorsed by the institution in which it will be conducted), screened by agency science staffs or by an advisory panel or study section of peers drawn from other higher education institutions. This is the vaunted project-and-panel system dear to the hearts of the articulate campus spokesmen. In its pure form, it is found primarily in NSF and NIH; there are no exact figures available to indicate the extent to which this system of screening applications is used by the other research supporting agencies, although we do know what they do not all use the external panel system in determining what to fund.

We also know that another kind of prototype—the Big Science syndrome—is coming to the fore, and that Big Science cannot be handled in the same manner as little science. Big Science centers upon (1) very large facilities and very expensive equipment—so large and so expensive that we could not even consider supplying every university, let alone every scientist; and (2) "highly coordinated group effort" (Kistiakowsky's phrase). Examples are the Stanford, Princeton-Pennsylvania, and Brookhaven accelerators (the latter brings in a third element of Big Science: management by an inter-university consortium), the Kitts Peak National Observatory, and an oceanographic ship. In each case, costs are measured in the millions or hundred millions (whereas the "unit costs"

of little science average $15–50,000); long lead time is required
when a new facility or research center is to be developed; and
the number of scientists whose research involves such facilities
is small. Also, Big Science facilities are often separated physi-
cally from university campuses; increasingly they are set up as
autonomous entities, operated under joint contract between
the sponsoring agency and a multi-university consortium, to
which involved scientists travel from their home bases for a
summer or an academic year (in addition to a small group
whose base is the facility itself).

The very high cost of Big Science facilities means that
direct competition exists among them: in any single year—or
even any single decade—many cannot be funded. If an accelerator, an oceanographic ship, a radio telescope, a biological
research program involving thousands of guinea pigs, and a
very large computer installation are proposed this year, a
choice is going to have to be made, because one or two of these
is the probable upper limit. And the impact carries over; the
running expenses of any one of these constitutes a multi-year
commitment that has to be taken into account when next year's
proposals are made.

Not only are these things costly; because of their size and
cost, they can have a real impact on the communities and
economic regions into which they are placed. This means that
geographic politics plays a real part in locational decisions in
Big Science. Also, because these represent a research potential
not to be copied on each campus, inter-field infighting is involved in making the choices: Big Science facilities cannot be
handed out by the usual single-discipline panels. Because each
one selected has an opportunity cost in the form of other programs or facilities *not* selected, inter-field rivalry demands
inter-field assessment in the choice process.

This is one area in which the spokesmen of science appear

to be largely in agreement on the need for priorities and conscious planning. Even though Big Science is, like its campus-based little counterpart, still basic research, one hears little argument that these major choices should be left to "idle curiosity" or determined by "proposal pressure." But while such agreement exists, the mechanisms and standards by which each decision is to be made are not at all clear yet, beyond the premise that such decisions are "more than scientific," that they involve questions of what Weinberg called extrinsic social merit, of mission-agency interest, and of just plain politics and economics.

Closely related to Big Science as a factor with high cost and also driving us away from the advisory panel mode of decision-making is the more general development of institutional, as opposed to individual, modes of science support. The shift toward institutional modes has not been sudden, but it has now reached a point where it cannot be ignored, and it has received added impetus from the President's memorandum of September 14, 1965, calling for broader institutional distribution of research funds and for more careful attention to the needs of the universities in making research support decisions.[8]

Institutional support takes a variety of forms: laboratory buildings and equipment; fellowships or traineeships to be awarded by the fund-receiving university rather than directly by the sponsoring agency; science development grants; support of both teaching and research institutes; NASA's university sustaining program; and what is called specifically the NSF "institutional grant," meaning that percentage of a university's project-supporting funds which is given to the institution who will use it flexibly in fulfilling needs not appropriately supported by grants to individual investigators.

Whatever the particular form taken by institutional support, it characteristically involves considerations additional to, or in place of, that of financing immediate research results. The overriding separate goal of institutional support is to develop the resources through which science will be performed and future scientists trained, whereas project grants directly support the research project. With these developmental, institutional, and educational goals goes a requirement for a different kind of advisory and decision-making apparatus and different, multiple-factor criteria of choice. Educational specialists perhaps become as relevant as scientific researchers, and the sponsoring agencies play a continuing role, instead of just supplying the funds and leaving the investigator alone until he reports at the end of his project. Even a different style of management—as well as simply *more* management from the government side—is required for large programs and for institutional development. Also, where aid to the universities is frankly admitted to be the goal, the institutions and their congressional delegations (i.e. the congressmen and senators from the districts and states in which the institutions are located) are appropriately more active in pressing their felt needs. The Office of Education and the Federal Interagency Committee on Education have strong reasons for claiming representation in such matters, along with NSF and OST. Like Big Science, institutional support moves us away from the individual project-peer-group, panel-style of operation. The panel system, if not on the way out, is at least declining in relative importance; if other advisory arrangements come into play, they will differ by being much broader in composition than the single-discipline panels to which academic scientists are accustomed, and which some of them seem to think are not just customary but decreed by the very nature of things.

NSF, the ideological central focus of the project-panel system since its inception in 1950, does not itself, nor did it even in the late 1950s, employ the majority of its funds in project support. In 1959, its basic research expenditure was $46 million, but its total budget was $133 million. In fiscal 1966, project support took $157 million, but Big Science programs (called National Research Programs and National Research Centers) got $78 million; and both of these together accounted for slightly under half of NSF's $480 million budget. Science education, equipment, buildings, training institutes, and the like comprised the remainder.

The movement toward an institutional pattern can be seen in the development of NSF's program over time: in 1958, when the cooperative fellowship program began, it gave receiving institutions the task of choosing the fellows instead of having this done directly by NSF; in 1961, NSF institutional grants were inaugurated; in 1964, the science development program began to bring second-rank institutions up to first rank; in 1966–67, college and departmental development programs were added to the mix, and the National Science Board was discussing the possibility of "master grants" that would lessen further the proportions of funding done through the project-panel system.

Since we lack firm, government-wide figures on Big-little science proportions, and on individual-institutional proportions, we are not certain how big, or how rapidly growing, is the challenge to ideology and institutions from these sources of change. We *can* safely assert that the challenge is substantial; and I fear that we can also safely say that it has yet to be faced squarely as a problem of substantive criteria or of governmental-advisory processes.

Also largely unrecognized so far is the fact that these developments constitute elements of planning for science, even though they are rarely called that. One day we will awaken to find that we have an extensive planning system within federal science programs, but it will not be a rationalized one because

we have failed to recognize what we have been doing for what
it is.

Perhaps the largest single change in the environment of
science policy development during the past 20 years has been
the emergency of congressional committees as major overseers
and style setters.

This is partly seen in the simple increase in the number of
committees and subcommittees of the Congress dealing with
one aspect or another of science and technology. After the
Joint Committee on Atomic Energy was created in 1946, there
was a twelve-year hiatus before Sputnik I brought about the
organization of a Senate Committee on Space and Astronautics
and a House Committee on Science and Astronautics. Then in
1963–64 came the first general coverage hearings on science
policy, through the House Science Committee and its temporary companion, the Select (Elliott) Committee on Government Research. Since 1962, Rep. Fountain's House Subcommittee on Intergovernmental Relations has kept close watch
on NIH; Rep. Henry S. Reuss has been developing a science
policy role through his Research and Technical Programs subcommittee; Rep. Daddario has adopted NSF as his "ward" with
his Subcommittee on Science, Research, and Development;
and Senator Fred Harris of Oklahoma has filled a gap in the
Senate's coverage through very active hearings of his Government Operations Committee Subcommittee on Government
Research.

If scientists once needed only to make their points in the
quiet atmosphere (relatively) of the advisory structure of the
executive branch, they have recently found it necessary to
enter the more public (and dangerous) arena of Capitol Hill

politics. To have persuaded the executive, assuming that it would carry the day unaided in the Congress, is a dream of the halcyon past. Today, the legislators have minds of their own in regard to science affairs: greater familiarity has not by any means bred contempt, but it has bred self-confidence, and that has led increasingly to a pattern in which Congress amends executive goals in science policy by interjection of its own goals.

So far, these have taken the form of (1) selecting particular fields of R&D for emphasis (oceanography, nuclear ships, for example) or de-emphasis (Project Mohole); (2) demanding much broader geographic distribution of the R&D "pork barrel"; and (3) demanding maximum attention to technological and social "pay-offs."

Senator Harris, whose home state of Oklahoma received one-tenth of 1 per cent of the $14.3 billion of R&D expenditures in fiscal 1964, has been a vehement proponent of a more "equitable" distribution. He held very vigorous hearings on this matter in 1966. The major burden-bearers from the executive branch were the Special Assistant, Hornig, and NSF's Director, Haworth. They claimed essentially that they shared the legislative concern—pointing to the President's directive of September 14, 1965, and to the actions being taken in accord with it to bring more institutions into the picture—and showed that things were really not so bad.

Harris called attention to the percentages of R&D funds going to particular states, ranging from California's 34.6 per cent and New York's 7.9 per cent through Ohio's 2.2 per cent, to five states (Maine, Delaware, Nebraska, Arkansas, and Vermont) that each received less than one-tenth of 1 per cent, and to the per capita expenditures which ranged from $315 in California to $3.21 in Arkansas. Hornig and Haworth, on the other hand, stressed the comparison of R&D funds in each state with production of Ph.D.'s, which comes out in much closer balance. For instance, New England had 12.8 per cent of the funds and produced 10.6 per cent of the doctorates in 1964; the West North Central states got 6.4 per cent of the money and produced 9.6 per cent of the Ph.D.'s. "Considered on this basis," Hornig told Harris, "there are certainly no gross inequities or maldistribution of Federal funds, even though there are some differences." [9]

Haworth and Hornig also stressed *institutional* rather than *per state* distribution, on the premise that they could show better results on that basis, and that it was, after all, only through university development that the other advantages sought by the legislators could accrue. Hornig pointed out that "the most rapid growth of support has taken place in institutions with little previous tradition in research. . . . Ninety per cent of the funds were spent in 65 universities in the late forties and 105 universities in fiscal 1965." He also shifted the burden of blame, as it were, by asserting that "the less favored regions are, in fact, the regions which have not built up academic institutions which can submit their share of meritorious applications. Consequently, the real problem is to expand and improve higher education in these regions." [10]

Haworth explained his "philosophy" of distribution in this manner:

> The key to the problem of greater geographic distribution of research funds lies in improving the scientific capability of those institutions which have the desire and the potential to become centers of high quality research and education in the sciences. This we can and should do, directing our aim toward special mechanisms designed to strengthen institutions, or major segments of them, as a whole, rather than attempting to accomplish this in a way that mixes the separate criteria required by the project system, where specific results count, with the quite different requirements of institution building. It is important

to recognize that it is not feasible for each and every institution of higher learning to become a first-class research center. But it is important that such centers exist in all regions of the country, both to give opportunity for the young people of the region inclined toward scientific careers the opportunity to pursue them effectively, and to provide intellectual leadership for other educational and economic components of the region at all levels." [11]

Senator Harris was not entirely pleased with Haworth's and Hornig's deflections of his points in their re-interpreting the problem:

it seems to me that you and Dr. Haworth [he told Hornig], from whom we have heard earlier, have been a little bit patronizing and condescending in your treatment of this committee by coming here and saying some things which are rather obvious; that educational excellence is primarily a local matter. We all know that. You can't divide research and development funds on any kind of rigid formula or geographic distribution—that is elementary.

And that you can't divide mission-oriented research and development funds on the basis of a need for more centers of excellence but that they have got to be on the basis of whether or not the mission will be accomplished. Now both of you have about the same kind of statement. You have spent half your time saying these things are not as bad as I think they are and are not really as important as I think, but that you are doing a whole lot about it anyway.

Now, I think if we would recognize this is of great concern, and a problem which is tied in with the economic development of this country, and with national policy, and quit talking down to Members of Congress, as you have done, I think, in the first half of this statement, then we would come a lot nearer to getting down to some cases, here and now. [12]

What particularly irritated Harris was that, despite the President's 1965 memorandum on broader distribution, Hornig had said that it did not seem to him that redistribution of existing research monies would solve the issue. He meant that new programs specifically geared to institutional development should be brought to play, not a twisting of the project system. But Harris, and other legislators, have not easily been persuaded that as much has been done as could be done, even within existing funds.

The point for us is not to pick who's right and who's wrong, but to see that congressional interjections of this kind are posing new challenges to the policy-makers, that considerations other than strictly scientific are being brought into the picture, whether the scientists like to have to think about them or not.

Closely related to the geographic distribution demand is, of course, the desire to maximize regional economic benefit and civilian "spin-off" from esoteric research. Almost every senator and representative harps on the "Route 128" theme, and increasingly on the civil technology use of arcane research. This is more than a little ironic, considering that the Kennedy Administration in fact proposed a specific civilian technology program, only to have it knocked down in Congress by the lobbying of industries fearful of having their established positions disrupted by new technologies. Despite that, however, there is now a good deal of pressure to use R&D for mass transit, housing, anti-pollution measures, resource development, and so forth; i.e. for Congress to press for more useful involvement of R&D. The legislators accept the need to develop our scientific potential, but they want to see much more attention paid to linking science-supporting with science-using considerations. It is no longer enough simply to aver that basic research pays off in time; the legislators want to know that the executive is working on ways to maximize and speed up pay-offs.

THE CHALLENGE OF CHANGE

The world of science affairs is undergoing substantial change, and change is the basic challenge to the existing system. A science framework in which R&D was done primarily to purchase defense and atomic energy, and to advance scientific knowledge itself only through one small agency (NSF), has become a framework in which many objectives are sought simultaneously, one in which some things that were originally accidental by-products have now become central objectives— development of more universities to the point of becoming "centers of excellence," for example. Because the elements do constitute a system, it was inevitable that what one element did would come to affect other segments. Perhaps we could not have predicted in advance what has developed, but at least with hindsight it is easy to see that universities could not have their faculties drawn into federally financed research projects without themselves being affected too. Certainly one would not *a priori* have picked the Department of Defense to be a primary source of funds for research in the nation's universities; since it has been that, however, we now find that we are expecting it to pursue a conscious policy of underwriting the health of the universities in the ways it conducts its research programs. Conversely, we have an Office of Education, which has a $3-billion annual budget but perhaps less impact on higher education (with the recent exception of large numbers of NDEA fellowships) than a number of departments and agencies not charged with aiding education at all.

In short, what academics would call the "functional specificity" of federal agencies is breaking down under the impact of new challenges: whatever an agency's ostensible primary field of operation or objectives, to the extent that it engages in R&D it becomes, like it or not, a part of the network of influence surrounding science affairs, education, and economic development. This brings us back to the first challenge: the challenge of planning. Given the complexity and number of challenges to the substantive goals of science policy today, it is clear that in equivalent proportions there is produced a challenge to our institutional structure, processes, and procedures. In the study of government, it is "old hat" that the ways in which we do things affects what gets done; it is equally true, though less often recognized, that as functions change substantively (e.g. as education and economic growth are added to scientific productivity as goals of science affairs policy) such changes reciprocally affect the ways in which we have to do things.

If our complex of goals is to be fruitful, we cannot count on this happening by the free play of pluralist competition. It is one thing to talk glibly about the benefits and joys of pluralism in providing support for science; it is quite another to ensure that different programs of different agencies do not work at cross-purposes, especially when they may be affecting the same institution at a given moment. Only through a structure of integration and conscious coordination can we ensure— or at least do our best toward ensuring—that we will get the most out of what we do in our multiple-purpose activities under the general heading of research and development.

Here we have covered several general challenges to things as they are. Next, we develop two more specific challenges: that of social science seeking a place in the politics of science support (Chapter 6), and in the following chapter, that of NSF's structure and role in a considerably more matured R&D system than existed when that agency began operations nearly two decades ago.

6| The Challenge of the Social Sciences

Where do the social sciences fit?

That question challenges the criteria, institutional arrangements, and processes that have been worked out in the natural science-government relationship. Because of the challenge, some of the issues of science policy development may stand out with greater clarity by examining them in relationship to this area in which they are arising afresh. Not that the social sciences are not already supported, for they are. But their support —and use—have not been rationalized to the same degree as have the physical and life sciences. The social sciences have no explicit home in government (i.e. no agency primarily concerned with their development and application), and they have little representation in the policy-making framework of government-science affairs. Their policy framework remains to be developed, almost from scratch.

The question of social science-government relationships is of considerable long-range importance to society, however, for if social science challenges government, it is in turn also being challenged by government on behalf of society—challenged to produce, to make an impact upon the solution or amelioration of a variety of societal problems ranging from smog control to birth control. It is hardly a novelty today to suggest that our technological capabilities may be outrunning our social capabilities, but Paul Miller, an assistant secretary of HEW, puts the need for the social sciences particularly well:

> If we direct our attention to the demands of today's world and the needs of tomorrow's, a great majority of our problems are clearly of the sort to which the social sciences have and should increasingly turn their attention. It makes no difference whether we look at our own country specifically or if we look at the world generally. Men face problems of building and renewing the economies of nations. Men are trying to create new kinds of political institutions which are more responsive to people. Men face the real problem of living with—in fact, preserving— diversity in a world brought closer and closer by new marvels of transportation and communication. For all these and other problems, we can no longer afford to relegate the social sciences to a second-rate, stepchild position.[1]

Government social science policy—like its older brother, natural science policy—may be divided into policies for the development of scientific capabilities and resources, and policies for the utilization of those resources in problem-solving situations. In the case of the social sciences, however, it is harder to separate these strands, for research that helps to advance a social science discipline may simultaneously have a direct application. Opinion survey research, for example, may be designed in a specific instance to contribute to methodological improvement of that kind of work and the training of graduate students; but the findings of any opinion survey may have an impact on electoral, party, or policy problems, depending on the subject matter of the questions posed.

The public image (and I definitely include the natural

scientists as part of the outside public, sharing in its attitudes and assumptions) of the social sciences further complicates matters because it tends to see them only in their applied uses —showing us how to avoid riots, establish administrative apparatus in developing countries, or solve the problem of poverty. There is little idea of what the development of social science theory does or can mean, little idea of the social sciences as bodies of systematic knowledge in process of development and having internal criteria for their own research, just as does, say, chemistry. Support of the social sciences is therefore often taken to mean support of their use rather than of their internal development. And the expectations of what the social sciences will be able to do often amount to a "conception of social science as a kind of supereffective, rational remedy for difficult situations." [2]

But that is to get ahead of ourselves slightly, for there are anterior problems to be considered. The fundamental issue, in fact, is whether the social sciences are sciences at all—in the same meaning as physics and chemistry. The range of opinions on this issue is large, among both natural and social scientists. The only consensus is on the proposition that *if* the social sciences do have anything definite to contribute, we surely need that contribution now!

What is a science? Strangely enough, the answer is unclear. In Europe, a broad meaning is given to the term; it is almost synonymous with "organized knowledge." In this country, however, science has taken on a much narrower denotation. A typical American characterization of a scientific truth "is that it can be put into quantitative statements that are testable." [3] Much social science would elude that definition. Jerome Weisner has commented on the different meanings, asserting that the narrow meaning causes problems in our handling of social science research:

> I think that the problem stems from the way we inter-
> pret the word "science" in this country. If we had the
> Russian or European interpretation of "science," which
> is just the development of knowledge, this probably
> wouldn't exist. All of us who have dealt with some of the
> foreign academies of science are surprised to find his-
> torians, economists, political scientists, as full-fledged
> members of their academies of science. I think this is
> unfortunate in our country for this separation has gen-
> erated a split among intellectuals which is undesirable.[4]

The split may be undesirable, but it appears likely to continue, if one examines comments upon the relationship of the
natural and the social sciences, or comments upon the diversity
of meanings within social science alone. Starting from a natural
scientist's image of the criteria of being scientific, W. O. Baker
of Bell Laboratories (where psychologists and sociologists are
at least in some degree integrated with physical scientists)
asserts that "Science . . . is science, whatever its particular
content may be. The work of a scientist must meet the same
criteria of verifiability and relevance whatever his field." [5]

If this be the criterion, then many scientists are dubious
about the scientific qualities of social science. Weinberg, for
example, calls attention to the variety of "schools" of social
science thought, and to the absence of a common language.
Because of these characteristics, he says that social science is in
a "pre-scientific stage," and that it is "not very ripe for exploitation." The questions it tries to grapple with are important, says Weinberg, but its ability to handle them is not great
enough to justify any greatly increased financial support.[6] A
much more sanguine view, on the other hand, is taken by
Wiesner, a former presidential adviser, whose reply to a Reuss
subcommittee questionnaire included these opinions:

> The social sciences are not going to point the way defini-
> tively to a solution of all our ills, but they can give us a

steadily deeper understanding of the working of our society, a better information base, and hence an enhanced ability to design our national programs to bring about desired objectives in the most efficient and productive manner. . . .

There is no question but that the multiplicity of variables in social relationships, and the difficulty of carrying out controlled experiments, necessarily makes the results complex and more controversial than in the natural sciences. However, the social sciences have made great progress in areas such as understanding the processes of political development of the emerging countries, human and group psychology, economies, foreign area studies and many others. Moreover, the promise inherent in the application of new tools such as modern data processing techniques open up enormous possibilities for enhanced ability to deal with multivariant situations.[7]

In NSF Director Haworth's view, too, "the proportion of research in social science subjects that is objective, independently verifiable, and subject to useful generalization has been growing in recent years." [8] It is this proportion that Haworth would call legitimately scientific, and NSF under his direction (as well as under his predecessor) confines its support to this part of the social sciences.

Despite such comments, Harold Orlans probably aptly characterizes a larger segment among natural scientists as being "skeptical, scornful, or commiserative about the scientific status of the social sciences." [9] One speaks of a "clear and identifiable gap between the natural and social sciences"; another says that the social sciences "are in many cases not yet ready" to deal with many problems one would like them to handle, and that (outside of the Council of Economic Advisers) the "soft" sciences will be slow to provide the hard facts needed by bodies like PSAC. Yet this same man also says that the social sciences "deserve strong support." Still another sees the basic approaches as "vastly different" and thinks it difficult to mesh social and natural sciences in joint efforts; however, he also sees a clear need to use social science as far as it can go today to provide "adequate analysis of the social-political-economic consequences" of technological programs, and thinks that physical scientists and engineers are "eager to include social scientists within their councils." At least some members of PSAC, however, think that body would be too "diluted" if social scientists were added to it.[10]

Thinking of scientific as meaning quantitative, replicable, independently verifiable, precise work, the natural scientists tend to take the position that either social science is respectably scientific or it is not. The notion of gradations, of a spectrum of work that runs from purely quantitative to purely qualitative, even speculative, is largely absent from their views. Among the social scientists themselves, there is great awareness of such a spectrum. The division among the social scientists is between those who would emphasize or legitimize only the quantitative end of the spectrum and those who see all parts of the con-tinuum as worthy of pursuit—even that which is closest to the opposite pole of humanism. Psychologists—much of whose work today is close to physiology and biology—tend to speak of the behavioral rather than the social sciences, and by doing so to stress the quantitative approach and the strength of linkages with the natural sciences. Political scientists and, to a lesser extent, sociologists and economists, more frequently have a broader conception of "proper" social science work—whether it would be called scientific or not by a physicist.

The natural scientists are not sure whether there is any-thing scientific about the social sciences, and the social scien-tists disagree about whether there ought to be anything about them that is not scientific. But at least both camps have *some* conception of research about man and society. Some legislators —and this is a major cause for concern about the fate of the social science-government relationship—have no conception at all. Thus Congressman Joe L. Evins of Tennessee, who heads the appropriations subcommittee that handles NSF and other independent agencies, once asked the NSF representative whether the agency was going to train politicians, when he saw that 17 grants were for political science. That could be a joke, but the conversation that followed indicated it was a joke only unconsciously, for Evins then asked what was the nature of books by political scientists: "how to become a candidate? how to enter politics? Somebody writes in and asks you to give them a grant?" [11] Evins was then assured that NSF was not getting into politics! Another example of complete misunderstanding occurred when Senator John McClellan of Arkansas was told about an Air Force-sponsored Harvard project on the Soviet social system that was "to determine how to carry on psychological warfare against the Soviet and the satellites." McClellan's response was this:

> What do you get, just a lot of professor theories and all that stuff? . . . To me, that is simply throwing money away, nothing else. If we have not sense enough in the Army and the Navy and the Defense Department and as American citizens to know how to counteract Soviet propaganda without hiring a bunch of college professors to write out a lot of theories, this Defense Department is in one darn bad shape. . . . [12]

One hopes that most legislative opinions of social research and its potential contributions will lie somewhere between such neanderthal views and those (of which there are a few more, perhaps) with too-high expectations for the social sciences.

The disagreements over how scientific the social sciences are or should be or can be—which of course have implications for the organizational relationship to be forged between the social sciences and the governmental structure—are paralleled by differences regarding the potential utility of the social sciences even among its practitioners. Arguing that it is much more difficult to solve problems with the social sciences because of differences in the way they are applied as compared with the natural sciences and engineering, an eminent sociologist, Kingsley Davis, has spoken of "The Perilous Promise of Behavioral Science" in this vein:

> the notion that one can solve social problems by studying society, just as one solves medical problems by studying the body, is a false analogy. Applied science, by definition, is instrumental. When the human goal is given, it seeks a solution by finding what effective means can be manipulated in the required way. Its function is to satisfy human desires and wants; otherwise nobody would bother. But when the science is concerned with human beings—not just as organisms but as goal-seeking individuals and members of groups—then it cannot be instrumental in this way, because the object of observation has a say in what is going on and, above all, is not willing to be treated as a pure instrumentality. Most so-called social problems are problems because people want certain things or because there is a conflict of desires or interests.

The social scientist, he goes on, is incapable of solving many problems because "he does not have control over the objects he is studying"—people. Conflicts over goals and means are the "fundamental source of trouble in human societies," and people in conflict will not accept solutions which require them to change their behavior radically. Thus warnings that cigarettes are a health hazard have had no effect at all on people's smoking habits—except possibly to increase them—but the technological solution (i.e. finding a way to eliminate the cancerous and heart-disease elements from the tobacco) would be immediately acceptable to everyone. The secret of applied social research, says Davis, "is absence of conflict." If the goal is agreed upon and people are open as to the means, social science can be used. The application of economics to problems of inflation and depression illustrates that social science sometimes can be applied successfully. But Davis is persuasive in arguing that there will be many occasions when we will call for the application of social science "engineering" in vain—not because of lack of knowledge but because of human obstreperousness.[13]

In considerable contrast stand the expectations of psychologist Donald N. Michael regarding social engineering. Michael, program director of the Center for Research on Utilization of Scientific Knowledge at the University of Michigan, believes that "if we are to cope with the impact of technology, we must have major social inventions as well as hardware inventions." To match the needs, he believes that there will be "an ever-accelerating accumulation of behavioral science knowledge for social engineering purposes," defining social engineering as "the deliberate application of systematically accumulated knowledge and theory about the nature of man and his institutions." This capacity we already have in its "early and relatively primitive forms," he says, and cites as examples:

> the human engineering of weapon systems, the use of systems analyses and program budgeting and planning systems in the development of long-range social and economic planning; Keynesian-type economic interventions; the application of behavioral science knowledge to urban design; the research leading to and the evaluation of Operation Headstart; the extensive work in new managerial theory and application, especially as applied in industry.

The computer, says Michael, provides the social scientist with a method for "combining in complex models as many variables as he needs," and a capacity for simulating "real life" conditions for testing the models. Although everything about man cannot be handled by computers, he believes that enough can be to bring about "substantial improvements in our ability to understand and predict and, hence, control behavior." (Whether understanding and prediction would necessarily mean a control ability is perhaps the point at which Michael and Davis would part company; I would share Davis's doubts.)

One wonders, after reviewing the bewildering range of opinion regarding the social sciences, their characteristics, and their potential utilities, if the sensible position is not the eclectic one: that various types, ranging from quite "hard" to quite "soft" (hard and soft, as used in such discussions, can be roughly equated with quantitative and empirical versus qualitative and judgmental), may all have their own legitimate place in the scheme of things, their own problem areas of applicability. Even if one were to accept the scientific ideal, one would have to admit that many important problems are not yet amenable to quantitative, conclusive treatment. That does not mean, however, that random views are equally good, that the softer kinds of social science may not have some relevant judgments to apply, even if they cannot offer complete solutions.

In my view, there are at least four types of social science work, each of which may fit certain governmental needs, and all of which merit public support for their development, from one source or another:

1. The experimental, quantitative, replicable study—of voting behavior, learning processes, emotional responses to a certain stimulus, congressional roll calls, or whatever.

2. Conceptualization and model-building studies. Models of economic or political development exemplify what hard thought by a perceptive mind may accomplish, even if experimentation possibilities are limited. And conceptualization is the crucial step in the creation of paradigms under which experimentation can become a fruitful pursuit and not just a random collection of facts. (Too often the social scientist wanting to be "scientific" too narrowly equates science with hyperfactualism, while the scientist himself testifies to the greater importance of seminal *ideas* in guiding quantitative work.)

3. Objective qualitative analysis. Without mathematics at all, the perceptive and well-trained social scientist can be socially useful and scientifically respectable in an applied manner by elucidating alternatives and examining their probable consequences. In the form of "If A is done, then B will probably follow," policy-makers can be considerably aided.

4. A small step farther on, the social scientist can engage in prescriptive judgments: "Since you want to reach A, you should do B, because it is most likely to get you there." In this work, as 3), the social scientist wants not just abstractions from reality; he must immerse himself in the concreteness of situations—which is one way of saying that he must use a humanistic approach to some extent. The physicist operates by simplifying the world he studies; but human beings and their problems always contain unique elements of particularity, and these may control what will work. They cannot be ignored, and this makes the use of social science expertise inherently different from physical science in at least one respect.

Given these types of operations, the totality of social science should include the totality of methodological approaches —not be restricted to one end of the spectrum.

THE QUESTION OF INSTITUTIONAL PATTERNS

For some years the social sciences have been trying to emulate the natural sciences intellectually. Now they are trying to follow the latter's lead in other respects: reliance on federal funds and influence in federal policy-making. The social sciences are now demanding equivalent *representation* in government.

Representation of two kinds is involved: first, a voice within government claiming the financial support that is thought necessary, just as the farmers have the Department of Agriculture and the natural scientists the National Science Foundation. Although NSF has a Division of Social Sciences, the agency is clearly run by the natural scientists—and many (possibly most) social scientists believe it is therefore run for the natural sciences, citing the very small proportion of NSF research funds that go to the social sciences, and the very limited representation of social scientists on the National Science Board.

Secondly, representation—perhaps through OST and PSAC—at the level of Presidentially connected policy-making, or at any rate policy-advising, bodies. The purpose here is dual: primarily, to have a position from which contributions can be made to the solution of national problems, to be sure of a place from which to be heard when problem-solving is being done; secondarily, as an additional locus for attention to the needs of social science development. In this, too, the roles of PSAC in relation to the natural sciences provide the model. In addition to studies of weapons systems, the use of pesticides, population control, and other problems where science is the means rather than the end, PSAC has also sponsored studies—such as one of high-energy physics—concerned with some field of science as a goal in itself. A PSAC panel on the needs of the social sciences would therefore be one possibility, in addition to the inclusion of social scientists in panels studying problems of, say, urban transit, educational technology, or pollution abatement.

In sum, as pure sciences, economics, psychology, sociology, social anthropology, political science, and possibly history and linguistics all want to make their developmental needs known to government through a regularized, internal, differentiated organizational position. As applied sciences (meaning simply as bodies of knowledge relevant and potentially useful to the resolution of societal problems), they want to be in on the choice of problems and of strategies for dealing with them, fearing (with good reason) that natural scientists alone, no matter how sympathetic to the need for social science inputs, will not, by training, be sufficiently sensitized to the contributions they can make—or even to the social science-related problems that physical science technology may produce as by-products of its own "solutions" to problems.

Support for and use of the social sciences are especially hard to separate. In tackling mission-oriented problems (and some mission relevance can be seen with almost any of even the "purest" social science research projects)—say, in evaluating Head Start programs or attempting to advise on urban renewal's social dimensions—the social scientists have to do fundamental research. They cannot just draw on the fruits of previous basic research, for there isn't yet a large enough basic research "bank account" to draw upon. At the same time, however, opportunities are needed to develop basic theory independently, when it is of a kind that no mission needs are likely to cover. (This will be a larger category than it need be, because of the limited understanding and imagination of the policy-makers who constitute the potential users of social science, for they tend to expect immediate relevance from all social science—even though they would know better than to expect that in the case of the physical sciences.) We cannot wait for the basic research bank to fill up before we begin using it, but we cannot ignore the need to build it up as rapidly as possible, either. Hence, organizational arrangements for social science will have to reflect both use and developmental needs, both mission and non-mission aspects.

In this regard, the social sciences are being challenged much more severely than were the natural sciences: the latter were permitted to become well-developed before society demanded they solve pressing problems, while the social sciences are being called upon to produce now, despite their admittedly primitive state of theoretical development.

The present situation of the social sciences might be analogized to the pre-take-off stage of economic development. These disciplines are just beginning to come into their own, to achieve some public recognition and acceptance as potential contributors to problem amelioration. Social science research is growing rapidly—in numbers of practitioners, in amplitude of studies, in cost, and in sophistication of strategies. A new impetus arising out of the Great Society programs is clearly evident. These programs have perhaps begun with more heart than mind, as it were; i.e. with more good intentions than substantial knowledge of effective actions. Yet their thrust is clearly in the direction of seeking and removing causes of social illness, and in this they differ considerably from the New Deal of the 1930s, for that dealt almost entirely with symptoms only. The attempt to go farther today could not, and probably would not, have been attempted unless the social sciences had already developed sufficiently so that they could show some "feel" for the underlying problems, even if not for the precise causation. Given appropriate conditions, further advance may be quite rapid; recall what 30 years have done for economics, from the bumbling of the 1930s to the sophistication of the 1964 tax cut. There is no reason in principle why the rest of the social sciences may not develop equally effective analyses of their respective areas of human behavior and social processes during the next 30 years.

Despite these hopeful augurs, we are still talking about the importance of the social sciences more than we are acting on it. Considering the billions involved in operational programs in the war on poverty, in education, in urban renewal and transportation, in race relations, in housing, in recreation, and in environmental pollution—to name but a few—the funds devoted to an investment in basic and problem-oriented social research that could back up these operational efforts is ridiculously infinitesimal.

What kinds of institutional patterns, then, are needed to fit the requirements of social science development and use? More specifically, to what extent can/should the social sciences be accommodated into existing patterns established by —and largely for—the natural sciences? To what extent would they be better off, and their societal pay-off larger, if separate organizations were established? What are the arguments pro and con various possible arrangements?

Thanks to congressional interest in the social sciences, we have both a substantial compendium of materials describing and evaluating social research in relation to the Federal Government, and much recent testimony by both natural and social scientists regarding possible institutional arrangements.[14]

REPRESENTATION AT THE PSAC LEVEL

Both natural and social scientists have been asked by congressional committees whether they think it more appropriate to parallel OST and PSAC with offices and advisory committees for the social sciences, or to add a substantial social scientist component to the existing bodies. Both groups are divided in their responses. Out of 50 social scientists, 14 expressed themselves as favoring a separate Office of Social Sciences, and 19 favored integration into PSAC and OST. Others ventured no reply to a question posed by the Reuss subcommittee.[15] Of 28 scientists and engineers (note that when we just say scientists, both writer and reader automatically assume that the natural sciences are being referred to, excluding the social scientists), nine were not in favor of enlarging PSAC to include social science representation in a substantial way, while about a dozen definitely favored social-natural scientist integration in the existing advisory apparatus.[16]

Commonality of positions by no means implies commonality of reasoning, and the arguments from both sides are quite diverse. Social scientists wanting separate organizations tend to argue that groups dominated by natural scientists would not adequately deal with or understand the needs and potential contributions of social science:

> there seems to be little question that a separate Office of the Social Sciences and a separate Advisory Committee for the Social Sciences are preferable. The problem is again one of divergent experiences and the need for persons experienced in the social sciences and their problems to be given opportunity to release social science skills in our country from restraints blocking their full use and the benefits derivable therefrom. In most areas of human activity we call upon those familiar with the activity to undertake tasks related to production of the greatest possible benefits from those activities. For example, we do not ask biologists to build bridges.[17]

Natural scientists opposed to PSAC-OST inclusion of social sciences tend to do so on the opposite ground that they doubt that the social sciences could make a sufficient contribution. Consider the implicit view of the social sciences contained in this quotation from a physicist's remarks:

> It is my belief that PSAC achieves its greatest effectiveness by maintaining its integrity as a dispassionate group advising in rather technical areas. It should include the social sciences where necessary to an adequate discussion of the technical problems, but should resist the temptation lightly to inject elements which lay it open to accusations of bias or lack of expert knowledge in its conclusions.[18]

Such views are perhaps representative of what a social psychologist had in mind when he argued for integration in PSAC:

> I am inclined to favor strengthening the role of social science in the present structure rather than the creation of a separate entity which would allow the physical science policy makers to continue to ignore the relevance of social science.[19]

What, then, are the major arguments for and against revising PSAC's membership to include meaningful representation from social science? One argument, by a prominent social scientist recently (1968) elected to the National Academy of Sciences and appointed as the first social science member of PSAC, stresses that group's need for a competence its natural scientists do not possess:

> A review of the activities of these agencies [PSAC, OST, FCST] would show that most of the time they are up to their necks in social science questions—and either forced to handle them on an amateur do-it-yourself basis, or to call for outside help. A separate-but-equal policy for the social sciences would not solve this problem. Incorporation of social science in the present agencies would meet it directly.[20]

The subjects on which PSAC advises are obviously relevant to the types of competencies required, and a major argument for social science inclusion derives from an expectation that technological applications to social problems will be an increasing part of PSAC's agenda, as distinguished from an earlier emphasis on defense "hardware" problems, where the social science component was not (or was not seen as) especially relevant. Handler's comments are representative of this view:

> As the Office of Science and Technology [Handler apparently subsumes PSAC under OST, and means his remarks to apply to both] becomes increasingly concerned with the utilization of technology for the management and solution of the problems of our society—poverty, pollution, population control, urban renewal, housing, transportation, education, etc.—it must learn to blend the scientific and engineering judgments with which it is accustomed to deal with social judgments provided by those knowledgeable in economics, sociology, and the behavioral sciences. . . . the national interest will be better served by extension of the term "science" in the titles of these organizations to mean *social* as well as *natural* science than it will be to erect independent advisory and administrative structures.[21]

If the problems attacked by the Executive Office groups are mixtures of social and technological factors, then the relationship between the worlds of the scientists and the social scientists becomes more crucial. Two variants of this theme are expressed by, respectively, former Special Assistant Wiesner:

> It is urgent, I believe, to bridge the communication gap, the lack of understanding, that exists between the natural sciences and the social sciences. Many of the most impor-

tant problems today require interaction between the two intellectual preserves. Furthermore, tools and concepts from the physical sciences . . . will have profound effects upon social science research during the next decade. On the other side . . . the natural scientists must become increasingly concerned with the social consequences of their work;

and by technologist-industrialist Simon Ramo:

Greater attention to social science is urgent, but equally urgent is the increasing of the bond and interaction between social science and the physical sciences and engineering. Indeed, the real problem and controlling bottleneck in application of science and technology for the good of society lies in the too severe demarkation that now exists. National programs re science and society must be seen as involving the two branches in intimate, inseparable relationship.[22]

Others would stress, toward the same end, that the natural and social sciences are already becoming more intertwined, especially those parts of the latter that—like psychology—have been able most closely to follow the methodological route of the physical sciences. This trend toward a symbiotic relationship should be further encouraged. Finally, it would seem that social scientists are needed in PSAC to ensure sufficient "sensitivity" to social science dimensions of problems and to apply social science techniques to their solutions. Although a number of scientists say that PSAC has been sensitive in these areas, few social scientists believe this to be the case.

OST provides staffing for PSAC and has its own responsibilities for staying on top of scientific and technological developments and applications. It has also been suggested that OST's staff should include a few outstanding social scientists. A precedent is found in the establishment during Wiesner's period of a Deputy Director position in OST for the biomedical and life sciences, a position that continues today. This was done as realization arose that "life science research activities required more surveillance and advocacy than they had previously received." If the same can be said today of the social sciences, perhaps the same step is in order: add a social science deputy director and a small staff—and perhaps have a PSAC panel on the social sciences for which these new elements would provide the framework.

Since its establishment in 1946 under the Employment Act, the Council of Economic Advisers has represented one explicit social science agency at the Presidential level. Charged with preparing the President's required annual Economic Report, CEA applies economics to national problems—and does so in a manner that has gained very considerable respect, among both social and natural scientists. (It does not, however, constitute an agency for representing and supporting economics as an academic discipline: it does *not* give grants for economists to do what they want, and it is *not* charged with assuring that economics gets "its share" from, say, NSF. It uses economics but is not an advocate for the academic discipline, except through the success of its own example.) What CEA has done in developing and using economic statistics to report and advise on the nation's economic health, a number of social scientists would now like to see done with the social sciences more generally. The suggestion is therefore heard that CEA become the Council of Economic *and Social* Advisers. "Social indicators"—i.e. statistics on a variety of non-Gross National Product matters such as education, health, and race relations— are being urged by more and more social scientists, and they could be incorporated into a new advisory committee or into a broadened CEA. In the minds of some, this development could be a substitute for social science representation in PSAC-OST;

for others, it would be a useful supplement, but would not—any more than CEA does now for economics—satisfy the full spectrum of representational needs.[23]

What are the arguments against substantial social science representation in the existing framework of scientific advisory bodies?

From the social scientists' side, one finds an apparent, though not well-articulated, fear that in any joint body they would be swamped by the predominance of natural scientists. And substantively, those who see the social sciences as inherently humanistic and methodologically distinct would not look upon such an integration as either feasible or desirable. The view that the social sciences are different is of course shared by a number of natural scientists—often with the implication that one of the differences is that the social sciences are weaker and have little to offer by way of "hard analysis." It is said by scientists that "the very nature of the social sciences is such that they will continually deal with problems on which definitive data are not available and theories not well established"; that outside of CEA "the 'soft' sciences will be slow to provide the hard facts of the sort which should be the concern of external advisory groups such as the PSAC"; and that the "problems and activities of the social sciences are quite different," so they need their own group if they are to be properly encouraged.[24]

Again, commentators are affected by their response to the kinds of questions with which the PSAC has to deal. Thus a physicist who sees PSAC as dealing with "hard technical analysis," concerning, for example, systems developments or tests for national defense, finds its role quite different from the social scientists'. On the other hand, he would include them in other areas, such as civil defense and world health and food studies.[25] Such differences lead Bode to put forth an unassailable proposition: "the only valid principle here should be . . . to adapt the membership to the kinds of problems which immediately need solving." [26] This can be done, and has been done, with sub-panels of PSAC set up to advise on a specific problem or problem area, and several times social scientists have been included in this manner. But that is different from membership on PSAC itself, the parent body that has to decide when to use the social sciences. If they are not represented on that level, they are not in on decisions affecting when their disciplines are used.

In defending PSAC's composition (which does not even include representatives of all natural science areas), spokesmen have pointed out that it is not intended to be more than generally representative, and that criteria for a person's inclusion depend on his general analytic breadth and ability to work with others toward a consensus based on reasoned analysis of technical data. An ideological emphasis on scientific consensus seems to exist, in fact. Hence, one objection to bringing in the social sciences is that they tend to provide "a greater opportunity for strongly divergent views on technical subjects." [27] Despite the Teller-Pauling kind of arguments (i.e. arguments over nuclear fall-out in which essentially identical data were so differently interpreted as to produce diametrically opposite policy positions), the scientists' image is that they have a system in which decisions are reached on the basis of pure facts. There is doubt that the social sciences will be able to provide their share of "facts"; hence their representation is thought to be of dubious value. That there are needs apart from hard facts—notably informed judgment and sensitivity to a broad range of phenomena—does not always seem to occur to those who think this way.

If the social sciences are different; if technical analyses can often be made without political or social analysis; and if one would have to include many social scientists (because there are so many schools of thought among them); then one might fear *dilution* of PSAC's existing competence if it were broadened. And several scientists do express this fear. The extent of dilution felt depends in part on whether one sees PSAC as dealing with social aspects of technological problems, or as also trying to play a coordinative and planning role for the support of the social sciences. George Kistiakowsky, Special Assistant under Eisenhower, argues that in performing the first role "valuable contacts with a large body of highly qualified consultants in the fields of the social sciences" have been developed and should continue to be used. But as regards problems arising out of social science sponsorship by government, he says that "neither OST with its statutorily limited staff nor PSAC with its fixed membership could undertake continuing coordination of this area without dangerous dilution of their competence and effectiveness in the area of natural sciences and technology." [28] Others, emphasizing problems more directly of a physical science nature, are less open to the use of social scientists. Thus we find a member of PSAC, apparently reflecting discussions held within that body, reporting a consensus "that it would not be profitable to dilute PSAC's limited manpower with two or more social scientists at a time when there are so many unsolved problems in the field of the physical sciences." [29]

Finally, evidencing either ignorance of social research or failure to think through what they are saying, a number of scientists maintain there is no need to add social scientists to PSAC-OST because they already are strongly represented in such staff agencies as CEA and BOB and in executive departments such as the Department of Housing and Urban Development and the Department of Health, Education, and Welfare. Political science and economics, for example, are said to be

much more intimate and vital parts of most governmental
concerns than the natural sciences can ever hope to be . . .
in the natural course of events they have many channels
to influence the government's actions which do not apply
in the natural science case.[30]

And one scientist's perception is that "the application of social
science to broad national problems is already assigned to
groups such as the Council of Economic Advisers and the
Bureau of the Budget."[31] Granting that CEA does have a
specific "assignment" in one area, its staff and the staff of BOB
would, I think, be a bit surprised to find that they have been
given such broad mandates in applied research! In BOB, for
example, political scientists are budget analysts or work at
legislative review (which is to say they are there as employees
with bureaucratic tasks) but do not constitute recognized
bodies of disciplinary advisers, and are not engaged in studies
of the social dimensions of technological problems (with
limited exceptions in CEA's case). None of the governmental
employees with social science backgrounds is charged with
overseeing and advocating the development of their disciplines
—and that is an essential part of what PSAC-OST does in the
representation of the natural sciences.

Even farther removed from an understanding of social
science is the comment that special social science machinery
is not needed because "our elected representatives in Washington, D.C. are quite good practical social scientists, whereas
they are not in any appreciable number trained, active natural
scientists."[32] In this usage, politician apparently means the
same thing as "trained, active" social scientist. It doesn't mean
that to the social scientists, however—or to the legislators
themselves, for that matter. That is like saying that the many,
many engineers in government service are "quite good practical physicists," so one doesn't need trained physicists in PSAC.

Granting that the social sciences have not yet (and some of them in some ways never will or should) become totally scientific, these "anti" arguments I think go farther than is warranted in rejecting social science representation. *Some* parts of social science are quite quantitative and precise; and *all* have professional sensitivity and judgment regarding their respective areas of concern. So there are definite contributions to be made beyond what would be accomplished by seeking out the common sense wisdom of the man in the street. It therefore seems merely parochial and obdurate not to permit a larger infusion of social scientists into policy advising at the OST-PSAC level. And the necessity for so trying is partly proven, in my judgment, by the apparent misconceptions held by men prominent in their own branches of the natural sciences. That is, I rather doubt that men who confuse a job in BOB with social research have sufficient sensitivity to social science's modes of operation and potential contributions to be in a position to decide themselves when they ought to call in social science consultants; they need social science consultants, rather, to help them know when to use social science.

What all this perhaps raises, most fundamentally, is the kinds of problems that should involve PSAC. If it were to concern itself exclusively with defense hardware and space system problems, perhaps the issue of social science representation would be moot. But if—as seems far more likely—it is becoming increasingly concerned with social problems arising out of technology, or problems to which both technology and social analysis are applicable, then true integration with the social sciences is required. And if (as is true) social scientists can improve their disciplines by rubbing elbows with physical scientists, perhaps also the latter have something to gain from professionals engaged in the much harder work of multivariate social research. Because the world is a mixture of scientific and social elements, our top-level advisory apparatus for dealing with the world's problems had best also constitute such a mixture. And the proper mix will be much better attained, I am certain, by bringing both elements together at the beginning of problem study than by establishing separate natural and social science bodies and trying to fuse their findings and viewpoints after the fact.

SUPPORTING SOCIAL SCIENCE: AN NFSS?

If the social sciences are to be utilized in national policy development, whether through integration into the framework of the Office of Science and Technology and the President's Science Advisory Committee, or through a separate Executive Office advisory system, then they need to be further supported and strengthened—for even the most hopeful spokesmen would concede that they are only in the very early stages of development, especially as regards theoretical structures and the incorporation of scientific methods. Widespread agreement exists that *more* support is needed; equally widespread disagreement emerges when the question shifts to the organizational locus of this increased support. Should it be through NSF's Division of Social Science, or should it take the form of a National Foundation for the Social Sciences, as advocated by Senator Fred R. Harris, who has used his Senate Subcommittee on Government Research to gather 800 pages of testimony on the subject?

The arguments on both sides are plausible, and some of the points are necessarily speculative (i.e. there is no "scientific" way to settle such an issue). When I first considered this question, I found myself dubious about the sense of creating another agency, thinking that the social sciences might better be integrated with the natural scienecs within NSF, and that

NFSS was not an appropriate way to improve the prestige and "visibility" of the social sciences. I now feel, however, that an NFSS is appropriate, and that it is needed—both for proper support of development as social science disciplines and as a way of increasing the use of social science for research on societal problems, research that can then be carried into the applied stage by mission-oriented agencies, such as the departments of HEW, HUD, and Transportation. Because the matter is quite debatable, it seems worthwhile to cover the arguments on both sides, while frankly explaining why I find the favorable case the more compelling.

That something is out of phase is clear when one considers that the social sciences receive less than 3 per cent of all federal basic research funds, and less than 5 per cent of the applied research budget—and this despite rather rapid growth in the past five years. The balance of research funds within NSF is 90 to 10 per cent in favor of the natural sciences; proponents of NFSS attribute this in part to NSF's narrow definition of what kind of social science it will support (the kind that is quantitative and replicable, and not policy-oriented) and in part to the simple fact that social science is unlikely to receive wholehearted support in an agency run by natural scientists for the natural sciences. Whatever the reasons, something needs to be changed. And it will, apparently, have to be through Federal Government action, for private foundation support is far from ample. For example, a major Social Science Research Council basic research program on governmental processes receives $600,000 worth of proposals in a year, but can fund only $60,000 worth.[33]

No one leads well from a position of weakness, and the present weak position of the social sciences may be a major reason why they receive little support and are so often ignored when technological applications having important social ramifications are under consideration. One of the first advantages of an NFSS, therefore, would be to create a locus of recognition, representation, and leadership equivalent to that which NSF and the National Foundation for the Arts and the Humanities (NFAH) provide for other areas of knowledge. NSF, says political scientist Harry Eckstein, "has always been legally able to support the social sciences, but has in fact always treated them as poor and stupid stepchildren."[34] To Senator Harris, NFSS would bring to the social sciences "the added visibility, recognition, and prestige necessary to give impetus for development."[35]

Somewhat more tangibly, it has been argued that when the President or Congress wants some "authoritative, top level" statement about the natural sciences or the humanities, they can go to the head of an agency; for social science, there is only the division director of the social sciences in NSF, a "subordinate official in a very large organization."[36] Would we put the social sciences under the natural sciences on a university campus? Hardly, yet that is the equivalent, Austin Ranney argues, to the present locus of the social sciences in NSF. Although it can be said that such considerations of bureaucratic status should not matter, it is universally the fact that they do.

Nor is it just a matter of status; rather, status provides the leverage through which leadership and adequate representation can emerge. Unless it be argued that natural scientists know better than social scientists what the latter want and need— and I do not see how that could be argued—social scientists need to be in a position to provide leadership. NFSS would provide the responsible senior positions from which the case for social science research can be made most effectively. Given NSF's primary orientation to the physical and biological sciences, its leadership can only adequately cover those needs of the social sciences that are most like natural science needs.

Thus it has been pointed out that NSF looks favorably on computer needs but less so on library needs—yet the latter are the "laboratory" for many social scientists. Similarly when social scientists go to NSF for building and equipment needs, applications for these are handled by a separate office, not by the Division of Social Sciences, and those who handle the applications would only accidentally include anyone with a social science background.

The social sciences are also different because they encompass both humanistic and scientific approaches. Curiously, the best expression of this situation has been made by a physicist, Gerald Holton:

> If . . . you see that there is a tension between two quite different traditions [the scientific and the normative-humanistic] within the social sciences, that a normative component quite legitimately exists and waits to be developed, then we should tend to look for an organization that in the context of other existing supporting agencies would allow social sciences more easily to find their particular indigenous existence, their style, their function, and their application. . . . [There is need for] one agency within which the indigenous strength of the social sciences in all their aspects can develop, and where the soft and hard traditions, the scientific and the humanistic traditions, the applied and the pure work, all would meet and mingle.[37]

At present, only a small part of social science approaches receives support from NSF—the part that is methodologically most like the natural sciences. One therefore finds psychologists, for example, most eager to continue with NSF as the supporter of social science, political scientists least eager, for the latter's work (except for public opinion and voting behavior) is not notably quantitative and the former's verges on biology. At the "soft" end of the spectrum, on the other hand, the new NFAH's National Endowment for the Humanities may provide some support for historical studies. But no agency has a primary mission for covering the very considerable area in the center of the social science spectrum.

The social sciences are still basically working out their methodologies and their basic theories. Until some consensus on theories and approaches emerges (and one can anticipate a good deal further basic research before that will occur in most areas), it is important that we avoid the premature imposition of a methodological or subject-matter orthodoxy—especially one that comes from physical scientists' ideas of what the social sciences "ought" to be like. As an economist, Gerhard Colm, puts it, a separate NFSS would "more likely make decisions on the merits of various social sciences rather than give preference to a social science approach which has the greatest appeal for people primarily trained and experienced in the physical sciences." [38]

This point may be particularly important because (1) policy-relevant studies are avoided by NSF as if they brought the plague (and maybe NSF fears a political plague arising out of the potential controversy inherent in policy-relevant studies), yet (2) it is the policy relevance of the social sciences that has led to recent calls for their greater support. Even more clearly than in the case of the natural sciences, public support for the social sciences will come for concrete reasons of expected pay-off, not for cultural reasons. To be basic and to be policy-relevant are not antithetical when applied to the social sciences as they would be for, say, high-energy physics. Very fundamental data and theory-building are needed in such areas as education and learning processes, human relationships in urban neighborhoods, or political attitudes among the electorate. Yet the basic work will have clear areas of application right from the start. So long, then, as NSF refuses to support policy-relevant studies, so long will it be inadequate as a support mechanism for a very large segment of social science.

Furthermore, the nature of social science and of the human problems with which we want it to deal seem to require different modes of support from those NSF feels most "at home" with. Much social science can be developed best by a problem-oriented approach, which also means an inter-disciplinary approach. Yet NSF is oriented toward a single-discipline pattern of organization and grant awards, and away from a problems approach. At the same time, the project system may not be as well-suited to the social sciences as to the physical and biological ones; institutional grants to a department or to a problem-oriented research group may be more sensible than project awards to individual scholars. And institutional awards may also be necessary to provide some insulation of social research: if the university groups decide on the particular projects, rather than having the funding agency do it, then the agency cannot be as easily blamed in Congress if a legislator gets upset (as some surely will) over a subject matter being explored or some findings he disapproves. Although it is possible, in principle, for NSF to develop modes of support in its social science program different from those it has traditionally employed for the natural sciences, one doubts whether this is likely to happen.

Then there is a question whether the social sciences, whose need for growth is apparent to all, can grow best in tandem or autonomously. Irving L. Horowitz points out that in the universities new disciplines have usually grown by being separated out organizationally,[39] and Margaret Mead made the point persuasively:

The social sciences need a chance to grow. Although social sciences can now benefit from any advance in the

natural sciences, the approaches are still sufficiently differentiated so that the two fields—one highly developed,
the other young and relatively undeveloped—cannot yet
work together within one institution as well as they are
able to work within separate institutions. Ten years from
now, the social sciences may well have developed to such
a position of competence and authority that the natural
sciences will welcome them as partners, but that time is
not yet.[40]

Although NSF spokesmen insist that the social sciences
can grow best in harness with the natural sciences, one can
point out that those sciences themselves have grown by separation. For instance, biophysics and biochemistry: no one argues
that these hybrid fields would be growing better than they are
if each were still just a sub-unit of one of the parent fields. It is
after a field has become well-developed—meaning partly
when it has developed *its own* approach and its own unified
theory—that its practitioners seem to feel strong enough to
collaborate with others. At the beginning, collaboration is
likely to be premature and to stunt the new field by forcing it
into a pre-established mold.

Similarly, the variety of approaches current and prospective in the social sciences augurs favorably for diversity in support. Some diversity there already is, since several operating
agencies fund some applied social science, while NSF and
NIH provide some basic research funds. But why not as much
pluralism in basic research support as there is pluralism in
approaches? Let three flowers bloom: NSF, for the portion
most like the natural sciences; NFSS for the whole spectrum,
with emphasis on working toward basic theories regardless of
methodological approaches; and NFAH for the most value-
involved, normative part of the spectrum—the part where
social science edges off into social philosophy. In this way, we

can permit all the proto-paradigms to compete freely with one another until one emerges victor by consensus—not by fiat.[41] Social scientists then would have three possible sponsors for a researcher's program, and none could complain that he was turned down because of an arbitrary dispute over appropriate methodology. The physical scientists, incidentally, have themselves insisted upon the importance of diverse sources of support; it is even more important for the social sciences because of the lack of agreed-upon theories in many areas.

So much for the arguments directly favoring the creation of a National Foundation for the Social Sciences. What are the arguments against it, and how can they be answered?

When Senator Harris first asked witnesses testifying on problems of federal support of overseas research to give him their thoughts also on an NFSS, he got some rather hesitant statements. Surely the most hesitant was that of the President of the Social Science Research Council, Pendleton Herring, who told Harris it would not hurt to have an NFSS, *if*

> other present agencies do not lessen their interest and support thereby; if Congress would be equally generous to one agency as it is now to numerous agencies with social science programs; if one chairman of an Appropriations Subcommittee would not decide to oppose what would then be the main source of social science support; if the social science disciplines did not get to squabbling among themselves for the favor of this single agency, if the one social science research foundation did not receive the brunt of criticism for all the controversial issues that might arise in various connections; and if the social sciences were not isolated from the natural sciences and from research in the humanities.[42]

(Herring assumed what Harris definitely did not; namely, that if NFSS came into being, all other support for social research might cease. Certainly other agencies in the "hard" sciences did not cease their support when NSF came into existence. In fact, it has been hard for NSF to get enough basic research to justify itself in competition with that funded through the mission agencies.)

Apart from Herring's "if-iness," the first argument is that recognition and status are not important enough reasons for creating a new agency, nor are they effectively furthered by an organizational "gimmick." Prestige and visibility will develop as the social sciences manage to make real contributions to national policy by solving problems. Certainly this is how the natural sciences came into prominence: by building a bomb and by aiding the executive branch in solving problems. NSF only came *after* the utility of the physical sciences had been demonstrated. It is the importance of science that has given NSF recognition, not the other way around. Similarly, if work on housing, race relations, or poverty shows pay-offs, then the social sciences will merit (and will receive) recognition. At the least, this argument is correct in denying that an organizational home, *by itself,* would create prestige. On the other hand, by aiding in the more rapid development of social science data and theories, and therefore in its capacity to solve problems, an NFSS could indirectly contribute much toward greater recognition.

Perhaps the larger problem here is that too much will be expected of a social science that has achieved the status of a government agency devoted to its interests. As Robert A. Nisbet has written, "formal and heralded establishment of these agencies [he was writing about a proposal for NFSS plus a White House Office of the Behavioral Science Adviser] could well lead to a burden of expectation by government and public opinion that the social sciences are ill-prepared to shoulder." And failure to meet those expectations would "promote disillusionment." [43] The extent to which this might be true will depend on making certain that NFSS is not itself intended or expected to solve problems but to develop the basic research approaches of the social sciences to the point where they can help solve problems when called upon by mission-oriented agencies. And that distinction will be hard to keep in focus.

One of the strongest arguments against NFSS is that it would fragment the world of science just when the social and natural sciences are beginning to draw together methodologically and to work together in problem-solving operations. There is "a great need for increasing cohesion," says Haworth, but NFSS might have a "splintering effect." It is a question, he adds, of having an "integrated point of view, of having people in daily contact with each other." [44] Similarly, the Director of the Center for Advanced Study in the Behavioral Sciences, Ralph W. Tyler, said NFSS would add "confusion and fragmentation." [45] And one of the few social scientists to be elected to NAS, Herbert A. Simon, adds, "This is the wrong moment in history to isolate the physical and biological science from the social sciences," for the boundaries "are becoming less and less definite, and the communications across them increasingly important." [46]

But would NFSS mean harmful isolation? Or simply helpful independence? We are talking now about supporting the internal development of fields, not using them to solve problems. In the latter circumstance, integration *is* clearly to be maximized; but in support, one fails to see a problem. As the social sciences grow stronger, through autonomous development, they will be better partners when they get together with the natural sciences. "There is no one so irrationally irritating at a family reunion as a poor relative," [47] says President Fred H. Harrington of the University of Wisconsin, arguing that healthy independent development of the social sciences will best fit them for joint ventures in the future.

If one sees the social sciences as essentially the same as the natural sciences in nature, and tosses aside the more qualitative studies that comprise a large part of social science, then one fears fragmentation also on the ground that the social sciences need to learn from maximum contact with the natural sciences. Thus Simon:

> An important goal of Federal social science policy should be to strengthen the best trends within the social sciences —the trends that will help them reach levels of effectiveness like those that have been attained by the natural sciences. Encouraging interaction between social and natural scientists, and encouraging social scientists to apply natural science standards of objectivity and technical ingenuity to their own research are important ways of moving toward that goal. . . . I would cite such examples as support for mathematical training, for empirical field research, for computer facilities. Creation of an independent agency would strengthen traditional and outmoded approaches.[48]

Given Simon's evident low opinion of non-quantitative social science, one cannot argue; one can just disagree, suggesting that NFSS would most likely itself encourage mathematical approaches, too, but would not do so exclusively at the expense of all other methodologies.

The impact of autonomy or integration upon the development of the disciplines into which knowledge is (unfortunately but fruitfully) divided is one side of a coin. The other side is the question of integration or autonomy in problem-solving activities. Then it is important to look at the social aspects of technologically defined problems, and conversely at the technological aspects of socially defined problems. As Haworth says:

> In problem-oriented or applied research—on problems of population, urbanization, transportation, foreign areas, and environmental quality—it is becoming impossible to obtain balanced results on the basis of compartmentalized approaches.[49]

He is right, but that has not much relevance to the issue of NFSS as an agency for basic research support. In NSF, for example, when a physicist comes in with a project, he deals with a physicist in the appropriate division, as a social scientist will deal with a social scientist—and they have no better chance of meeting one another through NSF than they had on the campus.

The character of an NFSS as regards its field of operation —i.e. basic research only, or basic and applied; disciplinary focus only, or disciplinary plus problems—is therefore important to the question of the integration-autonomy mixture. The substance of the work should determine the form of organization, and I would expect the bulk of NFSS' attention would be given to basic work in a disciplinary context, or through interdisciplinary teams of social scientists. It seems to me that social scientists and natural scientists and engineers would more likely join forces in the OST-PSAC or mission-oriented agency phase, when the data and theory scientists have developed are being applied to specific projects or problems. If my presumption is correct, then NFSS' separateness from NSF causes no great problem.

Apart from these intellectual arguments about separateness, there is a practical political question. Would NFSS be subject to pressure from neanderthal legislators or interest groups because of the controversial nature of the subjects that social sciences study? Dael Wolfle of the American Association for the Advancement of Science fears that an NFSS "would probably be more vulnerable to attacks on partisan grounds than any other agency of government." [50] That there is a great potential for controversy cannot be denied; that there *must* be trouble can be denied. It will depend partly on what kind of work NFSS supports, and it is quite unlikely to support work whose purpose is to evaluate normatively particular governmental programs or operations—that would come through mission-oriented studies, if through any financed by government. A PSAC report on pollution control measures would more likely be controversial than NFSS-sponsored basic studies of environmental problems—yet no one suggests that PSAC should be hidden under some other umbrella in the way that Haworth, for example, suggests that the 90 per cent of NSF's work in the natural sciences may protect the 10 per cent done in the social sciences.[51]

Maybe the time has come for the social sciences to try standing on their own two feet—and maybe doing so would create more public respect, rather than undermine it. I find Kingsley Davis's blunt words in this regard quite appropriate:

> If the Nation is to develop and utilize social science, it will have to face squarely the question of how to live with this field. The proper institutional mechanisms will have to be worked out and frankly supported. There is no doubt about the uneasy tension that prevails between objective social knowledge and the society that is the object of such knowledge. . . . But the first nation which breaks through the barrier and manages to put social science on a footing at least as sound as that of the natural sciences, will be way ahead of every other nation in the world. I would like to see the United States be that nation, and I believe that it can be. However, if the peculiar difficulties presented by social science are to be met in new and creative ways, it will not be done by pussy-footing and pretending. If the only way we are going to sup-

port social science is by hiding it under some other cloak, scattering it here and there so it will not be noticed, I for one will regard our social science policy as a failure, both from the standpoint of scholarly development and from the standpoint of national interest.

It is precisely because a separate foundation would bring social science into the open—into the focus of governmental and public attention—that it will be conducive to putting this aspect of knowledge on a new level of excellence and usefulness.[52]

I conclude that the best argument against an NFSS is that we might fail to maximize opportunities for greater understanding across fields by constant association; but I think the counter-argument for autonomous growth is more compelling. And in a positive sense, the best argument for NFSS is that the full range of social science approaches and sub-disciplines would be supported and given a chance to flower, without being held down by natural scientists' skewed pictures of what the social sciences are or can become.[53]

7 | The National Science Foundation: A Time for Change?

From its very beginnings, the National Science Foundation has had a split personality. It has been split structurally by an ambiguous authority relationship between the Director and the National Science Board. It has been split in functional orientation between its own program of grants to support basic research and its wider role in developing national science policy and evaluating federal research programs across the board. As a policy-making and evaluating body, it has simply failed to do the job assigned in its statutory charter; for its own support of basic research, it has, however, generally been accorded very high marks. The structural duality has, by and large, been resolved in favor of the Director. Even an ardent protagonist and former chairman of NSB has described the Board's situation as one of constant decline in importance:

> gradually, by successive steps, the National Science Board
> —originally envisaged as a largely autonomous group of
> leaders who were to have a powerful voice in the conduct
> of the scientific affairs of the nation—has become what
> amounts to little more than a routine committee for deter-
> mining the specific awards and contracts of the National
> Science Foundation, with little power to enforce policy
> decisions.[1]

Because NSF has had permanent authorization for funding until 1969 (i.e. it did not have to go before a substantive committee of the Congress to have funds authorized for its programs each year before seeking those funds from the appropriations committees—as NASA and the Agency for International Development have to), no legislative committee took a close look at NSF's course of development until the Daddario subcommittee began an intensive review in 1965—a review that led Daddario to write legislation amending its charter that was passed in July 1968.* Daddario's bill had four major purposes: to clarify relationships between the Director and NSB; to enlarge the NSB's role in overall policy development (reversing the trend of 15 years); to give explicit statutory stimulus to NSF support of the social sciences; and to add an applied science dimension to NSF's tasks. The latter two points arose out of the generally increasing concern in the Congress for strengthening and directing more research toward the solution of socio-technological problems, the hope being to make more use consciously of NSF's basic research support, rather than only to have it passively support projects in whatever areas academics chose to enter through their proposals to the Foundation.

Along with Daddario's amendments, a non-statutory issue also came to the fore in the same period: what proportion of federally funded basic research should be accounted for by NSF in order for it to operate as a "balance wheel" in the federal machinery for science? The idea of NSF as a balance wheel—which was publicized in the 1965 NAS report, *Basic Research and National Goals,* and received further attention in testimony on NSF during Daddario's hearings on the Foundation—is that it would continually review the basic research planned by other agencies, compare the expected amount with

* P.L. 90–407, 82 Stat. 360

independently determined needs field by field, and include in
its own budget sufficient funds to eliminate any expected gaps
between need and other agency support. It also means that
NSF looks at the total needs of academic science and tries to
put into its own budget the differences between what other
agencies plan to spend and the total needed, to provide continuity of support in the world of university researchers. In
fiscal 1965, for example, NSF's budget was held up until the
last moment, so that the amounts from other agencies could be
totaled and the gap-filling figure entered into the President's
budget request for NSF.[2]

Since structure should be fitted to function, organization
to tasks, we must see what NSF has done and what is expected
of it in the foreseeable future, and relate these matters to its
present and future organizational pattern. The Foundation's
past history gives some indications of what is possible and
what is inappropriate.

EARLY EXPECTATIONS AND NSF'S MAIN THRUST

NSF had its origins in a World War II realization that
military technology (and other technologies) would henceforth be science-based, and that the United States could no
longer afford to assume that Europe would provide the fundamental research required for a successful technological effort.
Vannevar Bush, the eminent scientist who headed the war-
time Office of Scientific Research and Development, provided
the primary leadership for the creation of a post-war agency to
replace OSRD. Characterizing basic science as "the endless
frontier," Bush pushed hard for a foundation which he visual-
ized as being funded by the government but operationally as
almost totally autonomous. His version of a national research
foundation would have established a part-time National Sci-

ence Board of non-governmental scientists and educators which would name its own chairman and appoint the executive direction for the foundation. The government's (i.e. the President's) only organizational connection would have been to name the members of the Board. A bill of this form (designed to obviate scientists' fears of too much political control over science) passed the Congress in 1947, but was vetoed by President Truman—even though he, too, wanted a science foundation—because it seemed to him too autonomous for our democratic system of government. Said the President, in vetoing this legislation in 1947:

> It would, in effect vest the determination of vital national policies, the expenditure of large public funds, and the administration of important governmental functions in a group of individuals who would be essentially private citizens. The proposed National Science Foundation would be divorced from control by the people to an extent that implies a distinct lack of faith in democratic processes.[3]

The National Science Foundation Act that passed Congress in 1950 was an uneasy compromise between what Bush wanted and what represented the normal structure for a government department. The Director was now to be appointed directly by the President (with Senate confirmation) for a fixed term of six years (still, the reader will note, trying to insulate NSF from politics) and would share the operational authority with the National Science Board. Although the Director would be the administrative head for internal management, all final decisions on grants as well as on policies had to be appproved by the National Science Board. (Some years later, in 1959, delegation of authority for grants below a certain size was made possible to the Director.) The Foundation consisted of both the Director and the Board, and it became clear during the 1965–66 Daddario hearings that no formula of words could very satisfactorily establish the exact relationship between them. However, it also emerged that power had gradually been moving toward the Director and away from the Board, both informally and formally. A reorganization act in 1962, for example, made the Director, not the Board chairman, the chairman of a reconstituted executive committee of the Board.

A highly prestigious list of persons eminent in science, educational administration, and public affairs generally was assembled for the initial appointments to the Board, with James B. Conant, President of Harvard and noted chemist, as chairman. In the first few years, an effort was made to act on the assumption that the Board was at the heart of the operation. The chairman of the Board wrote a forward to each annual report of the Foundation for the first half-dozen years, for example; more recently, the Director has made an initial statement instead. More importantly, the task of the Board and the Foundation, said the Second Annual Report, was *primarily* that of assessing government-wide research activities and formulating policy.[4] An early attempt was made to take some initiative in determining what kinds of research needed to be stimulated. For example, because of the urgency of developing jet engines and rockets, NSF undertook a study of high-temperature physics, chemistry, and metallurgy—to determine what was being done, the extent of need for greater support, and "the specific areas where basic research may be necessary to make maximum progress." It thus appears that in the earliest years an active role for the Foundation also meant an active role for the Board, for policies and operations going beyond NSF's own research activities were attempted.

It also appears, however, that this phase died rather quickly. The Foundation—reasonably enough—had to devote the bulk of its attention to getting its own research-supporting operations underway. This meant building staff, establishing sub-units of the organization, and formulating operating policies and programs of an internal nature. One surmises that little time was left for pondering government-wide research problems. Even if there had been time, there were more fundamental obstacles in the path of NSF's playing as large a role as its statutory authority and founders' expectations anticipated. As a recent chairman of NSB has said,

> because the budget of NSF constituted so small a fraction not only of total federally supported research and development but also of academic science, and because of the embarrassment inherent in the fact that the other science-supporting agencies are at the same hierarchical level in the government as is NSF, the Board of the Foundation considered that it must eschew its role as the "National Science Board." [5]

Instead, NSB increasingly became simply the Board of the Foundation. And it is not even clear that it has exercised much initiative (as distinguished from its unavoidable function of approving new programs brought forward from the Director's office) in that more limited sphere.

While NSB-NSF had no rival in science policy formulation until 1957, there was also little urgency attached to the development of government-wide policies. Sputnik I dramatically changed the degree of urgency, and it also brought into being the President's Special Assistant for Science and Technology and the President's Science Advisory Committee. In 1959, the Federal Council on Science and Technology was added, and in 1962, the Office of Science and Technology. By this time, it was widely recognized that NSF-NSB was doing little to develop policy and that it could never evaluate the research programs of coordinate-level agencies. Hence these powers (the latter

entirely, the former in part) were shifted to OST. (See Chapter
3 for more detail on organizational structure.) If Representative Daddario had not attempted to resuscitate NSB's role with
his amendments by assigning it the task of preparing an annual
report on the status and health of science for the President to
transmit to Congress, one would have expected the Board to
keep on declining in government-wide importance. Whether
Daddario's proposal will succeed remains to be seen, of course,
but I am dubious that this new task will give it sufficient
leverage to recoup the position it might once have had.

Thus NSB has little government-wide significance today
(whatever it may have tomorrow), and NSF settled, after its
early flurries with policy development and evaluation of urgent
research areas, for the not-insignificant role which Bush and
others had had in mind to begin with: the funding of basic
research in order to build up a "reserve" of basic science findings to be drawn on as technological needs required. As said
earlier, in this role all observers give great credit to the Foundation.

Drawing on the experience of the Office of Naval Research, which had served as a *de facto* science foundation between 1946 and 1950, Alan Waterman (who had been chief
scientist at ONR) and his associates at NSF designed an organization and a set of procedures (the peer-group assessment
system) whereby the best scientists in the universities would
have their proposals for research reviewed by others among
the best. The scientific community, through this kind of arrangement, ensured that science would remain uncontami-
nated by politics—that NSF's support would be awarded on
scientific merit alone, rather than by geography, log-rolling, or
other extraneous considerations. And the Board stood over it
all, as a preserver of insulation and as a further assurer of the
quality of the work to be supported.

Even in this aspect, however, another early, naïve expectation had to give way. It had been thought by some that the best scientists would be attracted to the Board; that they would select the work to be supported; and that in this way science would proceed under the immediate direction of its own leaders. The Board, however, could not long pretend to examine carefully each of thousands of project awards, and its own members were more scientist-administrators and educational administrators than they were men still active on the frontiers of science.

Project support rather quickly became NSF's most distinctive feature. University scientists came to count on it in increasing numbers, and they liked it because it was support with no programmatic strings attached. That is, one did not have to worry about making a contribution to defense (if DOD were one's supporter) or about health (if NIH were one's patron); one just investigated what one wanted in an area one had picked from personal considerations.

Later, ancillary enterprises were added—particularly direct support of the educational dimension through fellowships and equipment grants, along with science information systems and science-related statistical work. But the business of making grants to individual researchers in response to unsolicited proposals began first and has long been NSF's prime *raison d'être*.

Perhaps the best measure of its success in this field is the fact that NSF largely set the "style" of sponsor-investigator relationships, and came to symbolize government's concern for basic research—yet the agency funds well under 20 percent of academic research, and only 10 per cent of all federally funded basic research. One does not know how to apportion credit for NSF's effective patronage between the Director and the Board, but their operation was unquestionably successful. And in addition to its project support, NSF also devised the institutional grant, which aids the institution more directly. The institutional grant, so-called, consists of a percentage of all project grant sums received by a given campus; this percentage is given to the institution to use as it sees fit in developing science. Most recently has come another institutional support program, the so-called Science Development Program, which gives large chunks of money—typically $3–5 million—to universities that are now in the second rank, to help them on the way toward becoming first rank—or "additional centers of excellence," as the often-used phrase puts it. Thus NSF came to operate on several levels: support of individual researchers, institutional support programs, and scientific manpower development.

In the course of doing these things well, it went far to fill the gap that Bush had seen would occur when OSRD was phased out at the end of the war. But it did so somewhat at the expense of attention that might otherwise have been given to the development of government-wide policy for science. An operating agency, in the nature of things, is not often so adept at formulating policy that goes beyond its own bureaucratic concerns.

Also, the early effort to pick out areas of needed development and assess what research was being done, or needed to be done, in connection with them—the jet engines and high-temperature physics example was cited above—proved abortive. We have now come full circle, for this is the kind of basic role *vis-à-vis* possible applications of science that the Daddario committee has added back onto the Foundation's agenda. The concern for more even distribution of federal support among institutions and regions of the country now being expressed in Congress and followed up by NSF through its science development program was manifested in the first annual report of the Foundation, but it also seemed to be ignored until quite recently. In fact, Senator Fred Harris, Representative Daddario, and other legislators who have been trying to push the theme of broader geographic distribution since about 1964 might get an ironic laugh from reading NSF's first annual report, which stated that

> The National Science Foundation proposes to support basic research on as broad a geographic and institutional basis as possible. In the small institutions, many of which are operating on meager budgets, relatively small sums of money make it possible to retain the services of an unusually competent research investigator, for example, who could form the nucleus for a new and useful center of research. In other cases, colleges may be able to strengthen their research programs materially by the purchase of a few hundred dollars worth of needed equipment.[6]

This is not the way things worked. Rather, strong emphasis came to be placed on employing as the primary criterion the quality of the investigator and on the proposal to ensure that the greatest contributions to scientific findings were made. This is quite different from emphasizing the development of scientific manpower resources *for the future*, which would have led to greater concern for distribution. Even now, in fact, the claims of broader distribution must in part compete with monies awarded to keep the "haves" from slowing down at all: the "have-nots" will be aided to the extent that *additional* funds for that purpose are given to NSF, not by transfer of any existing funds. In this respect, at least, it is hard to avoid the conclusion that a Board composed of "establishment-type" figures, and panels whose members came predominantly from the "have" universities (where the best scientists resided), combined to thwart the kind of distribution urged in the first annual report—not intentionally, but as a consequence of the blinders that make all of us see our side of a case more clearly than we see the other fellow's.

There has also not been quite the development of basic research funding that NSF had anticipated at the time of its creation in 1950. Apparently it was originally expected that NSF would handle a very high proportion of federal basic research funds. In particular, the basic functions of the Foundation included, in the original legislation, a clause calling for NSF to initiate and support national defense-related research at the request of the Secretary of Defense. Had NSF ever taken over defense-related research (it never even began to do so), it would be a vastly larger, and much different agency today. DOD still accounts for a larger percentage of basic research than does NSF.

In 1953–54, the Bureau of the Budget apparently attempted to move all, or almost all, basic research into NSF. One draft of an executive order would have made NSF the "primary agency" for basic research, limiting other agencies to "such additional basic research as may be directly related to the solution of problems for which they have statutory responsibility." [7] These other agencies successfully warded off that particular formulation, but Executive Order 10521 of 17 March 1954 did state that NSF "shall be increasingly responsible for . . . general purpose basic research" and restricted other agencies to the performance of basic research "in areas which are closely related to their missions." Had this not been interpreted broadly in practice, it is likely that basic research would have suffered, for NSF's budget has never shown any likelihood of rising with sufficient rapidity to enable NSF to take over what the mission-oriented agencies would have had to drop if that guideline were rigidly enforced.

Despite increasing talk of NSF as a "balance wheel," and efforts by its friends to increase its importance in the federal scheme of things, other agencies are still taking on tasks that might have been thought more appropriate for NSF. President Johnson's 1965 memorandum directing all agencies using academic research to be concerned for the health of the academic institutions seems to have pushed things in this direction. For, in response to that memo, DOD inaugurated an imaginative and well-funded plan, Project Themis, by which $20 million would be distributed to 50 universities in 30 states in an effort to stimulate new relationships of continuing support between DOD and those universities for work of a basic nature but of mutual interest to defense and to the academics.

NSF: THE TASKS AHEAD

In 1953, the chairman of NSB, Chester I. Barnard, wrote in NSF's annual report that "Except for certain specified operating functions, the Foundation is essentially an authoritative advisory body" for national policy formation. That was wishful thinking: what NSF essentially became was an operating agency to transfer funds from the federal treasury to academic scientists. As a by-product, it did develop some general policies —for instance, regarding reimbursement of indirect costs or regarding loyalty-security aspects in fellowship programs. Only after the Foundation had been in operation for several years did it become apparent that the impact of its policies and programs upon the educational institutions wherein the researchers resided was becoming as significant as the scientific findings emerging from the projects. Instead of science in the abstract as the object of NSF's programs, in other words, it is very specifically academic science, and therefore the academic institutions, with which NSF is concerned. Thus Wiesner writes of the National Science Board's primary function as being "to insure the well-being of the basic research effort in universi-

ties," and Shannon of NIH sees "one imperative function for
NSF: . . . providing for the stability, vigor and balanced
growth of academic science." [8] NSF's clientele, we might say,
includes scientists as individual investigators, but it also includes universities and colleges (and to a lesser extent even
primary and secondary schools). What these groups want is
therefore important to NSF, and NSB is probably even better
suited, through its science-and-education-administrator composition, to represent the institutions than it is the interests of
the individual researchers. Perhaps this is simply to say that
NSF's major function has been to spearhead the government's
role in developing scientific resources, and that such resources
—we now realize—include the institutions where the research
is performed as well as the manpower that performs it.

Clearly, then, continued strong attention to the development of such resources can be listed as the first task of NSF, in
the future as up till now. Just how the task is to be fulfilled,
however, is subject to change. Support of the best research
project proposals was once the overwhelming mode; now, however, institutional grants, assurance of proper regional distribution of support, and support of educational efforts as well as
research efforts have been added to the roster of programmatic
approaches.

But this is not all. NSF is also being asked to assume additional functions. It is being asked to make a contribution to
applied research. It is being asked to help bring the social
sciences to a "state of the art" that would make them more useful to society in problem-solving. It is being asked to play a
balance-wheel role in federal planning of basic research support, and, by some, to reach for recapture of the important role
in overall government policy formulation that it had earlier let
slip out of its hands (and into those of OST) by default.

In light of these possible additional functions, beyond supporting research proposals, it is necessary to consider whether NSF's internal structure and institutional relationships with the rest of the government and with its natural clientele require any revision. For that matter, after 15 years of development without a thorough-going review, it was time enough for such a look at the fit of function to structure in any case.

The admonition to NSF to emphasize the applicability of basic research and to engage in sponsorship of at least certain kinds of applied research reflects a general atmosphere encouraged in President Johnson's Administration, an atmosphere which, while recognizing the need to continue developing science resources, emphasized deriving the maximum practical benefits that could be squeezed out of the basic effort. More specifically, this challenge came to NSF from the House Committee on Science and Astronautics, which has oversight jurisdiction over NSF and which the agency could ignore only at its peril. The flavor and extent of this warning are perhaps best illustrated by a substantial quotation from a 1966 committee report. In the context of discussing the Foundation's purposes and responsibilities, the Daddario subcommittee report had the following to say:

> For 15 years it [the Foundation] has worked to foster basic research and science education. Now it is time to make the Foundation into a broader instrument for forging and shaping, in company with the Federal mission-oriented agencies, the national policies to foster the national resources for science and to focus and direct them toward the attainment of great national goals. Full employment, a clean world to live in, a population in balance with resources, swift and ready transportation and communication, pure water to drink, education of the citizenry, discovery of new resources—all of these and other needs of the Nation must depend in part upon thorough, deliberate, and positive efforts to learn more about our

physical world, its creatures and its peoples, and their relations to one another; to apply this knowledge skillfully
and with judgment; and to have ready for application the
requisite science resources. The future of the NSF is
bound up with the cultivation and development of intellectual, personal and physical resources for science and
engineering throughout the country. Brought together by
this common purpose, its future programs should reflect
the interests and requirements of industry and government as well as the academic community. The NSF will
carry a far larger share of the responsibility for bringing
the understanding of and data for new fields of science to
the state where engineers and technologists can proceed
effectively with their task of applying the results of science
to new public and private purposes.[9]

Daddario then wrote into his amending legislation a provision authorizing NSF to initiate applied research at academic
and other non-profit institutions, and even further, a provision
authorizing more specific applied research "relevant to national problems involving the public interest," to be conducted
by profit-seeking firms, when NSF was "so directed by the
President."

What is the agency's reaction to these new mandates? The
answer has more than one part. First of all (and this has little
to do with what Daddario had in mind), Haworth asserted
NSF's pleasure in having a freer hand to support applied research in engineering (which would help its ability to support
engineering graduate education) and in the social sciences,
where basic and applied criteria are hard to separate, and
where the most useful education also may take place through
work on applied problems. Secondly, a doctrine of "hot pursuit" was expounded: that a man should not have to cease his
NSF support in a basic research project as soon as it appeared
that it might have some utility. That would really be cutting

off the nose to spite the face! Rather, when this occurred, the original investigator should be free to follow the applied lead up to the point at which some mission-oriented agency might take over the latter stages of research and the development into a product or system of practical dimensions. Thirdly, NSF expressed willingness to contribute to the solution of pressing social problems by exploring the question of what basic research might be needed to make applied research on such problems possible or easier, and then to initiate efforts to see that such basic research got done. Said Haworth, in 1965,

> I think we should concern ourselves a good deal more than we have with some of the scientific and engineering —and I include the social sciences here— problems that underlie some of the social problems such as transportation, urbanization, and many things of that sort. These are not areas where proposals are stimulated simply by a receptive attitude. . . . What I am trying to say is that we have to think how we can encourage concerted attacks by people in more than one discipline or more than one institution on some of these broader problems. I have to confess it is still fairly vague in my mind, but something needs to be done about these things.[10]

(It is worth noting parenthetically at this point that the first President of the National Academy of Engineering complained to the Daddario committee in 1965 that total government support of the engineering sciences was but 6.6 per cent of total government support for basic research. In his view, "the proportion the National Science Foundation devotes to the support of deriving useful results from knowledge would seem to be decidedly less than best judgment would dictate." Such a statement also indicates, if assumed to be a typical engineering reaction as I think it was, that the relative absence of engineers on the National Science Board, and on the top staff of NSF, has contributed to the organization's policy decisions.)[11]

NSF's relationship to the social sciences is likely to become stronger, both because of increasing recognition that we need their potential contributions and in order to forestall further demands for a separate foundation. With the Daddario amendments, NSF is now under some obligation (being the sole agency charged with basic responsibilities for the social sciences) to strengthen its social science staff, to cover a broader range of approaches in what it will fund, and to think through the probable need for innovations in its modes of support in order to suit the specific situation of the social sciences.

For example, it must face the issue of public policy-related studies having both basic and applied dimensions; the issue of controversiality that may well arise in the social sciences, but which has rarely been a problem in the natural sciences (with exceptions like Project Mohole and the case of a distinguished mathematician whose deviant political views, expressed in Moscow, led to congressional demands that NSF support be withdrawn from him); and the issue of appropriate changes in the composition of the National Science Board, which needs to include some distinguished social scientists. Here, perhaps more than in the case of the natural scientists, it is necessary that the Board members chosen as social science representatives be in fact active leaders in research, not surrogates in the form of once active researchers now gone administrative. Why? Because the approaches and concerns of social science are changing rapidly, and the ex-social scientist is unlikely to be thinking at the "cutting edge" of current research styles. Basic approaches having been established some time ago in the natural sciences, the same problem does not occur there.

Given NSF's position that the social and natural sciences should work together, NSF is also under some obligation to work out programs and institutional forms that would encourage closer relationships. Perhaps a Division of Interdisciplinary Problems needs to be created, where proposals can be considered from interdisciplinary groups, and which could more actively initiate plans for needed interdisciplinary research, and then invite proposals—in line with Haworth's own assertion that "in certain areas, our role must be a more active one. We must be more active in the promotion of, as distinguished from the support of, basic research." [12] Appropriate program ideas for the support of the natural sciences came naturally, as it were, to an NSF staff composed of physical scientists; appropriate ideas for the social sciences have obviously, on the other hand, come hard. Perhaps it would help if the NSF Director were to have a special assistant director, a social scientist, whose entire job would be to work on the challenges that the social sciences present. Such a post might well be filled by academic representatives on a two-year rotation basis.

As was mentioned earlier in this chapter, a number of spokesmen of the scientific community have recently been suggesting that NSF assume explicitly a role that has perhaps always been present implicitly—that the agency become the government's "balance wheel" for basic research. Although NSF did not and could not fulfil the function originally given it of evaluating the scientific research programs undertaken by federal agencies, it could investigate the coverage given to specific fields of science in the sum of agency activities, and then put into its own budget sufficient funds to fill any gaps. More actively, it could try to identify gaps explicitly and make an effort to stimulate research in the gaps, rather than just await the accidents of proposal pressures. That's one aspect of the balance wheel function.

Another meaning has also been suggested: that NSF be

the Federal Government's leader in basic research operations and in overseeing relationships between the government and the universities in relationship to research activities. It is, however, hard to be a leader or a coordinator if one encompasses only a small proportion of the funds over which leadership is to be expressed. For NSF only accounts for 10 to 15 per cent of federal basic research funds. Those who wish to see NSF's leadership role enhanced have therefore been urging in the past few years that its share of basic research funds be substantially increased.

Waterman, for example, felt that if NSF accounted for at least 50 per cent of academic research support, it could improve the distribution of research funds (because it could afford to fund more proposals of less than top quality, coming from the lesser institutions), and its participation and leadership within the government would be increased.[13] Weinberg has argued that NSF's share of academic research funds should be 60 per cent, or possibly even 80 per cent. This would, he has said, simplify the funding structure and focus debate appropriately over basic research policy onto a single agency's program.[14] And Wiesner has said that "the NSF share of the total Federal basic research effort is not great enough to allow it to be the dominant factor that it ought to be nor can it provide adequate national leadership." [15] It should be noted that none of these men was talking about increasing NSF's share by taking it away from mission-oriented agencies. Rather, they were assuming a leveling off of basic research budgets in those agencies (except for NIH and the biomedical sciences) and positing that future growth would take place within NSF, rather than across the board. It should also be noted that the first meaning of the balance wheel concept is not dependent upon the size of NSF's fund allotment, except that it will require a sufficient fund and sufficient flexibility in its allocation, to permit NSF to fill cracks wherever they appear.

If one asks mission-oriented agencies about their own basic research policies, and how they see the role of NSF in relation to their own, one finds the agencies very anxious to retain a good share of research for themselves, with an expectation that NSF will take care of any sub-fields not of interest to them.[16] Asked if an enlarged NSF share of basic research would be seen as a relief to their own budgets, or as an "unwelcome divorce of basic work from the environment of potential utilization," most agency spokesmen took the latter view. In reversal of the logic of Executive Order 10521 of 1954, the agencies see themselves as properly supporting a wide range of research for which some ultimate applicability is anticipated, and NSF as a residual category for whatever is left uncovered by the other agencies. The agencies would most definitely be opposed to any transfer of their own basic research to NSF, and they do not wish to define their own needs narrowly.

Partly, the mission agencies are concerned that undirected basic research of the kind handled by NSF would be likely to have only a "relatively small pay-off," compared to that which is programmed in response to a felt need and which creates communication between the scientists receiving the grants and the science-using agencies. The agencies feel that, although the results of particular projects cannot be predicted, nor a time limit set within which much basic research can pay off in practical applications, nevertheless they can rather easily identify some fields that are most likely to become useful and also some in which they will show no interest and thus are willing to leave to NSF. The Department of the Army, for example, wants to ensure that research is stimulated in such areas as explosives, tropical medicine, and chemical warfare, and states that the "Army must be the leader and actually perform the bulk of the research in these areas or the work would not be done, since it is the principal user." And in other fields—electronics, materials, meteorology—which are relevant to a much wider group, the Army nevertheless finds it necessary to support research itself "in order to fill the gaps, study fundamental problems having a direct bearing on its mission, and be an intelligent contractor." [17]

Although NSF may support effort in the same broad fields as a mission-oriented group, "they will not be aimed as nicely and as programmatically as the support given by agencies of the DOD," writes a Navy official. And the Navy, too, picks out fields of predictable application for its own program; e.g. the Navy makes more investment in "physics, chemistry, mathematics, oceanography and psychology, than in archeology, paleontology, philology or agronomy." It would be a "move in the wrong direction," says the Navy official, to have NSF take any research away from the mission agencies, for this would place the end user too far away from the person undertaking the research.[18]

Officials of several agencies, in addition to stressing the greater likelihood that basic research will be linked to end uses if it is performed under mission-agency sponsorship, believe that by doing and sponsoring their own basic research they can keep their own scientists at the frontiers of their fields through close association. They see basic research as a way of developing expert manpower that can be called upon to assist in development programs. The mission-oriented agencies are, of course, thinking of what they do themselves as well as by grant to university investigators. Since other agencies (unlike NSF, which does not run its own laboratories) have employee scientists to think about, they look at basic research as a way of attracting and holding good personnel (in both the applied and basic sectors), as well as of acquiring the findings that may emerge.

One also sees a difference—a significant one, I believe—

between NSF's and the mission agencies' ways of defining basic and applied research. NSF defines basic research as that in which the investigator's motive is knowledge for its own sake, while the other agencies tend to define basic research as that which involves the development of new knowledge, even if the purpose is an immediately practical one. The Agency for International Development provides a good illustration, when its research director writes:

> If we could afford it I would like nothing as much as to try to develop varieties of staple crops which would grow in highly saline solutions—for example, on saline soils irrigated by sea water. There are enough new hypotheses emerging out of plant physiology, chemistry and genetics to hint at the fact that this might be accomplishable. Its practical value would be, of course, that both the land and the water limitations on food production would be removed for decades or possibly centuries. Certainly this extremely important "applied" research problem would require very basic and fundamental research, and its outcome would be in doubt probably for 10 to 20 years.[19]

Looked at in this light, the question is not whether the investigator sees himself as seeking a way to apply his findings, or as simply seeking knowledge; rather, the question is whether the sponsoring or performing agency sees the work as relevant to the agency's mission—regardless of the investigator's motivation. If it does, then it wants to include such research in its own program, feeling that the pay-off will be greater if the work is part of a program connected to a mission, instead of being just another miscellaneous project supported by NSF.

In a sense, both NSF and the mission-oriented agencies can be seen as parts of a single "balance wheel" system. NSF plays its role by supporting undirected research generally and encouraging the filling of gaps left by the mission agencies in particular. The agencies play their role by ensuring that work relevant to their missions, but perhaps not otherwise likely to receive enough support, is covered. Thus both partners in basic research balance off each other's strengths and weaknesses. The one function likely to be filled *only* by NSF is to ensure basic research is supported sufficiently to keep pace with increasing numbers of investigators and graduate students in the universities, for the mission-oriented agencies have to determine the amount of the research they will support by reference to their own missions, not by any academic needs. Given the cogent reasons of the mission-oriented agencies for doing some basic research of their own without being required to limit themselves to what is presently of direct utility in their missions, and given their adamant stand against any shifting to NSF of work important to them, any growth of NSF's research budget is likely to come by increasing the pie, not by cutting the slices differently.

To the extent that NSF's share of the basic research total increased, its own policies and principles regarding grants and their administrative relationships with the universities would necessarily become more important because of the increased area of application. If it were ever to account for 75 or 80 per cent of basic research, then its policies would almost *ipso facto* be the government's policies as a whole. In that sense, the balance-wheel argument appears to be a good one. But in a different sense, NSF's ability to become the balance wheel of basic research would appear to depend even more on its own attitudes and efforts: if it exercises no initiative, if it were to continue the primary role of responding to academic scientists' individual initiatives in determining its own programs, then a larger share of funds would accomplish very little. An increased planning role—not the planning of individual projects, which is anathema to scientists, and properly so—regarding financial

and programmatic strategies would help make it a more significant factor in national policy development. There are signs,
including Haworth's own testimony, that the Foundation is
now trying to take more initiative along these lines—partly in
response to two years of review and probings by the Daddario
committee.

One potentially useful avenue open to NSF for enlarging
its policy voice is the Federal Council for Science and Technology, particularly FCST's relatively new Committee on
Academic Science and Engineering. Another would be the requirement imposed by the Daddario legislation for the National Science Board to present to the President and Congress
an annual report on the "status and health of science and its
various disciplines." By agreement with the Daddario committee, it is understood that this report need not be an annual,
quick survey of all fields and all problems, but can be a report
on a different specific field or problem area each year.

Just how this role will work out remains, of course, to be
seen. I see at least two difficulties, however. First, it is specifically the Board that is to issue the report, not the Director.
Since the Board meets for two days every other month on the
average, will this mean that a small staff, appointed by the
Director to work for the Board, will *de facto* do the reports,
and so determine what to report on each year, with its choices
and its finished products simply given a stamp of approval by
the Board? If the annual *Economic Report* is the model, there
is an obvious difference: the members of the Council of Economic Advisers, who write that report, are full-time officials,
working daily with their staff and with the President. Without
that degree of contact and involvement, one has some hesita-
tion about what NSB will be able to do.

Secondly, how will this NSB report relate to the work of
OST? Recall that NSF's original mandate to "develop and en-

courage the pursuit of a national policy for the promotion of basic research and education in the sciences" was partly lost by default; Reorganization Act No. 2 of 1962 moved to the Director of OST "so much (of this function) as will enable the Director to advise and assist the President in achieving coordinated Federal policies for the promotion of basic research and education in the sciences." While there is no reason why the President cannot receive advice from both sources, and while NSB's focus might be other than achievement of coordination, the visibility—even within the scientific community—of OST as a Presidential staff office is so much greater than that of NSB, which is really known as NSF's Board rather than the nation's, that one wonders if its voice can be resuscitated and made strong at this late date, just by legislative fiat. And one wonders if it *should* be made into a source of a Presidential report, or whether its studies and advice should be given to FCST and OST as information inputs for these offices to take into account. In other words, to put it bluntly, if we are to have an annual report to the Congress—and I think we should—it would be better, in my view, for it to follow the CEA precedent and emanate from OST rather than from NSB (see Chapter 9, below). Conceivably, NSB could be drawn upon to supply ideas and material for the basic research portion of a Presidential science report; or, even better, for the academic research and government-universities relationships aspects of basic research. Perhaps the annual authorization hearings to which NSF will now be subject in the House Subcommittee on Science, Research, and Development can include discussion in depth on some aspect of basic research, using an NSF-NSB presentation as the take-off point.

The last idea might be the best from an NSF-NSB standpoint, in fact, because one of the Foundation's problems in achieving the level of funding it believes it needs has always been, I believe, its relative lack of congressional contact outside of its annual appropriation hearings. Greater frequency of discussions with the House Subcommittee, as now required for formal financial authorization under the 1968 amendments, can serve an educational function and probably build a stronger political support base by giving NSF a group of friends in the legislature who would have more than random knowledge of the agency, its programs, and its field of activity. The Daddario legislation and the hearings held with regard to it have already demonstrated, I believe, that NSF can benefit from closer legislative contact. As a Daddario committee report said in 1965,

> it may be appropriate to suggest that the Foundation abandon any remnants of past aloofness in dealing with the Congress. . . . with due respect for the merits of keeping basic science in the pure atmosphere of "pursuit of knowledge for its own sake," science has nonetheless matured a great deal in recent years. We believe it can play in the political leagues without being corrupted or even unduly influenced by the character of the other players.[20]

NSF-NSB: THE ORGANIZATIONAL FRAMEWORK

Having glanced at what NSF and NSB are being asked to do, we now move our focus to the organizational structure through which the functions are carried on. Two levels are involved: the fit of NSF-NSB to the rest of the government and to the scientific and educational communities—their external relations, as it were—and the internal relationship of NSB to the Director of the Foundation.

Ever since President Truman rejected the first NSF legislation, which would have made the Director merely an executive secretary appointed by the Board, and a compromise between the scientists' wishes and normal governmental operation was worked out in the 1950 legislation, it has been difficult to answer the question, Who's in charge? By statute the Foundation consists of the Director and the Board, but without clear delineation of their respective authorities and responsibilities. Reorganization acts, executive orders, and amendatory legislation have both clarified and confused the relationships. On the whole, the Director's authority has been increased relative to that of the Board: the Director, not the chairman of the Board, chairs the Board's executive committee; by the Daddario amendments all actions taken by the Director "pursuant to the provisions" of the National Science Foundation Act "shall be final and binding upon the Foundation," and except as otherwise specifically provided "the Director shall exercise all of the authority granted to the Foundation." Under the 1950 legislation, on the other hand, the Board had to approve specifically in each instance the actions taken by the Director in awarding grants and fellowships, and the Director was only a non-voting member of the Board.

In the other direction, we have the new mandate for the Board, not the Director, to submit an annual report to the President on the health of science, and the Daddario amendments also state the Board's primary function as being to "establish and be responsible for the policies of the Foundation."

The purpose of these compromises from the viewpoint of the Daddario committee was clearly to strengthen the hand of the Director in operational and administrative direction of the Foundation's activities, while simultaneously emphasizing that basic policies are to remain the prerogative of the Board. Much of the trouble arises from the difficulty, if not the impossibility, of delineating a clear line between policy-making and operations. The devising of major programs—say, for institutional grants or a new kind of fellowship—is the bridge between policy and operations. It is very difficult to give the Director enough authority to make him responsible to the President (one can't be responsible for that over which one does not have authority), while giving the Board enough say to make it the body that establishes policies. From the viewpoint of governmental accountability and prestige, a strong director is needed; from the viewpoint of the scientific community, a strong board composed of men from the worlds of science and education is needed. Representative Daddario has persuaded the Congress that his amendments successfully walk this tightrope. I think, however, that the Act still contains contradictions in this regard and that Representative Weston E. Vivian expressed them succinctly when he made the following remarks:

> One of the purposes of our action is to raise the stature of the National Science Foundation. I concur with this, but I feel there is a very basic conflict. If we raise the stature of the Foundation in the scientific eyes, we may do so only publicly by increasing the stature of the Board relative to the status of the administration's presence in the agency through the Director [,] but to raise NSF's stature in the overall functions of Government related to science, the only way we are going to do this is to raise the stature of the Director and the President's role in the Foundation at the expense of the Board. I think this basic conflict has to be recognized.[21]

It seems to me important, in attempting to delineate the appropriate role for the Board, to consider whether it is fundamentally a part of the government or fundamentally a part of the science community; one or the other place has to be primary—although scientific community protagonists have wanted to have it both ways. For example, it has been suggested that the Board's role of policy and program determination within the Foundation (hence its governmental authority) should be strengthened, but that at the same time the Board should be free from "administrative discipline" so that it can raise questions publicly about science policies without approval of the executive branch (i.e. the President, BOB or the President's Special Assistant).[22] If it is to have governmental power, it *must* be subject to administrative discipline; if it wants to be free of administrative discipline, it should not have governmental power.

If one accepts the view that NSB members' "essential loyalty is not to the Congress, or to the Administration, but to science itself," [23] that seems to me a way of saying that freedom from administrative discipline should be more important to it than governmental power, and that no group whose basic loyalty runs to a locus outside of the government should have direct governmental decision-making power. Is it not more important for representatives of the scientific community to remain free to criticize public policy than that they have a final say in making policy without being free to criticize?

These considerations lead me to believe that the National Science Board should be *advisory* rather than determinative. And this position is reinforced by the general history of multi-headed boards as ineffective administrators. As Seitz remarked to the Daddario committee, "One man can be held responsible for the programs of a Government agency, but 24 cannot." [24] One might add, especially when those 24 are government personnel only a few days a year. If scientists want to ensure an effective voice for science within government, they should seek whatever administrative pattern will provide the greatest political strength for the agency that oversees the health of science. And an agency with pinpointed individual authority and responsibility would almost inevitably be stronger in the important respects than one with confused and divided authority. As Seitz has also said in suggesting that he thought the Board should *advise* the Director on matters of policy, "one will get a man of higher quality as Director if it is quite clear that while he has inputs from the Board on matters of policy, he, in the last analysis, is the person who is Director of the Foundation." [25]

In developing the Foundation's reorganization plan in 1962, then Special Assistant Wiesner says that he recommended that the Board be made advisory, that "all of the operating responsibilities be given by law directly to the Director, rather than being delegated by the Board." [26] Harvey Brooks took the same position, and in 1965 said that his subsequent service on the Board had reinforced his conviction.[27] To both Brooks and Haworth an advisory board might in fact be a *more* effective voice for science. Said Haworth in 1965:

> The importance of the Board is not that it has legal authority to make decisions but that as a truly independent body it can forcefully represent the views and needs of the scientific and educational communities. Its independence might even be enhanced if changed to an advisory body since there would then be no constraint on its openly questioning governmental policy with which it did not agree.[28]

As to whether the Foundation might ignore the Board if the Board were either advisory in law or delegated its powers *de facto* to the Director, Haworth correctly, in my view, thinks it unlikely "that any Director . . . would ever ignore or override the views of a distinguished group appointed by the President, with the advice and consent of the Senate, and representative of scientific research and education activities throughout the country."

Former NSB chairman Eric Walker is not persuaded.

Speaking of NSF as the one place where a lay board has policy authority, he has said that the scientific community is "very jealous of this position. We do not want to be reduced to an advisory board." [29] One of his reasons is that if NSB were made purely advisory, "it would be impossible to get the same calibre of men to serve on it. As an advisory board, it would lose even the vestige of influence in national affairs that has been left to it." [30] Walker would not only retain its policy-making authority; he would extend its authority to the determination of programs and responsibility for their implementation as well.

I think Walker is wrong on both counts: as an advisory body, there is no reason why high calibre men could not be obtained (look at PSAC, for example, which is advisory and has even greater prestige than NSB); and the influence of an advisory body in national affairs has proved considerable on numerous occasions. NSB is defended as an essential locus for government-university relations policies, but look at the record. In 1960 and 1964 respectively, there appeared two reports in this area; both came from advisory groups and had real influence on subsequent policy formation. One was the PSAC report, *Scientific Progress, the Universities and the Federal Government,* and the other was from NAS's Committee on Science and Public Policy, entitled *Federal Support of Basic Research in Institutions of Higher Learning.* If NSB should be jealous of anybody's position, it should be jealous of these advisory-only bodies, not of its own explicit governmental authority.

Protagonists of the Board should also be more aware that the Board's power in relation to the Director and the Foundation's internal operations is quite distinguishable from its influence upon federal research policies generally. Decline of internal power bears no necessary, or even probable, relationship to general policy-making influence. In fact, I would on the whole expect the latter to be increased if NSB were freed completely from its NSF responsibilities, for it could then concentrate upon, and comment freely upon, the whole spectrum of science, and might have time to do so effectively. It could certainly include NSF's policies and operations in its purview, but not be restricted by them. Divorced from NSF as such, NSB would finally be free to become what its name implies: a board of distinguished non-governmental figures charged with advising the government on science policies.

The only question then remaining would be: Would such a board merely duplicate PSAC? I think not, for the latter's focus is primarily the use of science in relationship to societal problems, and only secondarily upon the development of science resources. The two could well be complementary rather than competitive.[31]

If—though this would be less preferable—the Board were to move toward greater governmental authority rather than less, then it would be advisable to amend the Act and provide for Presidential appointment of the chairman of the Board. Both BOB and OST officials have testified in favor of such a move,[32] on the grounds that it would enhance the prestige of the Board within the government, and that it would appropriately make it clear that the Board was a part of the government and subject to Presidential oversight.

I would argue that if the Board is seen as intra-governmental rather than extramural advisory, then these arguments are strong ones. The Federal Reserve Board's history demonstrates rather clearly that independence from the President weakens an agency more than it strengthens it. If one is clearly "part of the family," one's internal position is stronger. This the protagonists of NSB have failed to realize.

Along this line should go one final structural change: the Director of the Foundation should serve, like cabinet department heads and those of other major agencies, at the pleasure of the President rather than for a fixed term of six years, which is the existing arrangement.[33] A new President might choose to retain the incumbent Director, but at least he would have the choice, and thus would be more likely to feel that it was his Director, and the latter would therefore gain in reciprocal loyalty from the White House.

Although the Daddario amendments are ambiguous in trying to strengthen both the Board and the Director, they contain two provisions that could be employed to place the Director clearly in charge without further legislative change. One is the authorization for the Board to delegate to the Director whatever of its powers (including policy-making) it deems appropriate. The other is the new eligibility of the Director to be elected chairman of the Board. Were these steps taken, the existing duality of authority would be largely resolved in the direction of executive vigor—and executive vigor is what NSF needs the most.

III | As Things Might Be

8| Policy and Process Requirements: An Overview

We have looked at the ways in which the science-government relationship has developed since World War II, and we have analyzed some of the stresses and strains that challenge what has been done so far. Now it is time to sift out the major requirements for more effective science policy in the future. Science imposes some requirements upon governmental institutions and processes; the character of our democratic polity reciprocally imposes its demands upon science and the scientific community. Both science and government have autonomous as well as common goals and needs; the problem is how best to fit their diverse needs together so as to support common goals most effectively. These are matters of judgment, not of scientific analysis, and what is presented in these last chapters represents one observer's prescriptive judgments after examining facts and trends as objectively as possible.

Perhaps the best place to begin is to examine why government plays the role of patron to science. In Chapter 2 we examined the reasoning of scientists in this regard, and found five major types of justifications. Although scientists would like to justify support on the intrinsic cultural merits of increased scientific knowledge, there can be little doubt that the major reason in fact for governmental support is the *use* that government can make of science. Government plays patron in the hope of obtaining a pay-off in return. Most of the R&D budget is allocated to developmental projects involving technological tasks that the political process has given approval to: supersonic aircraft, space exploration, weapons systems, improved public health. The basic research portion of the R&D budget clearly is supported not because the government is philanthropically inclined toward the value of knowledge for its own sake, but because the government has accepted the scientists' insistence that technological developments, governmental or private, increasingly depend upon the quality and size of our pool of basic knowledge. It is thus the "investment" justification that has created a two-billion-dollar basic research program. And this, I believe, is as it should be.

That is not to say that the cultural argument regarding science's intrinsic value is totally meaningless; just that it could not justify the *level* of support that has developed. In a sense, one might say that NSF's share of the basic research budget constitutes the cultural argument's share of the total. NSF funds proposals without regard to the utility of the prospective results, and its grantees have neither motivation nor obligation to relate their research to some agency's social mission. NSF itself seems to look upon its programs as supporting science both for its intrinsic values and for its development as a vital national resource. And if one looks at it from the legislative perspective, if it were not for the "investment" argument that relates even the most indirected research to eventual application, it is doubtful that the budget of NSF would be much higher than that for the National Foundation on the Arts and the Humanities. That is to say, government is not heavily in the business of patronizing culture as such. It has only very recently begun to do so at all. Therefore the main justification for science is its promise of ultimate utility. So long as our society still has to solve its problems of survival, of poverty, and of the creation of a livable environment, the priority given to cultural philanthropy whose fruits are of interest only to a minority of the population will not be—and should not be, in my scheme of values—a very high one.

It follows that in its relationships with science government will seek patterns that promise the greatest and most expeditious links between the development of the body of basic scientific knowledge and the application of that body of knowledge to societal problems. It does not follow, however, that government is interested *only* in the use of science and not in its development. The health of the scientific community, the scientific enterprise as some have called it, is of very great concern to government, though the reasons be utilitarian rather than aesthetic. And in developing science resources, what counts is that the job be done in ways that fit the integrity of science itself, regardless of how practical the government's motives may be.

In other words, scientists should not be worried by the differences between their own and the government's reasons for patronizing science; but they will from time to time find good reason to worry about the ways in which government develops and uses science, for those ways will not always be correctly calculated to advance science to best advantage. For example, the scientific community would have good reason to complain if *all* basic research came from mission-oriented agencies, no matter how much of it there might be. Some share of research must be financed on a non-mission basis if the integrity of science is to be maintained, if its own values are to receive the support they require for their most fruitful development. And within mission-related basic research care must be taken not to let the agency mission alter what is being supported as basic research.

On these premises, then, we can say that government

should continue to support basic research, doing so for its reasons rather than those of scientists; that it should do so in ways consistent with the best development of science as such, even though the health of science resources is a derived rather than a primary concern of government; and that arrangements should be developed accordingly to maximize the feedback of governmentally supported science into government's technological programs.

To develop science resources adequately, and relate that development to governmental needs, we need a clearer and more definite science policy, agreed to by the legislature as well as by the executive. R&D has grown in separate pieces and with great rapidity. It has outstripped the existing formal premises of policy. What is badly needed now is an overall framework by which both the executive and the Congress may jointly declare their intentions and policy presuppositions in regard to science. As with economic policy, science policy needs a fundamental charter at this point. The National Science Foundation Act and the reorganization plan that created OST in 1962 provide some of the elements needed, but not an overall framework and not in a joint executive-legislative framework. Our $17 billion for R&D is still in search of a policy.

In a span of but 25 years, science in the Federal Government has grown from a minor relation ($100 million support in 1940) into a major beneficiary. No other area of discretionary expenditure is larger in today's budget. Yet none is less well rationalized, less satisfactorily justified or distributed among competing claimants. Science constitutes the cutting edge of governmental activity today, from anti-missile-missiles to mass transportation, from pollution abatement to cancer and heart disease research. That much is clear. But over overall national policy regarding science and technology is not clear.

We have discerned a *de facto* set of policies for science (Chapter 4), but it is time now for a formal science policy to be set forth, although some would argue that in a pluralistic society there will be as many policies as there are agencies dealing with science. Organizations are useless without ideas, and effective planning and coordination presume common premises among the institutions involved. The larger gap in science policy, therefore, is not the organizational but the substantive one. William D. Carey of BOB has succinctly stated the present situation:

> We have had great strength, I think, in administration, in program operations throughout the Government. But the rationalizing of it all, the attempt to shape a framework in connection with which we do all of this research and development and technology—there I think . . . too little has been accomplished. . . .

I believe the point has been reached at which we need a careful statement of the total governmental position *vis-à-vis* science and technology—something equivalent to the oft-quoted mandate of the Employment Act of 1946 that the Federal Government is to "promote maximum employment, production and purchasing power." We need, therefore, both an equivalent statement of national science policy to underly agency programs and a set of institutions well-designed to provide continuous oversight of this large sector of activity.

We need also to improve the representational structure of science and technology and to rationalize the special mechanisms for science affairs that can be differentiated from what is needed for other areas of policy. For example: do we see NSB as *the* locus of representation for basic science? For academic science as a 60-per-cent segment of basic science? Is the advisory panel for research project choices as developed by NSF and NIH an essential or an accidental part of the basic science support scene? If the former, should we extend it to all the other agencies that now rely more on internal review of project proposals?

There is greater reliance upon advisory bodies in science policy and administration than anywhere else in government, I believe. And advice is surely needed. But does our advisory system undercut our normal insistence that governmental decisions must be made by accountable officials of the government and cannot be "farmed out" to interested groups? One high-level participant in the science affairs of a military department, for example, has expressed strong feelings about agency accountability in this way:

> We expect our people to be informed enough to make their own decisions as to the relevance, worth, and need of a particular proposal. If they rely on the priority listing of an outside panel, they certainly are not running a program but only acting as secretary to carry out the wishes of an outside body. There is no reason to believe that this outside body has the intimate knowledge of, the feeling of, the need of, or requirements for particular work by a specific agency. To acquire these is a full time job, not the weekend spent on selecting proposals for their scientific worth only.[1]

At another level, are PSAC and NAS to be taken as representative of the scientific community's views without further examination? Both are bodies whose members get there by cooptation rather than by any formal mechanism of representation, which leaves open the question of whether and how far they in fact reflect the scientific community at large. We saw in Chapter 2 that the views of leading articulators of science are not always identical with those obtained by a broader survey; how far should we go in assuming that those who speak up adequately represent those who go silently about their work "at the bench"? And if, realistically, we have little choice but to use professional organizations as *de facto* representatives of the scientific community, do we receive inputs of ideas and opinions from a sufficiently broad range of such organizations? Until the recent creation of the National Academy of Engineering as a coordinate body to NAS, for example, it is probable that the contributions of engineers were not given proper consideration.

In any area of expertise, technical advice is needed by government. But science policy, whether for the development of science or for its use, raises this need to a higher level than in other areas. In this area we sometimes almost seem to have "government by advice," so strong is the supposition that what is advised from outside is what should be done. One wonders if, given a government that itself includes a great number of scientists, the views of governmental scientists might not properly be brought more often and more strongly into the picture. If so, how? By larger representation on PSAC and in NAS, perhaps? By greater reliance on the Federal Council on Science and Technology? Whatever the mechanism, it is important that we lean back and take a look at the advisory apparatus that has developed, and see whether it fits all our needs, or whether it perhaps represents only some segments of the scientific community at the expense of others.

Representation is a political concept, not a scientific one, and it can be argued that it is a misplaced effort to apply it to scientific advisory mechanisms. What is needed, it can be said, is not accurate representation of different segments of the scientific community but simply the selection of the most appropriate backgrounds for the advisory group in relation to the specific problem upon which advice is sought. If environmental pollution is the problem, for example, we need an advisory panel of those most expert in this field—not one representative from each scientific discipline or professional organization for the sake of representativeness.

On the other hand, when it is not a question of using science to solve a problem but one of the government's posture toward science generally, then the representativeness of the body advising the government and being used as its sounding board is appropriately a question of importance. For example, academic spokesmen for science have in recent years discussed at length the balance of individual project support versus institutional support as forms of patronage in regard to universities. But do these spokesmen represent more than their own views? Have we any assurance that their views accurately reflect the preponderant opinions among all academic scientists? No, we have not. Yet all will be affected. If government's modes of support are to serve academic scientists' needs as seen by the scientists, perhaps survey research would occasionally be useful in helping to determine more definitely what they define as their needs, rather than taking on faith the representative nature of the views of the few people who serve as surrogates for the scientists in PSAC, NSB, and NAS.

The needs of government are just as much at stake as the needs of the scientific community, and the danger in this regard is less that scientists won't be heard clearly enough than it is that a rather small group of (mostly) academically oriented scientists will (by unchallenged advice) impose on government a pattern that suits the separate interests of science without sufficient regard for the interests of government and the public. That this is not just an empty fear is indicated, I believe, by the fact that President Johnson's expression of concern over whether adequate attention was being given in the field of biomedical research to the stage of delivering health services occasioned such a pained reaction from the biomedical research community. If the scientists thought more about why government was supporting their work, they would not have been either surprised or chagrined to find that a time came when a call was made to show that they cared about the public pay-off from their work. The basic researchers may perfectly well say that utilization of research results in hospitals and patient care is not their problem, but they have no basis for complaining when the suggestion is made that somewhat greater a share of total resources be thrown into the task of ensuring maximum utilization. Otherwise, we would have a very arid situation of research for its own sake—and in bio-medical science particularly that would be a ridiculous situation.

The relationship between undirected research and government's need to use research for social purposes poses a need for a more strongly developed planning system. We need to tie together science resources development and science utilization more explicitly and more effectively than we have done in the past. This requirement arises from the logic of governmental patronage and from the increasing public-political expectation that scientific and technological resources be directed more fully and effectively in relation to pressing societal problems. So far, our institutional pattern emphasizes concern with science resources development in NSF and concern with utilization in PSAC, but only in OST are the two brought together. The role of OST therefore needs to be enlarged to provide more effective linkage between the two major aspects of science planning.

The need for planning has already been identified as a challenge. The dominant reason for the need lies, I believe, in the apparent situation that a high-technology society such as ours continually creates technologically derived problems, which in turn call for further technological advances to contribute to their solution. So far, this has been primarily a matter of after-the-fact realizations that a problem has been created (e.g. sudsy water in home taps because of detergents that did not disintegrate). Increasingly, we should try to anticipate and prevent unwanted side effects. But that means more careful planning of the technological use of research results. It means careful assessment of technological innovations. Just as we now have a mechanism for the screening of drugs before they can be marketed, so we seem to need a "technology screening" mechanism more broadly. Although this might be done in the various agencies in accord with their particular areas of concern, some overall planning of a screening process is also needed, and that part should be the specific concern of a central body.

To the extent that OST, using PSAC panels, can attempt to identify areas of research need, it might then also stimulate one agency or another, as appropriate, to sponsor or perform research directed toward filling gaps and supplying the basic knowledge needed for anticipated societal needs. This would mean a more active role for OST than the present one of reviewing what the agencies are doing seriatim and then attempting to impose some minimal coordination through the budgetary process. Whether in OST or elsewhere, this function is needed if science's contribution to society is to be most effective.

Basic research poses some peculiar problems from the viewpoint of ordinary government operations. Funds are spent on the recommendations of non-governmental advisers, and no specific "product" can be required in return. The government spends its money, yet "buys" nothing; rather, it is granting funds to be used by scientists for their purposes, which are only indirectly the purposes of government. The meaning of accountability is not easy to determine in such a sphere of operation. Certainly we cannot insist on a "dollar's worth" of research findings for each dollar of research financing. The most we can ask, in fact, is for an assurance that the researcher has done his best to accomplish what he set forth in his project proposal. If nothing comes of it, there is no complaint to be filed. The appropriate policy premise can only be that we can by and large assume the integrity of researchers and their home institutions. Accountability in this area has been difficult all along. Gripes about "time and effort" reporting are perpetual, yet the government must insist on some kind of accounting for the expenditure of taxpayers' funds. Money cannot, as was once suggested to be the desire of scientists, be left in a hollow log in the dead of night, to be picked up anonymously by scientists who would then need to make no accounting whatsoever.

Perhaps the most meaningful kind of accountability in basic research, however, might consist of the papers that result from the research. If these are of good quality, then the support was worthwhile and the investigator has shown his good faith. This would be a kind of accountability quite different from that normally connected with governmental affairs, yet it would be appropriate to the integrity of science. Given the nature of scientific creativity, the ordinary administrative modes of accountability have little meaning as applied to basic science. Rather than force scientists into arbitrary and essentially meaningless forms of accountability, it is government's obligation to work out a pattern that provides a meaningful basis for evaluation of the work supported, and the scientists' papers would constitute such a pattern. In project support, what counts is not the number of hours a scientist puts into his work, but the quality of his thinking and his experimentation. Only papers and research reports at the end of a project enable us to judge that quality, as a basis for determining whether

that investigator merits further support or not. Such judgments, which a man's peers are inevitably making in any case,
would constitute a meaningful kind of accountability from
both the scientific and the governmental viewpoints.

No matter what form of accountability is employed, a
basic tension will continue to exist between the scientific
community's requirement of substantive autonomy and the
government's requirement that public funds be used to maximum effectiveness. Government is the immediate patron, but
the ultimate patron is the taxpaying public, and government
must act as the public's financial guardian as well as being a
patron. The tension between responsible government and
autonomous science depends primarily upon the integrity of
the institutional arrangements through which the two spheres
are linked. If those are well-designed, we can confidently do
without some of the particularistic kinds of accountability
derived from other spheres.

With 60 per cent of federally funded basic research being
done in the universities, the health of basic research is indis-
tinguishable from the health of the universities. Institutional
grants are one kind of recognition of this fact, but others are
needed. In turn, the universities consist of their faculty and
their students, and support of the latter as an element of national educational policy is closely tied to the development of
science resources in the form of skilled manpower. It is therefore necessary to broaden the discussion somewhat to take the
educational situation more broadly and directly into account.

Today there is probably no major university that does not
count on the national government—the Department of Defense, the Atomic Energy Commission, the National Institutes
of Health, the Office of Education, the National Science Foundation, and the National Foundation on the Arts and the
Humanities—for a basic, irreplaceable share of its budget.

Even one-third of the operating funds for Harvard come from the Federal Government. Furthermore, some 80,000 graduate students depend on research assistantships and traineeships provided by these agencies, plus NSF and National Defense Education Act fellowships. About 25 per cent of higher education costs are now underwritten by the Federal Government. And since the most money goes to the "best" campuses, the ironic fact is that it is the leaders of American education who have been effectively made wards of the House and Senate Appropriations Committees, not the less meaningful rank and file of college establishments.

Because our conventional wisdom did not permit outright aid to education until very recently, much aid has had to take the form of funds to support a faculty member's research, with a tacitly agreed upon myth that only the man, not the institution, was being supported. With this myth, the project system became a prime mode of educational support. But it has been an unsatisfactory one educationally, no matter how effective with respect to scientific results, for by its nature project support goes to the already leading institutions: the stronger faculties at the better institutions write the better proposals.

Although broader distribution has been developing in recent years, there remains a marked concentration. In 1966 the top 100 university receivers of R&D funds accounted for 88.7 per cent of such funds; the top ten receivers picked up 29.64 per cent of federal academic R&D in 1966—though this was at least down from 1963, when they accounted for 36 per cent. As aid to scientific research, such a distribution makes sense in terms of research output; as aid to education, however, it is much too concentrated: financial needs do not only exist, or even primarily exist, in the leading institutions. A 1960 PSAC report put the educational aid role of the national government squarely in the center of the situation: *Either [the federal gov-*

ernment] will find the policies—and the resources—which permit our universities to flourish and their duties to be adequately discharged—or no one will.[2]

Although spokesmen for science insist that graduate education beyond the M.A. level is impossible without research, the emphasis has been on the research, rather than on the contribution to education. Now that scientists are themselves stressing the contribution of research awards to graduate education as a justification for increased federal funds, it is time to admit that the institution as well as the researcher is being aided, and it is time to give money directly to the institutions —as so-called institutional grants are beginning to do. In doing so, the research criteria emphasize existing quality of researchers; educational aid will emphasize the need to generate quality in new locations, the need of every institution for more funds.

As aid to higher education increases, programs of strengthened support should not be looked upon as simply charitable gifts from the federal patron. Society gets cultural, technological, and economic returns from its investments in education. Furthermore, most of the existing funds from Washington are being used to advance governmental goals directly: the mission agencies pay for the universities to perform research that will contribute to solutions of the problems they face.

Although the awarders of federal funds have placed as few restrictions as possible on their university grants, some universities—and all should—worry about their integrity as independent centers of thought when they are dependent upon government for 75 per cent of their research funds, and when 80 per cent of those funds come from agencies not charged with aiding education but with landing a man on the moon, or developing an artificial heart or a new aircraft. Only NSF and the Office of Education in HEW have a primary responsibility for the health and autonomy of those receiving their grants.

Thus the crisis of the universities is not just over how much money, but also over its sources and the ways in which it is allocated.

What needs to be done? First of all, more money is needed, both for students and for institutions. Our national educational policy, based on the concept of education as an area of investment that pays off both for aided individuals and for the society as a whole, should be to ensure that every student who can qualify academically is not prevented by financial need from going as far as he can in the educational system, whether that be the M.A., the M.D., or the Ph.D. This means a universal, federally financed fellowship program. It should be open-ended: instead of funding a given number of fellowships each year, there should be a congressional commitment to provide whatever funds are needed to meet the demand of qualified applicants—just as agricultural parity subsidies are open-ended, or aid to veterans is.

Secondly, it is time that we became frank about aiding institutions as well as individual investigators and individual students. It is no longer necessary to hide what is done for the campuses behind the mantle of research support. We can now give money directly to the campuses, and can thus afford to clarify for ourselves what is funded for its potential discoveries and what is funded to provide student apprenticeships. And there is every reason to distribute the latter category very widely, using, perhaps, some sort of per capita measure plus an equalization formula so that the most needy states and institutions receive more than what their per capita share would be. Then the true research funds could continue to be awarded to the scientifically best proposals, which means that a fair degree of concentration in such funds is likely to continue for a long time—since new "centers of excellence" cannot be brought into being overnight.

By such steps, it will be possible to retain the integrity of both science and the educational institutions, for we need no longer pretend that what is done for one purpose is actually done for another. Because research and educational needs overlap considerably, the possibilities of institutional amalgamation of research and educational programs—should also be considered—but that fits into the next chapter. Here we simply conclude that a stronger research-education program is needed, and that an appropriate policy will clarify the two areas, aiding both scientists and educators in retaining their integrity of purpose.

9| Toward Improved Federal Organization for Science

In the study of government, it has long been recognized that institutional patterns and substantive policies interact with one another. We often attribute a direction of policy to an organizational framework of a certain kind. Thus we expect the Federal Reserve Board to be financially conservative because its structure gives the banking community special access, and we know that the peculiar structure of the independent regulatory commissions—such as the Federal Power Commission or the Interstate Commerce Commission—affects their outlook toward the industries they regulate. Any organization is, among other things, a way of structuring inputs; i.e. a way of determining who will be heard in what ways in the formulation of policies and programs. In the science area, for example, the structure of NSF-NSB is such as to accentuate the attention given to the views of the universities in formulating basic research programs.

It is equally true, though much less studied, that particular policies and areas of policy tend to call forth certain types of organization. Thus the nature of scientific research is such that the formation and use of advisory groups from outside the government is much more noticeable an element of organization than in other areas of policy. The nature of economic

241

planning is such that a centralized focus had to be developed organizationally if the pieces were to be coordinated into a coherent whole.

In this chapter, therefore, we try to suggest possible avenues of institutional change that might strengthen government's ability to support science effectively, to improve its policy formulation process regarding science, and to relate what goes on in science affairs to the larger governmental context.

THE OVERALL FRAMEWORK

We have noted earlier that the organizational pattern of science in the Federal Government has grown piecemeal, with the creation of OST in 1962 providing the first overall locus of attention apart from specific agency programs. In addition to the need for a centripetal, Presidential-level organ to integrate the rapidly increasing R&D programs of the government, OST was also created to provide a place in the executive to which the legislature could come for information and ideas and from which the legislators could learn in broader terms about the purposes and major directions of the executive.

Creation of OST therefore meant a new linkage between Congress and federal science policy (for such policy as there was had developed mainly in the executive agencies rather than on Capitol Hill), but that linkage now needs, in my judgment, to be strengthened further. Congress has become much more active itself in science affairs. It now injects its own ideas—for example, about geographic distribution or the role of the social sciences or a revised charter for NSF—about what is needed, rather than just listening to the executive. Congress does so, however, through a plethora of subcommittees, each of which has only a partial view. In *ad hoc* fashion, a broad view of the whole is sometimes taken, but this is accidental in the sense that no single committee has a specific mandate to serve as a legislative sounding board or policy initiator across the whole spectrum of problems and policies.

I believe that the time is now ripe to fill this gap, to create a legislative base for science policy and a new mechanism for relating legislative to executive thinking. And, as suggested earlier, I believe the best way to do this is to follow the model of the Employment Act. That act, by establishing a Council of Economic Advisers (CEA) in the Executive Office of the President and a Joint Economic Committee (JEC) in the legislature, did much to encourage both a coherent economic policy in the executive and constructive legislative attention both to the policies put forward by the President and to other economic problem areas regarding which JEC has frequently taken the initiative in instigating governmental action. JEC does not itself write legislation; what it does is to act as a centripetal focus in an organization noted for the autonomy and often the narrow views of its sub-units, the committees, and subcommittees. Of at least equal importance has been the so-called mandate of the Employment Act of 1946, which calls upon the national government to promote maximum employment, production, and purchasing power. The declaration of purpose has served as a rallying cry for more than twenty years now, and has achieved the *de facto* status of a constitutional statement regarding the government's responsibilities regarding the economy. However men may differ on the appropriate economic programs of a particular time, all must argue within the framework of that act's adjuration to the government to promote maximum employment, production, and purchasing power.

CEA and JEC did not become effective organizations overnight. Their roles developed gradually and, indeed, may

244 AS THINGS MIGHT BE

not be entirely settled now. But they did evolve as a focus for
economic policy in ways that both stimulated governmental
actions and contributed greatly to public education regarding
modern economic policy. The latter contribution has been
partly direct, through public reports, and indirect, through
education of the President and legislative colleagues in informal ways.

A science and technology act might set in motion a
similar sequence of events. I therefore propose such an act. It
would establish OST as *the* centripetal executive agency for
policy development regarding science and technology programs
and would create a counterpart Joint Committee on Science
and Technology in the Congress. OST would be charged with
aiding the President in the preparation of an annual report
on science and technology, a report which, like the *Economic
Report,* would review the previous year's major accomplish-
ments and problems, analyze the current state of governmental
programs, describe science and technology goals for the coming year, and propose a "strategy" for achieving those goals.
Such a report would provide a much-needed stimulus to the
executive's taking a broad view and a long-range perspective,
and would give Congress a better feel for what is being done
with $17 billion of the taxpayers' money. It would encourage
attempts to shape a framework that would make R&D more
understandable than is presently the case.

Because plans and programs mean little apart from funds
for implementing them, the annual science report should be
done in close consultation with the Bureau of the Budget, utilizing the effort that already has been institutionalized there of
preparing an annual analysis of the distribution of all R&D
funds, by agencies and by major program areas. BOB's analyses
are already quite valuable, but their focus is more narrowly
financial than should be the President's science report. OST

would bring the substantive scientific elements into sharper focus, and supply the philosophic framework within which the budget should be developed. It is exactly this kind of overall view, taken repeatedly and on an annual schedule, that is needed to fill our largest gap in science affairs: we perform the science well enough, but we are not always certain of the purpose of what we are doing.

While formal assignments of policy-articulating responsibility can never pretend to define entirely and exclusively the actual locus from which ideas and influence will emerge (e.g. despite the Council of Economic Advisers' formal primacy in economic policy, the Secretary of the Treasury or the Chairman of the Federal Reserve Board may in fact be the dominant voice at a given time, depending on who has the President's ear), some mechanism is required to ensure continuing, high-level attention to an area of governmental activity as all-pervasive as science and technology.

Exactly because science is all-pervasive, an annual report on it needs to come from the presidential level, not from an agency that covers only part of the spectrum, no matter how important that part may be. My thinking therefore runs contrary to the NSF amendments legislated in 1968 that impose a requirement that the National Science Board prepare an annual report on basic research for the President to transmit to Congress. NSB is no better situated now to do a report on a government-wide matter than it was to develop a national science policy and review agency programs when such functions were first given to it in 1950 and then largely transferred to OST in 1962.

If my proposal were adopted, any NSB report on basic research policy should become either a statement in the NSF annual report (the Director's annual statements have sometimes been of the same nature as the report would be), or else incorporated into OST's report, perhaps as a separate appendix. NSB's utility would lie primarily in its comments on the universities-federal agencies relationship, and on that topic it could make a real contribution. It is overdoing NSB's role, however, to charge it with a report that would be taken as representing the President when transmitted to Congress, as the Daddario amendments provide. NSB is perhaps well structured to provide comments on the health of university science but not on the "status and health of science" as a whole; nor is it well-suited to indicate those aspects of basic research "which might be applied to the needs of American society," as the recent amendments also require. OST, with the help of PSAC panels, is far better equipped to do these jobs, because it does cover the whole range of science policy; it is not restricted to one set of interests as NSF-NSB is tied to the academic community; and it is in touch with both basic research efforts and technological development needs, in a way that NSF is not.

A parenthetical comment is in order here. Contrary to popular assumptions about "empire building," an official of OST indicated to the author in 1967 that OST lacks the staff or the time to prepare an annual report of the kind envisaged here. Apparently it is too enmeshed in fighting bureaucratic brush fires, and sees its function as limited to imposing some minimal coordination upon the operating agencies. A legislative directive could change this, however, and CEA's experience proves that this kind of job can be done with a small staff. Certainly OST, which is a full-time organization, would not find it harder to accomplish this task than would NSB, which is a body of men with primary outside obligations who devote 24 days a year to NSB meetings. Either body might require more staff to do the job; Congress would serve itself well by providing that additional staff to OST.

The science and technology act should have a broad

declaration of legislative purpose, to provide a permanent underpinning for the government's support of research, one that would disarm any efforts to eliminate or drastically reduce appropriations to a level inconsistent with the health of science. By way of illustration, I suggest the following wording:

> *The Congress declares:*
>
> *that the health of the basic and applied sciences (mathematical, physical, biological, social and engineering) is a matter of appropriate and necessary federal concern;*
>
> *that the preservation and development of scientific resources, including universities and scientific manpower, is a matter of appropriate and necessary federal concern;*
>
> *that the Federal Government, in using the resources of universities, non-profit institutes, and other science-related institutions, shall so arrange its programs as to provide for maximum strengthening of the capabilities of such institutions as national resources; and*
>
> *that the Federal Government shall encourage the application of government-sponsored research to areas of civilian technology need, by appropriate means.*

Such a statement would provide a bit of leverage for research whenever attacks are made on its utility, and would formalize what is already clear in fact: that science and government have entered into a permanent alliance. By its breadth, this declaration would apply to all departments and agencies and thus create a set of common policy premises. In turn, such premises would constitute a beginning in developing that overall rationale which has so far escaped us. As time went on, administrative actions would further elucidate and sharpen the policy premises, just as the concrete, practical meaning of the Employment Act mandate has developed over two decades. We would have made a start in the direction of a national science policy, as distinguished from separate policies for separate agencies.

SCIENCE IN CONGRESS

Today it is hard to find legislative topics that do not have some research and development aspects, that do not draw upon or have a potential impact upon science and technology. So many are the involvements of the Congress with science that a 127-page report was required just to list what was done, affecting or utilizing science, in the 89th Congress.[1] Yet many legislators express themselves as unhappy over the relationship of Congress to science. It is the ancient question, in a particularly virulent form, of the generalist having to make decisions with the advice of experts. Very few legislators have any background in science or engineering, although those who have served several years on a science-oriented committee do seem to be adept at learning how to evaluate the testimony of experts and are neither overawed by them nor overbearing toward them. How Congress should advise itself on science and technology is therefore an oft-posed question. Partly it involves, too, a matter of inter-institutional pride: Congress does not want to feel that it is at the mercy of scientists in the executive branch or allied with it; it wants its own corps of experts.

And related to the question of appropriate forms of scientific advice for Congress is the question of the committee structure. Historical accidents, strong personalities, and a tradition of fragmentation have in combination produced a structure that defies rationalization. (Not that Congress often tries to rationalize its structure in any case!)

In recent years a number of steps have been taken to improve legislative capacity for dealing with science, both through establishment of committees and through new arrangements for receiving advice untainted by executive hands. The committees that have been developed, and the advisory arrangements currently in use, have been described in Chapter Three, so we need not repeat them here. What we want to ask now is: What else does Congress need that it does not have?

A Joint Committee on Science and Technology, as urged above, would go far toward filling the remaining gap. If developed as perspicaciously as the Joint Economic Committee has been, a JCST would provide the countervailing overall view that the other committees of narrow or only partly scientific jurisdiction find it so hard to provide. JCST could explore the long-range questions of the impact of science on society, the long-range assessments of where current programs and policies are leading, that are missing today. And it would provide a focal point to which would be drawn the outside experts who now gravitate to OST-PSAC and NSF-NSB for lack of a legislative sounding board.

JCST might also perform some of the tasks that Rep. Daddario has suggested be assigned to a Technology Assessment Board. That is, Daddario wants some organization, closely related to the Congress, to look ahead at impending technological developments and assess both what they promise and what they threaten. Since no single staff group could possibly be sufficiently *au courant* of all science and technology to do this job across the board, it might be better for JCST to take on the job. It could operate through *ad hoc* advisory panels, just as OST uses PSAC. Only these would be advisory *to the Congress* rather than the executive, and thus their findings would receive greater legislative attention—assuming the caliber of panels were as high as PSAC's. Exactly because

JCST would not itself write legislation, it would be in a position of acting for the whole Congress in seeking advice, without any need or fear that it would offend some other committee's legislative jurisdiction. Through such a committee and such a function, Congress could have an internal source of ideas related to science programs, a way of determining where technology is going, and a better locus for obtaining external advice than any it now possesses.

Beyond this, it seems appropriate to strengthen the ties of Congress to the National Academy of Sciences. The House Science and Astronautics Committee has already made a good start in getting advice on basic and applied research policies from NAS, and other committees could get into the habit of using NAS, too. If JCST is created, one of its major links should be with NAS, both for direct advice, and for procedural suggestions on a "consulting" basis whenever JCST came upon an area it wanted to explore.

Within the past few years a number of suggestions have been made for some kind of science advisory staff in Congress. For instance, one was for each house of Congress to have a small scientific group of a physicist, a chemist, and a biologist; another sought to create a Congressional Office of Science and Technology with the duties of advising individual congressmen and committees, of making studies at the request of committees, and of reporting significant scientific and technological developments to relevant committees.

While one can sympathize with the ideal behind such proposals—to keep legislators as well informed as executive branch officials are regarding technical matters—one doubts that they would be effective. No small group could duplicate all the specialized branches of knowledge needed from time to time (which is why OST itself relies on PSAC panels instead of doing all its own work). One day a seismologist might be needed; the next day perhaps a biochemist or a marine biologist. Instead of having a staff that itself included all relevant scientific specialties, the most that could be done would be to have a congressional staff that knew how to locate and draw upon the relevant specialties as needed. Further, it is not straight science that Congress generally needs, but the ability to assess the policy and managerial aspects of technical problems. Most legislative decisions concern matters in which science is a *part* of the problem to be considered, but not the whole. As one careful assessment of the congressional advisory process has observed,

> The legislative task requires a generalist who can identify those elements whose consideration is essential to the passage of laws which regulate and guide public affairs. In making generalist decisions involving science and technology, it is not necessary for Members of Congress to know physics, chemistry, biology, electronic engineering, etc., in detail. For example, a legislator need not know the chemical formula for liquid and solid propellants in order to make up his mind whether or not to vote money to develop both fuels. If it is important for national defense that the Navy have missiles, if ships and men would be endangered by liquid-fueled rockets, a decision can be made to develop Polaris missiles on the basis of these additional factors. Similarly, if the feasibility of separating salt from water is established, if some regions of the United States need more water, it is not necessary to know the molecular structure of ocean water in order to decide upon appropriations for research and development looking toward a desalinization program. . . .
> Specialist scientists are unlikely to have the qualifications to identify and analyze all the pertinent elements necessary for the formulation of Government policy. The additional elements which must be weighed are economic, political, military, national, and international. If a biologist explained various forms of cancer, for example, it would

still be necessary for someone on a committee staff to relate this information in a meaningful way to committee decisions on appropriating more or less money for the construction of health research centers, medical personnel, and fellowships; how to prevent overlapping and duplication among Government departments; and what criteria should govern Federal grants to universities.[2]

It would be inappropriate, as well as impossible, for Congress to attempt to make scientific choices as such. But it is both appropriate and possible for Congress to make decisions about societal goals whose achievement requires science and technology. That is, Congress is quite well-fitted to make choices of ends, though not to make choices about scientific means. And most of the questions that arise are not the strictly technical ones. As Wiesner said to the Daddario committee,

> the 90 percent of the [R&D] budget which is not basic research is for things which nonscientists can make judgments about. Your committee has made judgments about many things in the space field, communications satellites, meteorological satellites, even the objectives of going to the moon which themselves may not be basically scientific questions. It may take some research and development to achieve these objectives, but the value of the objective is one that you can judge.[3]

Congress may need "its own" scientific advice, but not through its own staff of experts in its chambers and not through *purely* scientific advice. The use of consultants and panels, and the ability of committee staffers to find the right specialist when one is required—these are the ways Congress may best obtain the advice it needs. Like the executive, it may find it hard to locate the right persons, for it is not every scientist who is equally at home in the policy and managerial aspects of government programs as he is in his own realm of research. The paragon of a science adviser or committee staff member would "have an appreciation of the values and ways of the legislative process, a feeling for public policy, and a capacity for sorting out public issues, competing values, and alternative solutions."[4]

These qualities of a generalist with, probably, an engineering or scientific background are the ones needed—not a staff of basic research scientists ignorant of or insensitive to the policy framework in which Congress operates. The most effective way to draw upon such people would be to have them as staff to the Joint Committee on Science and Technology I have proposed. The next best would be to attach such persons to substantive committees like the House Committee on Science and Astronautics. The least useful way to arrange the use of both generalists and purely technical advisers would be through an isolated advisory group out of touch with ongoing legislation or investigations of technical programs.

In assessing policies and programs, Congress needs advice; but it does not need to duplicate the staffs of the executive agencies, and would be moving in the wrong direction if it tried to do so. Its job is the political one of determining which programs are *desirable,* not that of choosing the scientific means for achieving them—although it does need to be advised regarding the technical *feasibility* of what it thinks to be desirable.

A DEPARTMENT OF SCIENCE?

During the period 1958–60, the issue of the desirability of creating a cabinet-level department of science was raised and considered in Congress. The executive opposed the creation of such a department, as did most of the scientists. Ten years later, and with an R&D budget approximately doubled in the interim, it is worth looking at that issue again.

The major protagonist was the then Senator Hubert Humphrey, using as his forum the Subcommittee on Reorganization and International Organizations of the Senate Committee on Government Operations. A staff study prepared under his direction in 1958 gave as the objective for a proposed Department of Science and Technology "the coordination and centralization of certain Federal civilian science functions now vested in agencies which carry on science activities and which have some general relationship, and should, therefore, be brought into closer cooperation with other similar or related activities of all Federal agencies operating in various fields of science and technology." The study spoke of an "urgent need" to coordinate the activities of such agencies as the Atomic Energy Commission, the National Science Foundation, the National Bureau of Standards, and the National Advisory Committee for Aeronautics. Centralization of several agencies into a cabinet department, it was argued, would "insure better coordination and proper administrative direction and control of civilian science programs." [5] Coordination is always a "good" word in the legislative lexicon, and it is often invoked on an axiomatic basis: if a kind of activity goes on in several agencies, it is assumed that better coordination is needed, even in the absence of concrete evidence that the activity in question is suffering from any lack of coordination. So far as the public record is concerned, that seems to have been the case in this instance.

Besides coordination, and often providing a primary reason for its need, is the "bad" thing of duplication. Senator Humphrey was equally concerned with this, charging "multitudinous duplications and waste." [6] Presumably any activity consuming several billions of dollars will have some duplication and waste, although the senator did not supply details. But duplication and its eradication through coordination were his first reasons for proposing a Department of Science and Technology.

His second, perhaps even co-equal reason arose from a legislator's normal frustration when encountering the doctrine of "executive privilege" as a justification made by a representative of the executive branch for being unwilling to testify before Congress. Any executive agency may from time to time refuse to supply certain information to Congress, and there is generally little the legislators can do about it. They have learned to live with this situation, even though they don't like it. In this instance, however, Humphrey ran up against a more substantial problem. The one source from which he might have been able to obtain the information and testimony by which to assess what was going on in government science was the President's Special Assistant for Science and Technology, a post only created a few months before Humphrey began his investigations into the coordination of science. But the Special Assistant was located in the specific framework of the White House Office.

This is the more personal part of the President's staff, as compared with those persons and offices located in other segments of the Executive Office of the President. The two are often confused, but office heads in the latter (such as the head of the Office of Economic Opportunity and members of the Council of Economic Advisers) are appointed with the advice and consent of the Senate, and their offices are statutorily based. In the White House Office, special assistants are appointed without a requirement of Senate confirmation, and their positions may be created or erased at the will of the Chief Executive. Furthermore, *everything* in the White House Office is subject to the doctrine of executive privilege. Thus when the Special Assistant declined to testify at all before the Congress, Humphrey and his colleagues were stymied. If they could bring science policy formation and coordination into a regular department, however, there would be a statutory basis, Senate confirmation of the department head, and a normal requirement of congressional access to the secretary and to information suppliable by his department. Senator Humphrey's feelings about being told that he could not have certain information or access to certain officials because of executive privilege were strongly expressed during the 1959 hearings on his bill:

> I use this opportunity to say that I protest this kind of treatment and withholding of privileged material. It just makes it impossible for a committee of Congress to ever get full information upon which to take constructive action. That is why I feel that many of us who are keenly interested in the subject matter now under discussion have little or no information. . . .

Again, referring to the then recently established Federal Council for Science and Technology, also in the White House Office, Humphrey learned from Dr. Alan Waterman, the NSF Director, that FCST would handle problems of duplication and coordination, that it would engage in forward planning, and that it would discuss any problems of program administration. He was incensed that its discussions would be unavailable to his committee:

> I can understand from the Executive point of view how they would like to keep that all to themselves, but I have a feeling that only when these councils in the Executive Office of the President share frankly with legislative representatives openly, candidly, and cooperatively, that there will be real cooperation and coordination of the Federal science activities.
>
> I have the feeling when there isn't that kind of esprit de corps or that kind of feeling between the two branches, executive and legislative, and a legislative sub-committee has to dig around and do its own investigation and sleuth-

ing; that is when the trouble starts. That is when the half-truths come out. That is when you get the misrepresentation that takes place. That is when the arguments start.[7]

At the time, the executive had no effective answer to this criticism, and it was a major one.

These reasons, plus a generalized feeling that overall science policy formation would be enhanced and given a permanent footing if moved to a cabinet-level department, were the primary ones behind Senator Humphrey's proposal. While he was generally opposed by the scientific community, he did have some support. The late Lloyd V. Berkner, then head of Associated Universities, was pushing a variant form of a Department of Science concept.

Berkner's thought was to pull together into a department some of the emerging Big Science fields that had no settled institutional "home base." Among these he suggested weather modification, oceanography, seismology, and antarctic studies —all of which required "integrated planning" and large-scale "package support." He also would include in such a department those currently existing bureaus which had no strong functional relationship to the overall purposes of the departments within which they were lodged—such as the Weather Bureau, the Bureau of Standards, the Coast and Geodetic Survey, and the Naval Observatory. Berkner did not include NSF, NASA, or AEC, so his version would be more supplement than a supplanting of existing agencies. In a way, his proposal might have been called a "Department of Environmental Sciences," and in that respect may have had something to do with stimulating what came in 1965: the Environmental Science Services Administration which pulled together (in the Commerce Department) the Coast and Geodetic Survey, the Weather Bureau, and certain functions of the National Bureau of Standards.[8]

The problem emphasized by Berkner—fields without a

fixed reference point in federal organization—is one that still creates bothersome situations, although FCST and subsidiary bodies (such as the Interagency Committee on Oceanography) have worked hard to achieve adequate coordination without a department of science structure, and apparently with some success.

A related but more general point was also put forward in favor of a department: that it would provide an enhanced capacity to recognize and seize new opportunities in science, and to handle new problems in the support and use of science. One might have assigned such responsibilities to NSF, but that agency then had no reputation for vigor or imagination outside of its own relatively small primary program of supplying funds in reaction to proposal pressures.

In a careful review of the issues concerning government organization of science, it was also suggested that another objective of creating a Department of Science could be to enhance the status of science in government by bringing it into the cabinet, and perhaps thereby also increasing its financial support.[9]

The concept of a Department of Science and Technology drew criticism when first formulated, and some of the original reasons at least have been outpaced by other developments—which is not to say that a new case might not be made. One of the criticisms was that to incorporate AEC and NSF into a department would require wholesale restructuring of these agencies. AEC is headed by a five-man board—would that be placed under the secretary of the new department, or abandoned for a single administrator? NSF has a 24-man policy board, the NSB—what would happen to that? Humphrey too easily assumed that these structures could be left as is, at least at first, while the new department was given a sort of overall administrative leadership status. It is unlikely, to say the least, that such an arrangement could prove workable. Secondly, a catch-all department that included AEC, NASA, NSF, and an assortment of bureaus pulled in from Commerce, Interior, and perhaps some other departments would be dominated by its largest mission-oriented element. As of the time Humphrey first proposed a department, this would have been AEC; today it would be NASA, and it is hard indeed to conceive of NASA as being anything but dominant if mixed with other organizations. It is already larger in budget than most departments, and at least as important in the public eye as any of the cabinet departments, except perhaps Defense or Health, Education and Welfare. A Department of Science that included NASA would not find its other components so much coordinated as submerged.

More importantly, as the Bureau of the Budget pointed out in testimony before the Humphrey committee, it is hard to see what the major purpose of such a department would be.[10] It is a standard principle of departmental organization that there be a major social end—health, defense, promotion of commerce, etc.—for each department. But science and technology do not constitute a goal in themselves (except in the limited sense applicable only to NSF, whose goal is to promote basic research); rather, they are means toward the attainment of non-scientific ends. As such, they need to be tied not to a department that would try to make the means into an end but to the missions of departments and agencies: "Since each agency is and must be the best judge of how to perform its mission, it follows that each agency should have authority and funds to plan and pursue its own research and development in order to carry out this mission." [11] This means that one could not feasibly pull science programs out of, say, the departments of Agriculture or Health, Education and Welfare in order to centralize them in a Department of Science, to the extent that those programs were integral parts of the departmental missions. And without doing so, the proposed Department of Science would not have social purposes to provide the linkage between science as a means and social goals as ends.

If a Department of Science left what is tied closely to agency missions where it is, and if it left out AEC and NASA because of their size and their well-established positions in the federal scheme of things, it could include NSF as a possible core, plus those basic research bureaus not tied closely to the missions of the agencies in which they were located. This could conceivably be of some utility in strengthening the group included, but it would have little to do with the Department of Science proponents' major theme: that a department is needed to coordinate *all* federal R&D activities and to develop an *overall* federal science policy. The department would only be speaking for the areas of science it included, not for all of science. This is the point at which the proposal meets perhaps the most telling objections, and also the point at which events have superseded it.

On general administrative grounds, a coordinating body should be outside of and hierarchically superior to the programs it coordinates. Although NSF was originally given a mission of evaluating research programs in all agencies, it never tried to do so, Waterman realizing that as one agency on a level with the others (or even slightly below, since it is not a cabinet department) it just could not impose itself. Even with departmental status this picture does not change. All other departments would fight to keep their research bureaus from being moved, or to get them back, and the secretary of the Department of Science would be "committed to constant political warfare." [12]

Ironically, it is because science *is* so important that it cannot be appropriately contained in a departmental structure.

It is too pervasive in the entire government to be constrained in that manner. Since research is a means to almost every agency program, to put all of it under one structure would be like trying to move all governmental typing of letters into a single "Department of Typing." Granting that Humphrey and others have not really advocated putting all science into one department, their coordinative goal could only be achieved by a departmental arrangement if it did include most science activities.

If one grants a need for coordination—not to prevent duplication (which is rarely a real problem) but to integrate and stimulate various areas of science and technology and for the development of an overall federal science policy—through what mechanism are these goals to be accomplished? If the "blind clash of competing agencies" [13] is to be avoided as the determining mode of policy, but a department cannot be the coordinator and policy developer, how else do we proceed?

The answer given is to organize coordinating and policy developing activities at the Presidential level. The primary organizational vehicle has become the Office of Science and Technology in the Executive Office of the President. Created, as will be recalled, in 1962, OST was not on the scene when Humphrey first made his proposals. It, and the affiliated FCST, are the developments that largely undercut the science department proponents' ground. They coordinate; they develop policy; and OST provides an executive focus for contact with, and providing of information to, the legislative branch. Statutorily based, and in the Executive Office rather than the White House Office, OST acts much like an ordinary department or agency in its relationships with Congress. Top officials of OST testify frequently and at length before legislative committees.[14] No longer need a legislator complain that everything important about federal science policy is withheld behind the cloak of executive privilege. While there are still limits (the Special Assistant does not testify before Congress on the advice he has given the President when wearing his White House hat, so to speak), they are no longer so restrictive as to undermine the essential informational function. It appears to be the case, in fact, that OST's creation may have been motivated in part by a desire to accommodate a legitimate gripe from the Congress without creating a Department of Science.

If one turns from the question of informing the Congress to that of coordinating policy for the whole Federal Government, the Executive Office of the President again seems to be the logical place. Science pervades the entire structure, and cannot be completely contained within a single department. Hunter Dupree speaks of the presidential office as "the only spot in the country where real hope exists for creating a central scientific organization." He continues:

> The main advantage of the Office of the President as the place to begin this new effort [of science policy formation and coordination] lies in the President's position clearly above all the agencies, both public and private, which together make up the total scientific establishment of the Nation. Many of the Government research agencies are under one or another of the departments, especially Defense, Agriculture, Interior, and Health, Education and Welfare. Still others report to the President alone—the Atomic Energy Commission, the National Science Foundation, the National Advisory Committee for Aeronautics. With the proliferation of research contracts and Federal grants, the Government's action has profound effects on the universities, the foundations, and industrial research. Conversely a supremely important problem area such as missiles research can be influenced only by actions far transcending the program itself. Corporations, universities, and a wide scattering of Government agencies must come together to solve it. *Only a power very near the summit of the Federal structure can hope for success.*[15]

Whether OST has done a superb, an adequate, or an inadequate job may be open to dispute (the truth is probably better than adequate, less than superb), but I think there is little basis for questioning the *locus* of the effort, in comparison to a department. Also, incidentally, the statutory foundation of OST provides yet another element sought by Humphrey: some assurance of permanence in the science policy apparatus. It is now no longer a matter of Presidential whim that there be a science policy focus at the Presidential level.

I conclude that whatever case may once have existed for a Department of Science to coordinate science programs and develop overall policy (and it was a weak case to begin with) has been effectively answered for the foreseeable future by the Executive Office structure that has developed since 1957. The combination of OST, FCST, PSAC, and the Special Assistant fills the bill as far as it is likely to be filled at the present time. Such inadequacies as may now exist in this area are more likely to require extension and further development of existing apparatus than to call for supplantation by a Department of Science.

To say this, however, is not necessarily to say that there is no present case for structural change. I think there is a case for change, but toward different ends than those in Humphrey's mind in 1958 and involving a different set of agencies. In brief, I think a strong case exists for some kind of department-like amalgamation of NSF, the National Foundation for the Arts and the Humanities, perhaps the Office of Education, and perhaps (though most unlikely) NIH. Let me spell this out, including the range of alternatives.

A DEPARTMENT OF RESEARCH AND HIGHER EDUCATION

First of all, NSF began as a straightforward effort to stimulate with federal funds a considerable increase over the pre-

war years in the size of the basic research effort of the natural
sciences in the United States. Until World War II, America
had relied primarily on basic research done in Europe for the
findings on which our own technological advances depended.
Vannevar Bush's war-time operation, the Office of Scientific
Research and Development, made a strong start toward developing a stronger basic research base in the United States.
It was to prevent this start from atrophying that NSF was proposed (with the Office of Naval Research filling the gap informally between the end of the war and when NSF finally
got under way in the 1950s). The orientation of NSF was
toward scientific findings and the direct research efforts of
scientists. It was not initially toward the support of universities
or toward the support of graduate education. That is, not in
any but a very ancillary fashion.

To put it another way, the explicit function of NSF lay
originally almost entirely in science—its support and the
development of federal policy regarding research in the natural sciences; its functions, despite a necessary connection
with the educational world, were not thought of as lying in
education or in federal policy regarding the universities. In
contrast, today it would not be too great an exaggeration to say
that NSF's *de facto* major functions are to ensure (so far as lies
within its power) *the health of the educational institutions* in
which science is performed and to support the *education of
scientists*—at least as much as their subsequent research. NSF's
share of federally funded basic research is less than its share
of federal support of students and universities.

While, as said above, science is not as such a governmental
purpose but a means to non-scientific missions of federal agencies, NSF forms a kind of exception. For undirected science and
the higher education institutions in which the majority of it is
performed *are* the organizing purpose of NSF. And in the

name of this organizing purpose the agency's budget is now a significant one: half a billion dollars annually. But to say that NSF is a "science agency" is to define its mission too narrowly today. It is far more than that, in the sense that its support of science is intimately linked with its university and education related functions, which have become of equal importance to the science as such (if not in the minds of its officers, at least in the impact felt by the institutions). Yet in another sense it is less than the Federal Government's science agency, for its share of the total federal science effort is so small.

What must be recognized, then, is that NSF has gradually developed a special niche, but one that was surely not entirely foreseen in the beginning. And the niche it occupied may be said to be expanding, in conjunction with other agencies, as well as in its own program.

Whether the Federal Government-social sciences relationship develops through a separate National Foundation for the Social Sciences, through a considerable expansion of NSF's activities in this area, or both—it is clear that in the next few years a research-and-education support pattern of sizeable dimensions is going to develop in relationship to the social sciences, paralleling what has happened in the natural sciences. Further, we have begun the same process in relationship to the arts and the humanities, through NFAH. In short, the Federal Government is becoming the patron, not just of science, but of *research* of all descriptions. The physical sciences may in some sense form the prototype of research, but they are far from being the only disciplines performing research. As the government's patronage is extended to cover the entire research arena, the question naturally arises whether the agencies whose major purpose is the health of undirected research should not be closely related to one another, or fused into a single organizational unit, whether as an agency called a "foundation" or as a department. And within this framework, mention should be made of NIH, too. Seen in one way, the Institutes of Health comprise an agency with a health mission, using science as the primary means. Seen in another way, they comprise another important element in the federal government-university relations pattern, for NIH accounts for more than one-third of federal support of research at universities and for 20 per cent of federal support for research, training, and facilities combined, in the universities. Because of this sizeable impact, it shares with NSF the responsibility for the health of higher education institutions. It is difficult to decide whether to call it a health agency or a science-education institution, like NSF, although in terms of internal purpose, the nod would be clearly given to the health orientation.

Given the research-education purposes and impacts of NSF and these other agencies, there is a growing relationship between them and the Office of Education in the Department of Health, Education, and Welfare. This would not have been as obvious as it may seem just a few years ago, for OE traditionally had little to do with university-level education. This has changed, however, thanks to the National Defense Education Act graduate fellowships administered by OE, and to the higher education legislation enacted more recently. Now OE is very much in the higher education picture. It accounts for very little university research (though even that may be changing rapidly), but does account for about one-fourth of all federal support to the universities for research, training, and facilities —because of the last two categories. Since 1964 there has been a Federal Interagency Committee on Education, in recognition of the government's increased activity in this field and especially of the fact that several agencies are involved. While this committee has not made much of a splash on the Washington scene, it at least symbolizes the fact that there is a felt need for coordination in this area. Some effective liaison, between NSF and OE on fellowship programs, for example, indeed antedated the interagency committee's formation.

If, then, we think of supporting the healthy development of basic research, education of future researchers, and the institutions through which these are pursued as a major organizing purpose in the federal government today, we see that some ground does exist for a unification thrust, whether as a department or as an independent agency. Like every other function of American national government, this has grown piecemeal, largely in an unplanned manner. But it has grown, and interconnections among the parts have developed to the point where perhaps some restructuring would be in order. Program coordination would be one reason, but perhaps the larger reasons would be similar to those that earlier impelled the demand for a department of science: the need for more effective policy development on common premises, and for the encouragement of leadership through an agency of "critical mass" size. Only now it would not be a department of science with the objectives of 1958, but possibly a department of research. Several possibilities of amalgamation present themselves.

The least change from existing structure would be involved if one recognized the need for a common thrust and orientation among these agencies by appointment of a research and education advisory board that would meet with the heads of NSF, NFAH, NIH, and OE (and NFSS, if created). This could take the place of NSB: disband NSB as an authoritative administrative overseer of NSF policies, and create in its place, but with broader agency coverage, a Research and Education Advisory Board. It is with respect to university relations that NSB seems to have its most important role, and university relations are important to all of these agencies. So why not a single, prestigious advisory board to relate to all of them?

Going farther, there could be created a Department of Research, or of Research and Education, or a National Research Foundation. A common research agency, under whatever rubric, would provide a broad frame of reference for decisions on comparative priorities, and an opportunity and incentive to develop common patterns of relationship with the universities. The university relationship now suffers from a plethora of arrangements with, and requirements emanating from, the different agencies; a common agency might be able to restrain the government from splintering the universities through too many separate relationships. Furthermore, programmatic alliances and amalgamations would be encouraged, perhaps not only simplifying the existing structure but also providing an opportunity for imaginative cross-fusions to take place.

Just what might be included in a common department or agency is hard to determine. A minimum arrangement might see NSF, NFAH, and NFSS, if created, combined into a National Research Foundation or Department of Research. Conceivably NIH might also be included, although I incline to think that its health-mission orientation gives it a sufficiently different thrust so that it would be better to leave it outside, but with some formal liaison structure established between it and the new organization focused on more undirected research.

The difficulty with this pattern is that it does not take account of the Office of Education relationship, or of the general educational dimension that is so important a part of the research picture. So an alternative would be to make it a Department of Research and Education, or a National Research and Education Foundation, bringing into it either all of the Office of Education or at least the higher education functions of OE. The problem here is that either one splits the higher education function from what OE does at lower levels, requiring liaison between the two split parts, or else one adds to the research agency the elementary and secondary education functions, many of which do not have a close relationship to research and serve a quite different clientele, with long-established relationships to a separate set of professional organizations, too. On balance, I think the research-higher education linkage is so important as to justify separating the higher education functions out from the rest and bringing them in with the research. It would be easier, I judge, to establish necessary liaison and coordination between split educational agencies than between research and education. That is, it would be easier for the higher education part of the new agency to coordinate when necessary with an OE that kept the secondary and elementary education functions than for higher education left where it is to be related satisfactorily to the research body.

A further option to be determined is whether, if some such agency is formed at all, it should be at the cabinet level or not. There are no abstract principles to decide this; it depends on one's feel of the permanent importance of the function and of the political importance to the function of being represented in the cabinet. Without any very strong feeling on the matter, I would think it probably appropriate to make it a *Department* of Research and Higher Education. Surely the purposes served will be of great importance in the governmental picture for a long time to come, and the size of operations will be considerable. Further, the social prestige of the subject matter additionally argues for cabinet status. And, finally, it would seem appropriate to establish this organization at the same level as the perhaps comparable Department of Health, Education, and Welfare.

10| An Approach to the Priorities Problem

We come now to the nub of the matter: the making of choices in allocating government funds for science. This is what the agencies and departments, the Executive Office organizations and the advisory groups, the congressional science committees and the appropriations process, are all about. Their fundamental test comes in their ability to allocate resources in a pattern that will satisfy both the scientific community and the larger society that rational use is being made of funds and manpower.

For almost a decade and a half we lived in a protected world; we avoided many hard choices because the R&D budget seemed to expand fast enough to permit everything to be done simultaneously. All fields of science were pursued, and, as new research problems emerged, new funds were poured into projects to solve them. When the Apollo project came along, requiring billions of dollars annually, it was added onto atomic energy, defense research, etc.; it did not have to take funds away from them. In basic university research, the expansion of funds apparently kept pace rather well with expanding demands—at least no screams were heard from the suddenly affluent (by comparison with all past history) research laboratories of academia. Graduate fellowship programs were being established and increased each year, so potential conflicts between funds for research as such and funds for graduate science education did not arise.

Choices were of course being made, nevertheless: some fields received more support than others. More attention was paid to defense and space R&D than to research that might create new civilian technologies or help in solving pressing social problems. Indeed, in the 1950s the nation seemed hardly aware that it had any pressing social problems, let alone concerned to see if science and technology could aid in their resolution. In recent years, our awareness of problems has increased, and so has the volume of criticism of the choices that have been made. These have been criticisms of the overall R&D pattern more than of choices within and among the basic science disciplines. That is, the criticisms (at least those reaching public visibility) have been of alleged imbalances between military and civilian directions of the R&D effort, between development projects aimed at space exploration and those aimed at clearing up air and water pollution, between resources directed toward supersonic flight and those directed toward a workable mass transit system for our metropolitan areas.

Even before the R&D budget began leveling off (about 1964–65, therefore, the *priorities* among competing projects were being disputed. There may have been some funds for all, but it was increasingly said that the larger amounts went to the wrong places. These disputes have not been over choices among sciences as such, however, but over the social values embedded in the *uses* to which R&D was being applied.

Now a new note is added. Questions have been raised about *scientific* priorities as such: are we putting enough into chemistry compared with physics and biology? Is a new high-energy accelerator needed as much as more funds for little science in the universities? Should oceanographic studies be singled out for special attention and extra funds? These questions are arising because the total money spent on science has become so large; because an increasing proportion of the total (though no exact measure exists) goes into Big Science projects; and because the demand for basic research funds from an expanding universe of scholars and graduate students is increasing much more rapidly than are the funds available. Now the harder choices have to be faced at all points of the R&D spectrum: not just whether one area is receiving more than it merits; but whether this one or that one should be funded at all, and whether one will have to be cut down in order to increase another.

Even apart from Vietnam war costs, it seems dubious that the exceptional rate of growth of the R&D budget during 1950–64 will be matched again. Yet costs are rising, and so are the number of projects that might be done and the number of researchers to be supported. The end result is that hard choices will have to be made henceforth both in the development of science and in the application of science to social-technological problems. Indeed, to the basic researchers, it appears that the basic allocational problem is the proportionate share to be awarded to each of these ends of the spectrum. Their fear is that a tighter R&D budget will squeeze basic research more than technological development projects, because the social value of the former is less politically visible. In any case, the ability of the system we have established to come up with viable judgments in making comparative allocations decisions is the crucial test of a science policy, and we are now facing that test in its harder forms for the first time.

Furthermore, a recent assessment of the American effort in planning science and technology by European experts throws down a challenge for us to try something harder than what we have been doing. According to C. H. Waddington, a former member of the United Kingdom Advisory Council on Science Policy, the "strategic thinking" in American science has been remiss. We have tended, he asserts, to look at our present situation at a given moment and ask, "Where do we go from here?" Instead, he says, we should be more actively deciding where we want to go and then asking, "How do we get there?" Had we done the latter, he thinks we would not be emphasizing the development of a supersonic aircraft while relatively neglecting the development of ways to double the world output of food by the year A.D. 2000. His strongest criticism of American science planning is that we failed to formulate a comprehensive research program aimed at "ensuring that life is biologically enjoyable." [1]

Is Waddington criticizing our science planning, however, or our sense of values as expressed politically? The latter seems to me to be the case, but the very question points up what has to be the basic premise of priority planning: it cannot be a strictly scientific matter. The decisions cannot be made on scientific grounds only, but must incorporate a blend of scientific and social elements, of criteria of scientific merit—What pattern of allocations will produce the greatest advance in scientific knowledge?—with criteria of social merit—What pattern of allocations will produce the most important advances in the practical utilization of science and technology to improve human welfare?

Although the advancement of the public welfare is the ultimate ground on which public support of science rests, we built for some years a protected enclave in which all but criteria of scientific merit were firmly excluded—at least in the ideology and wishful thinking of the basic research community. This was never entirely so, and could not have been, in a system that provided even the bulk of basic research funds through mission-oriented agencies; but it is only recently that we have attempted to build this fact into our system of thought for science planning. We are only now realizing that the advancement of science and the advancement of social objectives through science must be kept in balance, even if balanced tension. The head of an organization particularly sensitive to the balance between social and scientific merit in a research program, James A. Shannon, director of the National Institutes of Health, poses the situation clearly:

> Our national program in support of science is entering a phase in which the decision whether to support a given field depends less upon technical considerations than upon social need. If we are to continue to have adequate support for the fundamental as well as the applied . . . then the aggregate effort must be to develop some sense of balance between the two approaches. Take, for example, the problem of water pollution, which has long since ceased to challenge the medical investigator. Water pollution, beyond a doubt, will yield to techniques of management—to an approach that relates the capacity of the nation's water resources to the ways in which we use them. The field of air pollution affords a comparable case. We certainly inhale numerous carcinogens in perhaps dangerous amounts, not only from cigarettes but from a wide variety of hydrocarbon wastes; but knowledge of these carcinogens does not provide the thrust for their elimination nearly so much as the social pressure of people living within our metropolitan areas who insist on clean air as essential for comfort.[2]

Our R&D effort can become badly imbalanced in either of two ways. Either by social pressures skewing science so that we ignore basic research's needs because we fail to see practical applications, thus leading us to try to solve problems technologically before the appropriate science is ready for them.

Or, in the other direction, by too completely separating science development from science use in an effort to protect the former, with the result that we produce an arid and precious science remote from the concerns of its human sponsors. The public that sees science as technological wonders would tend toward the first type of imbalance; some scientists would tend toward the latter.

Alvin Weinberg, in the articles cited in Chapter 2, took a balanced view—a politically realistic view. As criteria for establishing priorities he advocated a mixture of scientific and extra-scientific considerations. The competence of the scientists and the ripeness of a field were joined in his scheme by the technological and social merit of the field. Thus, the behavioral sciences he judged to be of high social relevance, but not yet developed sufficiently as sciences to warrant much support. Molecular biology, on the other hand, he gave high points to, both for its scientific qualities and for its social merit in terms of potential applications to health problems. The manned space effort he derided as important neither scientifically nor socially —perhaps reflecting primarily a personal value position more than the result of examination in the light of formal criteria.

In attempting to develop a single set of criteria to apply to the entire spectrum of R&D, from high-energy physics to the manned space program, Weinberg was perhaps overly ambitious. I would take the position that there can be no single set of criteria across the board; that we must categorize different areas and develop both substantive criteria and decision-making mechanisms appropriate to each area. In only a limited sense, at the level of OST and BOB, is it fruitful to attempt an across-the-board evaluation, and then not by comparing particular fields or projects at different points along the research-development continuum but by providing major directions and assessing the total balance between undirected basic research, applied research, and technological development in the nation's R&D program. For the most part, we must establish sub-universes of science policy and develop approaches individualized to each.[3] And in doing so, it is important that we distinguish in each area the varying proportions of scientific and non-scientific factors to be "cranked in" to the decision-making process. At many levels, science *policy* must also be in part science *politics*, not in the pejorative sense of politics, but meaning that non-scientific values and interests are legitimately to be considered along with scientific criteria. The correct mixture at each level is the important—and difficult—consideration.

The allocations processes must also explicitly recognize by-product values. Science does not exist in isolation; it is ineluctably related to other social spheres: education, industrial growth, regional development, for example. Sometimes the science-related values are the ones to which we will seek to give priority, as much as to science itself. In formulating allocations policies, therefore, we will sometimes be formulating policies *for* science in its own right and sometimes supporting science instrumentally, as a way of achieving related objectives. Again, we must particularize. Support of undirected basic research relates especially closely to support of graduate education; major space program decisions may especially affect regional economic growth. The important point is that in each area we have a multi-value focus. This in turn reinforces the point that in making science allocations it is not just scientists and criteria of scientific merit that are involved.

The question of priorities is an extension of the question of justifications for support of science that we examined in Chapter 2. There we analyzed the reasons given by scientists for federal support, both of science generally and of particular fields. Although there were some implications for priorities, none were stated explicitly. We found that reports on individual disciplines and areas each offered statements of needs and opportunities that justified federal funds, but almost no clues were given to ways in which the needs of one field might be compared with those of another. The NAS Committee on Science and Public Policy, which sponsored several "needs and opportunities" studies, has not felt it possible to arrange any priority listing among the disciplines on the basis of the individual studies. Perhaps the closest approach to comparative criteria that emerge out of such studies lies in the frequent references to manpower projections, showing increases in graduate students and professional investigators, and to proposal pressures: the number and dollar amount of projects proposed by investigators compared with the funds available from granting agencies. Chemistry, for example, was able to demonstrate that a lower proportion of its proposals were being funded than those of some other disciplines, and this fact has apparently been taken into account by NSF as justifying a priority for an increase in chemistry funds.

Not only do we lack comparative substantive criteria for justifying priorities; we also lack a clear mechanism for utilizing such knowledge of the situation as "needs and opportunities" reports are able to make available. Because there is no priority planning system as such, it is so far a matter of informal feedback: NAS or similar studies of fields are picked up by NSF and OST, perhaps referred to an FCST group, and eventually some incremental budgetary adjustments may filter through BOB and be reflected in agency budgets.[4] The concept of NSF as a balance wheel for basic research may be relevant here, since the practical meaning of giving a basic research field a priority may be to give it extra funds in the NSF budget, if gaps in its support are found to be developing from other agencies. Some organizational engineering is called for.

In any case, since scientists have been able to rationalize

criteria for federal support of science but have not been able to provide clear priorities criteria or to suggest a mechanism through which comparative allocations determinations might be made, that task still lies before the science affairs community. Not pretending to greater insights than the spokesmen of science have themselves been able to bring to bear on these problems, I nevertheless venture now to suggest a set of categories for priority decisions—a set of categories that also constitutes a ranked priority listing for R&D support—and to comment on some of the considerations that an allocations system will have to grapple with. Perhaps doing so will move us a little bit further forward by provoking others to correct, amplify, or replace what I say.

A PRIORITIES FRAMEWORK

To propose categories of science and science-related activities within which allocations decisions are to be made requires analysis of the science affairs universe. To propose a priority ranking of the categories themselves requires both analysis and the application of a set of extra-scientific values. Ultimately, each of us has his own, individual scale of values; practicably, we can propose a pattern that would seem to fit the politically relevant values for this time in this society. The scheme below embodies the fundamental premise that human needs of an urgent, even if elementary, level—such as attacks on disease or making the environment humane—provide a more fundamental guideline determining what fields to support than do the needs and opportunities of science disciplines considered in themselves. The overall case for science support by the taxpaying public, that is to say, must rest upon social benefit, but this is not to be narrowly construed. The cultural enrichment of the community through greater understanding of the universe is as much a social benefit as the advance of the economy. Since a major justification for research support is that research pays, it would be logically contradictory not to relate priorities in research to areas from which a pay-off is most urgently desired. Development goals should thus play a role even in planning basic research priorities. With that premise understood, this is the priority pattern and set of categories I propose:

> *First priority* goes to those *social objectives which are defined as most urgent politically* and to which scientific research can most clearly make a contribution.
>
> *Second priority* goes to *science-related educational needs,* from the elementary schools to the graduate education-research laboratory level.
>
> *Third priority* goes to *undirected small-scale research*—so-called little science.
>
> *Fourth priority* goes to *Big Science:* those fields having very high equipment costs or requiring large teams of researchers or large facilities, yet which are part of basic research.

These categories cover the R&D spectrum, and they cover both science clearly related to extra-science missions and science done to add to the intellectual capital out of which eventual, but not now predictable, technological advances will be derived. Within each category, separate criteria and processes of decision-making need to be elucidated. Scientific criteria as such will be most important in the last two, social merit criteria in the first two. Just as the criteria need to be accommodated to each subject area, so also will the appropriate mix of those making decisions vary from one category to another,

No single "priorities planning board" could be established that would have a character appropriate to making decisions for all of these areas, although the overall balance among them must be looked at by a coordinating body with overall responsibility for science policy—presumably OST-BOB.

Now let us comment on each category in turn.

First Priority. Our area of first priority—urgent social objectives that require science for their achievement—is the one least encompassable in a purely scientific framework. The criteria are primarily those of social merit, politically defined. Yet this is not to say that a technical input is not also necessary, for what is socially desirable may not always be technically feasible. The technical "state of the art" necessarily affects the pace at which, for example, we can introduce effective air pollution control programs.

How we define social merit is the first question, the fundamental one, though. It is here that the European criticism mentioned above is perhaps most applicable: that our system of technological planning does not always seem to cause us to emphasize what we ourselves know to be most urgent. There is surely more unhappiness over pollution and more need for an improved urban transportation system than there is public demand for supersonic flight, yet the latter seemed for some time to receive greater governmental attention. Why? The answer may be that we really do not engage in technological planning at all, but that instead we let technology plan *us.* That is, we seem to do what the state of the art tells us will be possible, following the path of least social resistance. The supersonic plane and the man shoot are projects that might be called "technologically sweet." They excite the engineering imagination; they challenge our ingenuity—but within limits we know are possible. And they do *not* challenge our social system: there are few social-economic-political obstacles to their achievement, so long as the government puts up the money. They therefore constitute a path of technological least resistance.

Perhaps we follow this path because we lack a mechanism for forcing ourselves to think through the comparative advantages to be gained from pursuing any of several technological options—or a mechanism for asking ourselves, "Where do we most want to go?" and, "Can technology take us there?" And in the absence of such mechanisms, we let technology direct us by default.

At one level, this is basically a problem of our entire political system. The President and the Congress are supposed to provide leadership in analyzing choices open to us and in proposing social priorities. This they do not always do well. Vested interests in government agencies and outside groups are always active on behalf of their pet projects, and they often succeed by default because we do not sufficiently engage in conscious priority planning. This is why Rep. Daddario's concept of a Technology Assessment Board has much to recommend it, whether in the particular form he has proposed it or in some other form.

The need for more conscious appraisals of what we want from science and technology, and of the ramifications of what we are told is possible, might be partially met by a combination of OST-PSAC efforts along lines of technology assessment in this sense and related studies by the proposed Joint Committee on Science and Technology in Congress. PSAC has done several studies of social problems having technical aspects, including population control and pollution, but it has not been asked to broaden its net and advise the government regarding which social problems science and technology may best contribute solutions to. If it could do that, suggesting a range of problems and possible technical approaches, we might have a

better information base upon which to make our political decisions. This is not to say that the social choices should be
turned over to the scientists, but that by clarifying the relationships between social problems and the technical state of the
art they would also be clarifying the larger social choices.

The essential role of the scientific community in the sphere
of urgent social problems is to analyze and point up the contributions that research and development can make toward
their solution. Given the degree of specialization in our society,
it is not often going to happen that those most concerned about
some societal problem are also those most knowledgeable concerning the contributions that science might make. And the
most important aspect of the scientists' role will be to suggest
ways in which science may be relevant when the non-scientist
would not suspect its relevance. Often they will be able to
suggest ways in which social requirements and statements of
problems may be redefined because of technical potentialities
unsuspected by social analysts. One thinks in this connection
of the war-time history of the Office of Scientific Research and
Development. OSRD was most effective because the scientists
were free to think of new weapons possibilities that required
new strategies, rather than just to operate within the boundaries of existing strategic requirements as defined by the
military. In the field of mass transit, for example, scientists and
engineers may be able to think much more imaginatively about
possibilities than the transportation economists and practitioners of transportation who are "culture bound" by existing
modes of transportation.

Choices of priorities among societal problems having technical dimensions will, to the extent that basic research is involved, also mean the setting of some priorities in basic research, too. To the extent that some area of basic research
relates predictably to a priority problem, that research shares

in the priority. Because imbalances in basic research support might thus be engendered, this possibility makes more important the balance-wheel function within the basic research sector, and it means that all sectors need to be kept in close communication with one another.

Second Priority. It would seem to fit both the scientific community's and the public's sense of needs to give a high priority to educational support. While some scientists are dubious about almost all efforts to engage in science planning, fearing the imposition of irrelevant or ill-informed non-scientific criteria, I think none would take exception to planning that has as its objective the maximizing of the future potential of science through building appropriate resources. And the most important resource is trained scientists themselves. Science education, from kindergarten through post-doctoral research training, is therefore perhaps the strategic focal point in the expansion of science resources for the future.

As we observed in Chapter 2, one of the major arguments offered on behalf of scientific research support by the Federal Government has been the contribution that research makes to graduate education. And we have seen that this relationship has been stressed ever more strongly in the past couple of years, to the extent that at least one spokesman would make the educational by-product of basic research almost the only reason for increased federal support at the present time. While science education has been a by-product of research support, it demands attention as a more autonomous goal. That it is becoming so is clear from the shift we have observed in the focus of federal programs from exclusive concern with the individual investigator and his research toward equal concern with the support of the educational institutions in which the research is conducted. For the universities are themselves part and an essential part, of science's resource base. If educational support has been a "spin-off" benefit of research support, it is equally true that research support is in part a "spin-off" of educational support. Educational and scientific criteria must therefore be carefully blended to get the most out of federal programs that affect both. There are some problems in achieving the appropriate blend.

To argue a high priority for science education is easy; to determine how much money is needed and what rate of increase is required each year are difficult. Brooks has pointed out that the educational justification for federal funds for science can be more easily quantified than the cultural or other justifications. One can know the number of students at every level; one can measure the rate of increase in graduate students for each discipline for the past x-years, and estimate the manpower needs of each field; an estimate can be made of equipment needs per student and researcher, etc. Some of the NAS Committee on Science and Public Policy studies of scientific fields' needs and opportunities have therefore relied heavily on graduate student enrollments, present and projected, in justification of desired support levels for fellowships and research.

Certainly the statistics of enrollments and equipment costs provide a useful base line for estimating support needs for science education. But Stephen Toulmin has brought out some difficulties that prevent such statistics from being adequate when used in their raw form:

1. Recent increases in graduate students in specific fields may reflect nothing more than "the effectiveness of past Federal support in attracting graduate students into one field or another."

2. We have no "reason to suppose that these projected rates of increase reflect either the probability of utility or the intrinsic intellectual value of the competing fields of science."

(This suggests that relative support levels for education in each discipline logically require prior determination of the intellectual/practical importance of each field.)

3. "If we tie levels of support for different sciences to the number of graduate students in the different sciences," says Toulmin, "we are giving support in direct proportion to the educational relevance." [5] Yet that relevance is not the *only* significant basis for determining needed levels of support in different fields. This is a point at which the precise blending of educational and intrinsic scientific criteria becomes most difficult and most important. In granting project awards, educational criteria are generally thought to be irrelevant, or at best ancillary to such criteria as the quality of the researcher and the promise of his project design. The use of graduate student enrollments to determine allocations for research support therefore contradicts in part the desire to maximize research criteria as such rather than educational criteria in granting project awards.

We may therefore need to distinguish those aspects of science education that can be supported in themselves from those that flow out of and must share criteria with research objectives. At the pre-college levels, science education efforts can presumably be separated almost entirely from research support questions. Equipment for laboratories and demonstration teaching purposes can be provided to elementary and secondary schools on something approaching a per capita enrollment basis, and teachers can be brought up to date in summer seminars without raising research support questions, or concern about the relative distribution of support between fields. At the undergraduate college level, the picture is becoming mixed; as acceleration in education occurs, and the belief grows that research experience is essential, it is harder to support science education without supporting the research of science faculty.

Finally, at the graduate level, the research and educational criteria come together in a tight merger. It is at this level that some additional tough questions need to be faced.

To aver that basic research and graduate education are mutual requisites, and that a major reason for supporting science is to produce more scientists through graduate research training, has become a truism. In fact, it has become an unthinking slogan, especially since the definitive statement of the position was made in the 1964 NAS report, *Federal Support of Basic Research in Institutions of Higher Learning.* Too many simplistic generalizations are being propounded, without recognition of their inconsistency with existing patterns of support for science and for education.

The problem is not that the research-education link is not as strong as claimed, for it is. The problem is that it states but a part of the truth, while policy must embrace a larger number of facets. For example: the scientist as educator is more than a researcher; science education includes the dissemination and reception of information and ideas, as well as the research experience; the man with the best project may not be the one who will do the best job of bringing his students into the work and insuring that they get the most out of it; the production of scientists requires educational support at all levels, not all of which are as closely tied to research experience as is doctoral work. The view that implicitly assumes that science education needs will be taken care of if all individual university-based project applications are funded is therefore a myopic one.

Since so much of graduate education support has taken the form of research project support, a crucial question lies in the relationship between project support as research and project support as a means to education. Should contribution to graduate education be a factor (an important one) in awarding research grants from NSF or NIH? What role does this factor play now? If the role is minimal, then is it the case that the vaunted contribution of basic research to graduate education is nearly ignored at a vital point?

A statement of the guidelines used by NSF in evaluating research proposals states that the principal criterion is the predictability that the research will "result in significant advancement of knowledge in a field of interest and importance." Six sub-criteria are then listed, after which comes this statement:

> Account is also taken of the contribution which the research will make to science education and training, particularly at the graduate level. This is generally judged on the basis of proposed student participation in the work. The extent to which the research will stimulate the total science enterprise of the institution is an additional factor.

It is also stated that proposals of middle-range quality "are supported at lesser institutions in order to encourage development and improvement of their research and instructional programs." [6]

From most comments of scientists upon the project research system, one gets the impression that these ancillary educational criteria are of very minor importance in the evaluative process. Whatever the agency's intentions, most scientists seem to feel that in advising on research awards, purely scientific criteria should prevail: the quality of the investigator and of the project. The peer judgments on which the system rests are judgments of scientific, not educational, competence; the value system of science would be skewed to the extent that scientific criteria were diluted by any others in determining research support. The two facets, most scientists would say, require different approaches. I think most of them would prefer that educational support as such be offered in other forms, other packages, to preserve the purity of the project system. Yet this position is clearly inconsistent with the notion that a major reason for supporting faculty research, and especially for measuring needed increases in the support rate, is the need thereby to support graduate education. This latter value, especially now that emphasis is being placed upon building up centers of excellence in the "underdeveloped" regions of the nation, seems logically to require that the educational aspects be placed on a par with the scientific ones. Either that, or else less should be made of the relationship and educational support should be considered a separate category to be handled by other types of programs: fellowships and traineeships, principally, and equipment support.

I may perhaps state the matter too starkly, for it may be contended that the educational value of a research project depends strongly on its value as research. From this point of view, it may be a waste of funds to support less-than-first-rate research at lesser institutions in order to support education. Perhaps more general institutional aid is needed for such institutions, in order to build them up to the point where project support can be both scientifically and educationally justifiable for them. This makes much sense, yet poses difficulties for the base-broadening objectives of current policy, for it implies a high degree of continued concentration of project support in the "best" places, at the same time that scientists are asserting that such support is essential to graduate education.

Undoubtedly, the research-education relationship is that of a continuum rather than an either-or opposition. Yet I think it important to state the matter rather starkly because so many misleadingly simple assertions have been made about the relationship. Furthermore, the priority given to some of basic research is affected by the relationship it bears to education support, since in this scheme education support as such receives the higher priority. It may carry some research *per se* along with it, to the extent that the case is made effectively that the research support makes a necessary contribution to the educational objective. My purpose is not, I repeat, to deny the assumed connection, but to urge scientists and science-education administrators to think through the particular modes of connection more explicitly and carefully.

Third Priority. The third priority, I have suggested, should be for undirected small-scale basic research—the investment capital upon which rest technology and the application of science to areas of social need. Although this is the heart of the whole R&D spectrum in the thinking of basic scientists, it does not receive the highest priority in this scheme for the reason that (like capital investment versus current operations in industrial planning) its long-run importance is greater than any single year's exact level. In any one year there is undoubtedly a minimum amount required for continuity of effort, but the appropriate amount above that, or for expansion, is not easily established. What we need to do is to ensure a healthy, continuing research program so that the well-springs do not dry up in areas not presently tied to a higher priority objective (but which may become tied in the future, and unpredictably so).

In analyzing the basic research allocations problem, the fundamental fact is that, in the nature of basic research, one cannot establish concrete objectives and then estimate the costs of reaching them. There is no way to measure the added "output" in knowledge or utility to be gained by an extra dollar in the basic science budget—and equally no way to measure the loss for a dollar subtracted. At least in the present state of our knowledge about the processes by which intellectual advances are translated into technological innovations, nothing but the vaguest predictions can be made as to the ultimate effect of either halving or doubling the basic research budget in a given year. The construction of a science budget cannot proceed entirely from the intrinsic elements of research but must be calculated in considerable part from essentially extrinsic factors, be these graduate student enrollments, proposal pressures, or whatever. There is no scientific method for constructing a science budget.

As is often the case, it is easier to begin by rejecting what one believes to be unworkable than by proposing what one believes to be appropriate. I therefore begin by rejecting the possibility of determining an independent total figure for basic research, whether based on a percentage of all R&D, a percentage of Gross National Product, or the number of scientists multiplied by an average support figure.[7]

The concept of "overhead," borrowed from economics and business practice, has been put forward as a convenient handle for rationalizing basic research support in relationship to the large sums of money put into technological developments. About the only thing to be said for this, however, is that it at least recognizes that there is a relationship between the R and the D, a relationship which basic scientists too often want to ignore in the interests of keeping science "pure." In the business world, I understand that the overhead concept is a slippery one: it is difficult to give it a precise quantity except after the fact. What is difficult in business is, I think, almost impossible in research and development. Unless and until we develop better ways of tracing back technological developments to their basic research origins, we cannot measure the amount of basic research to be allocated as overhead to a particular technological development. And without the ability to make such measurements, we have no way of knowing whether the appropriate overhead is 5, 20, or 90 per cent of total R&D.

As a practical matter, I would expect this argument to be

less vigorously pushed now that the R&D budget has leveled off. Neither the number of scientists nor the research cost per scientist has leveled off, so continuance of the overhead percentage of recent years (9 to 11 per cent) would mean declining support per scientist—which is hardly what the research community is arguing for.

All of these shortcomings exist in even stronger form as criticisms of the suggestion that basic research be budgeted as a given percentage of Gross National Product. Tying basic research to GNP would have the advantage that the growth of GNP is steadier than growth of the R&D budget; but there is little else to recommend it, when we have no way of knowing what percentage of GNP devoted to basic research is needed for eventual technological utility nor what percentage is needed to achieve an acceptable rate of increase in scientific knowledge. While in principle some connection exists between the amount of research the society does and its rate of industrial progress, we know too little about the long, complicated chain of relationships involved to permit their embodiment in a research support formula.

Another approach to an overall support formula would be to proceed from the number of scientists to be supported. In one version (that of Seitz) the government should support all the "good scientists" at $50,000 each annually. Another (Brooks) has suggested full support for all the "most talented and creative people," a group which he estimates as perhaps 5 per cent of all those "capable of doing competent and significant basic and applied research." Since the scientific community demonstrates an unwillingness to make judgments of the comparative merits of different fields, it is difficult to believe that any workable system of public judgments can be devised by which scientists will tell us who among them represent the top 5 per cent. Furthermore, even if we had a way of identifying the elite, the problem remains of determining the amount of support for the remaining 95 per cent. Brooks's answer for the remainder appears to be to use faculty and graduate student numbers as the base, so far as university research is concerned. Verhoogen, on the other hand, proposes that "every scientist who is capable of raising a valid scientific question and of contributing significantly to its solution . . . should be given an opportunity to do so by means of a research grant." On the basis of $20,000 per year, and estimating that the "number of competent scientists with good ideas" is between 50,000 and 100,000, the little science research expenditure would perhaps amount to one billion dollars annually. The choice of competent scientists to receive these grants Verhoogen would determine by the total sum requested for all proposals rated "good" by advisory panels. The injection of proposal pressure at least provides some check beyond a simple head count.

I doubt that it is either sensible or practicable to support everyone calling himself a scientist any more than we would support every person with a Master of Fine Arts degree as an artist. And for reasons indicated earlier I am dubious about using graduate student enrollment as the crucial determinant, although it certainly needs to enter into the picture.

Finally, it appears to be a major shortcoming of all the formulae for overall support that they are farther removed even than is necessary from the intrinsic questions of basic research: what are the gaps in our knowledge and understanding; what are the areas most ripe for exploitation? And they ignore the fact that most of the basic research funds come from agencies with extra-scientific missions, which means that the needs of those missions must enter the picture, as well as the needs of scientists. Even though we are discussing undirected basic research, we are not talking just about NSF funds; yet it is only regarding NSF's small portion of basic research that one could meaningfully contemplate an autonomous basic research formula.

Turning to the more positive side, therefore, I would suggest that the construction of the basic research budget proceed from field-by-field analyses of needs and opportunities; from Weinberg-type criteria questions; from proposal pressures; and from higher education institutional needs. The combining of these related yet partly disparate criteria would be no simple feat, but it would provide a balanced approach, even if informed judgment would play a larger role than quantitative calculation.

Weinberg's criteria of scientific, technological, and social merit still provide the best checklist that has been suggested for evaluating the claims of scientific fields. A comparative priority of a kind would be provided by ranking fields that stood high on several counts above those with lower "scores." The problem is: who will do the evaluating and ranking? Much as it might hate to take on the task, COSPUP is the likely candidate. Composed of an interdisciplinary team which reviews NAS field reports before giving them its endorsement, COSPUP cannot help but have some feel for the strong and weak points of each field. It is in a better position than any other group to make the comparative assessment that will be needed if there is to be a priorities system at all. A COSPUP report on comparative merits need not be taken as gospel but would be most significant for further decision-making.

The kind of assessment that application of Weinberg-type criteria would provide could usefully be supplemented with proposal pressure information. Not just the number of proposals in each field, but more significantly their average quality as indicated by review panel ratings. If field A has more proposals than field B, but a higher proportion are low-rated, then field B would have a higher rating as a field. Proposal pressures should not become the dominant criterion in establishing priorities, however, because a priority may be needed exactly to fill gaps left in areas that are not currently popular and which therefore do not attract many proposals. Sometimes a more active approach is required, one in which relevant agencies seek to stimulate proposals to build up a field, rather than just respond to the current fads among investigators. It is at this point that needs and opportunities studies may be most important—in identifying gaps left by proposal pressures. In this sense, basic research planning partakes of the notion of management by exception: the giving of special attention to what is not being taken care of spontaneously. Given the explosion in research publications, it becomes increasingly difficult for individual investigators to review their own fields in order to determine where the best opportunities lie. This has to become a specialized function today, and NAS field reports and agency advices based on them and on analysis of proposal pressures can be most helpful in providing intellectual maps of the various fields, emphasizing gaps, as clues by which individual investigators—particularly perhaps the young ones not already totally immersed in a certain line of investigation—may select their own work areas. In this way, the next year's set of proposals may be encouraged into better balance.

Assuming that one could work out some qualitative weighting of the various components of a basic research budget, the next question is the practical one of how to organize the mechanism to accomplish an inter-disciplinary, inter-agency comparative review. Such a review might be accomplished along the following lines.

First would come single field reviews. The agency having the largest commitment to a given field (e.g. AEC for high-energy physics; NIH for the biomedical sciences) would establish a review panel to which *all* agencies supporting that field would send the proposals they received, with endorsing comments indicating the relevance of each proposal to their missions.

Second would come an inter-field review to compare the quality of marginal proposals in each field, and to identify areas of unusual activity or areas of insufficient activity. This second-level review might be performed by an interdisciplinary and inter-agency group of program administrators, perhaps organized by NSF as part of its balance-wheel role.

Thirdly, the results of the marginal assessment process would be embodied in an overall basic research plan for final review by OST-BOB. After such review, there would be a choice. The plan could be made binding on the constituent agencies, or the judgments about inter-field comparisons and suggested differing levels of support for each field might simply be forwarded to all the participating agencies as recommendations. Then NSF could try to compensate in its own allocations for what it felt to be out-of-line results in the decisions made cumulatively by all the other agencies.

The latter—looser—approach is probably not only the more realistic one in the light of normal agency jealousies over external dictates, but also better suited to fitting the basic research plan to mission considerations: an agency will sometimes feel that mission needs must override the more purely intellectual judgments that the panel review process would embody, and it will insist on doing either more or less than a disciplinary viewpoint alone would call for.

An approach such as this would seem to constitute a way of striking a reasonable balance between agency autonomy and over-centralized administrative priority setting. Basic research support in the American system is dispersed among too many agencies, and derived too strongly as a by-product of extra-scientific missions, for there to be a very rational overall structure if everything is left entirely to agency-level decisions. That same extreme diversity, however, makes it unwise, as well as administratively impossible, to impose a central plan on the agencies by fiat from above. As compared with existing practices, however, some movement in the direction indicated (i.e. toward the injection of a larger central-review element) is, I believe, in order today. It will become more necessary over time if we are correct in our expectation that the priorities question will become more rather than less pressing as the increasing costs of science bump against the ceiling of political resistance to ever-expanding budgets.

Fourth Priority. Our last priority goes to Big Science—the segment of basic research that departs most obviously from the classic picture of the individual investigator pursuing his curiosity wheresoever it may lead. Big Science is characterized by organized team efforts, by tremendous equipment and organization costs, and, in consequence, by a degree of planning and programming unknown to, and unneeded by, little science. Furthermore, Big Science is likely to be done in research centers separated in more or less degree from the regular university campus, and there are but a few such centers for each field. This in turn carries the implication that Big Science fields typically have a relatively small number of practitioners with very high costs per investigator.

The prototype of the Big Science field is high-energy physics: a basic installation costs hundreds of millions of dollars to build and many millions annually to operate. Radio astronomy, oceanography with its ships, and certain lines of investigation requiring major computer installations are other components of Big Science. The characteristics emerged first in the physical sciences, but are now spreading to the life sciences. One can even foresee Big Science in the social sciences, as we learn to formulate large-scale surveys involving large populations through the use of investigatory teams and computers. In educational sociology, for example, one can easily envisage very large-scale projects attempting to isolate familial and environmental influences upon educational achievement of the child.

So far as high-energy physics and radio astronomy are concerned, Big Science has also meant very pure science: our cultural enrichment by learning more about the nature of matter and the origins of the universe is the primary goal; practical applications of the knowledge are extremely remote. But oceanography is both pure science and a field of vast discernable applications for navigation, food supplies, weather analysis, and mineral resources, among other things. And in biology, Big Science is emerging in the form, for example, of genetic experiments involving multitudes of test animals, and biomedical applications can be readily envisaged. So Big Science is becoming applied as well as basic, and the criteria involved in making choices among competing Big Science programs have to include the comparative social significance of missions as well as the respective intrinsic scientific merits.

Some Big Science—for example, a large-scale social survey—can be organized without requiring any single huge instrument or other great capital investment. But in oceanography, astronomy, and high-energy physics major facilities are required and raise capital investment questions not met elsewhere in basic science. As the recent competition among 85 locations for the next-generation accelerator showed, some extremely non-scientific influences loom large in planning for Big Science facilities. The assumption that a major scientific installation will in some (almost mystical) way contribute greatly to a region's economic growth through the attraction of high-salary, high-technology industries leads to vigorous political struggle over who will get which Big Science facilities. Further, the costs of such facilities are sufficiently great to make an impact even on today's large federal budget; more particularly, anything that will cost $100 million or more seems inevitably to become a matter of political hassling. Take Project Mohole, for example. When its costs were estimated at $5–$20 million no one but NSF and the scientists involved were much concerned. When estimates reached $120 million and a contract of $35–$40 million for a drilling platform became involved, political hell broke loose.

Non-scientific criteria thus loom large in the political choices in which Big Science becomes embroiled. Its environment is that of the larger world, not just the internal world of science. At the same time, choices here perhaps involve a more manageable number of variables than in the complexities of little science. The number of agencies concerned with any one Big Science program will be small; the educational dimension is minimized numerically; and in at least some Big Science fields there does not have to be a concern with utilitarian pay-off, for none is expected. Concentration can therefore be placed on the field itself, and on the state of the federal budget. Planning is generally simpler, in at least some respects, when a few big decisions have to be made rather than a continuing series of diversified smaller decisions. And Big Science facilities do have to be planned for, both because of their costs and because by their nature there can be few of a type. Every campus cannot have its own accelerator or oceanographic vessel. Rather, a few national centers are constructed, and an essential element of the operational planning is the provision for access to those centers by investigators from a large number of home institutions, as well as the gathering of a permanent center staff. The managerial arrangements—the prototype is a non-profit consortium of universities—must be planned as well as the physical facility itself.

Such planning of capital equipment and its organizational blueprint does not occur spontaneously or as the simple result of proposal pressures. Conscious administrative decisions are required, decisions that include but are not limited to scientific considerations as such. The decision-making framework for Big Science therefore must be more tightly knit than that for little science. And it must be competent in management, budgeting, and administrative politics as well as in the science itself.

One of the big differences between Big Science and little science is that in the latter area one can contemplate supporting all fields to some extent each year, but in the former there has to be a "waiting list" of investments, for the costs preclude simultaneous funding of all scientifically worthwhile projects. This means a much tighter competition, and a more urgent problem of establishing inter-field priorities. Which in turn means that reviews transcending disciplinary panels are more essential. Consensus within a field on its next Big Science facilities need is but the first step. Impact on adjoining fields, which Weinberg stresses, has to be assessed by a group broader than those immediately concerned, and then OST-BOB level judgments have to be made to establish an inter-field rating. Given the size of Big Science budgets, such planning has to be made over a number of years. Ten-year projections of facilities in relationship to expected field activities are needed, partly because large facilities have very long lead times between the initial go-ahead signal and the point of operability.

Because Big Science priority setting involves saying "no" to whole fields in a given year, it will be even harder than in little science to find any *a priori* substantive criteria on which all participants would agree. The integrity of the institutional process by which the decisions are made, and in particular an assurance that all affected parties are represented in the decision-making, becomes more important than the criteria themselves. Carl Kaysen proposes a high-level committee representing both the affected sciences and the funding agencies, to scrutinize each year the entire shopping list in relation to available funds. The funds he would set at some fixed proportion of total basic research expenditures, perhaps in the neighborhood of one-half. His description of the proposed committee's functioning merits extended quotation:

> The evaluation process in practice could be expected to involve a fusion of two elements. The first is an element of professional judgment as to the "ripeness" of particular projects, in terms of their ability at that time to make a substantial contribution to the forward progress of the particular science in which they were to be used. The second is an element of political compromise, so that neither any single science nor any single group of closely related problems is the recipient of the lion's share of the funds over any period of years. This political element is necessary. In the absence of an objective standard for judging whether, say, particle physics ought to be developed faster than radio astronomy, and in the presence of a budgetary constraint, the allocational decision must inevitably represent somebody's preferences or prejudices. The present proposal incorporates an explicit mechanism for registering the preferences and prejudices of those who are both affected and knowledgeable. The mechanism is broadly a representative one, though informally rather than formally such, and similar in character to consultative organizations in other areas, and which the Government relies for advice with respect to decisions affecting the interests of particular small groups in the society. The result of this process would be an approved list of projects, which typically would involve funding commitments over a number of years, and which in total would fall within the limits of the formula, with the exceptions set forth above.
>
> The user representatives on the allocating committee might include people drawn from the President's Science Advisory Committee, the National Science Board, and the

outside scientific advisory groups to the various operating agencies; while the fundling agencies might be represented through the Office of Science and Technology. Behind this top committee might well be a structure of appropriately chosen subcommittees screening the requests from each field of science. Special ad hoc arrangements might be needed from time to time to deal with proposals cutting across traditional fields.[8]

Between this category and the preceding one of little science there is bound to be some budgetary competition. One accelerator's construction and operating costs equal the support of hundreds, even thousands, of individual campus researchers. OST and NSF need to be alert to the trade-offs between Big Science and little science, to ensure that the demands of the former do not impinge too heavily on the latter. Perhaps NSB-NSF representation on Kaysen's committee would sufficiently ensure representation of the little science viewpoint.

One final point: why is Big Science given the lowest priority in this scheme? There are two reasons. First, its cost in relation to little science, and the fear that a higher priority for it would squeeze out too much of the latter. Secondly, Big Science is less closely involved in the educational function of science support. Because its installations are often national research centers set apart from campuses, and because the number of scientists using any one Big Science facility is comparatively small, no great number of graduate students are trained through these facilities, compared with the training function of little science. Since we give high priority to the educational justification for science support, we give less to the area that contributes proportionately less in this regard.

In this chapter I have tried to suggest a set of priorities that accord with the values of the society as patron, and which fit not too badly with the justifications that scientists themselves have offered for federal support. And I have tried to sketch some of the considerations involved within each category, to show that the setting of priorities cannot be done in the same way for every area of science policy, but must be fitted to the circumstances of each.

The reader who rejects the priority order given to the four categories may still find the categories themselves useful in organizing thought about the priorities problem. This is certainly the most intractable problem in federal science policy, one that no one has wanted to face. It has only recently, therefore, begun to receive the attention it demands. Much more hard thought by both scientists and administrators will be needed before a satisfactory priority system is developed.

11| Science, the Federal Patron and Society

What we have been looking at is a developing tripartite partnership between government, science, and the public. But one of these has been largely a silent, almost an unconscious partner: the public. It is the ultimate patron of science and the ultimate beneficiary of or sufferer from the technological results of science, yet it has had little or no direct say in the development of the partnership. A poll would surely show that it has had little awareness of its role as patron.

In fact, were ours a town-meeting democracy in which the support of science had to win a direct popular vote, it is a moot question whether a sufficient base of understanding and approval exists for such a vote to be carried. Happily for science, in our representative system the voters leave many decisions to their representatives and to the leadership of the executive branch, enabling government to undertake many things that the active elites consider "good," but for which widespread public support may not exist. Science, like many other functions of government, receives support because the public does not object—not because the public demands it. The governed consent implicitly, but the scientific community has been able to do little to build an *active* favorable constituency beyond itself. Space and defense aspects of R&D have a sizeable constituency in the industrial community of contracting firms. The closest analog for pure science lies in the universities and their faculties who benefit from federal support. But the universities themselves have not done an effective job of explaining research and its values to their publics.

Strong as the support for basic research may be in the federal agencies and the Executive Office of the President, and willing as Congress has been to include basic research in the funds it awards largely in the name of technological developments, the ultimate foundation of public patronage—an understanding by the public of why basic research is important and merits large-scale support—remains shaky and incomplete. In the short run, scientists perhaps need not worry much about this, for the public has not shown any sign of interjecting itself directly into science affairs. But in the long run, either the scientific community will manage to make itself better understood with a wider public or the voter-patron may simply become aware that large federal expenditures are being made for something not adequately justified and react with a disfavor that would be very quickly and easily reflected in congressional budgetary actions. When legislators call for more "equitable" distribution of research funds, and seem to the scientists to mean by this a distribution more on the basis of state populations and less on the basis of the quality of researchers and higher education institutions, we are perhaps seeing a mild form of the kind of intervention in the name of the public that could occur if the public were to assert itself directly in the absence of adequate understanding.

One consequence—so far unfaced—of the development of publicly financed patronage for science is, therefore, that the scientific community needs as never before to explain itself to the outside public. Given the nature of modern science, this is not intrinsically an easy task. It is perhaps made harder by the traditions of the scientific community. Although Big Science is changing the pattern now, the tradition of science is individualistic and privatized. That is, scientists have tended to operate as "loners" and to communicate only with one another; they have been a sub-community set apart from most of society by their own habits and wishes. Now they must develop external relationships. They must try to make themselves understood— and they have an obligation, too, to try to understand the system through which they are supported by their immediate and ultimate patrons, the government and the general public. Instead of sneering at the political process and assuming all persons not scientifically trained to be dunderheads(as sometimes seem to be the feelings of scientists), scientists must learn that political processes have their own rationality, different as that may be from the laboratory variety. Spokesmen of science who are actively engaged in the patronage process understand this need better than those who live only in the laboratory. Said John T. Wilson, Deputy Director of NSF, in 1967:

> I really wish that the academic and scientific communities would work as hard at understanding what the Congress is trying to do, as the Congress does in trying to understand what the academic and scientific communities are trying to accomplish.[1]

Congress and the public are the patrons, but it is the scientists who often act most patronizingly.

How science is to develop rapport with its public patron is a difficult question. More time out from the laboratory to explain what one is doing to lay audiences would be one route, and there are an increasing number of good books about sci-

ence and scientists for the layman—thanks perhaps more to the
initiative of publishers than to spontaneous efforts of scientists.
Science magazine does a good job of covering public policy
aspects of science in an understandable way, but presumably
it is a journal that reaches only the already convinced. The
general press has its own obligation to staff itself for covering
science affairs adequately, and has some distance to go in
meeting that obligation, with notable exceptions.

In addition, and of equal importance to the establishment
of direct contacts with the voting public, scientists can cultivate congressmen and other public officials. I don't mean
crude lobbying—though there are sometimes appropriate occasions for that, too—but efforts at increasing mutual understanding in a long-range and fundamental way, through the
respect that may be engendered by closer acquaintanceship
and frank discussions. The sad fate of Project Mohole shows
how the support even of friendly legislators can evaporate
when scientists have failed to attain a secure base of understanding with their public patrons.

The impact of science (taken in the broader sense that
includes technology) on society has been very widely, if not
always deeply, discussed; but that society is also having, and
will continue to have, an impact on science has not been so
widely realized. The patronage partnership, however, ensures
that there will be such an impact, and whether it is on balance
beneficial or harmful will depend not a little on the ability of
scientists to explain their needs and their ways to their direct
and indirect patrons. So far, the experience has, I believe, been
clearly on the beneficial side. This is largely attributable to the
wide discretion the public patron has accorded the scientists in
designing and helping to administer their own programs of
support. Whether that discretionary latitude will be continued
as the public becomes more aware of its own stake in the game

depends on the state of communication between scientists and society.

GOVERNMENT'S IMPACT ON SCIENCE

Science, which is one of the major causes of social change in our society, is not itself immune to change.[2] Not all that change, of course, can be attributed to the Federal Government's support for and use of science, but we can discern some effects that are fairly clearly derived from the partnership.

The most obvious of these is the growth of science in the past quarter-century. In terms of both the number of scientists pursuing basic research and the number of qualitatively important discoveries, science has grown prodigiously. At the least, this growth would not have been possible without the vastly increased support made possible by government policies; and the atmosphere of the way in which the support has been provided, it seems safe to say, has on the whole been conducive to good science. That is, support has largely been given in accord with conditions that scientists have themselves deemed necessary for effective work. In this respect, there can be no question but that federal policies have been effective and beneficial.

Another change—about the beneficence of which there could be considerable argument—might be called the end of idle curiosity. Many discussions of basic research motivation contain rather romantic references to the scientist choosing research topics out of "idle curiosity." Partly this meant chosen apart from considerations of utility: he just wanted to find out something. Partly, too, however, the phrase has connoted an almost random choice, an unprogrammed choice. It is in the latter respect that the federal grant system has clearly compelled a change. No scientist hoping for project support would write a proposal simply stating that he wondered if such-and-such were true and he would like to conduct experiments to find out. Rather, the prospective investigator ascertains the state of existing knowledge in his general area of research, hypothesizes a researchable question whose answer would add a predictable brick to the edifice of knowledge in that area, and describes a particular research methodology that he intends to employ in attacking the problem.

Although I have seen no writings about this, it seems clear that the proposal requirements of the federal agencies supporting science must be having a considerable impact on the spirit of science—making it more professional, less amateurish (in the good sense of that word), more clearly goal-directed, less random—as that spirit has often been described. For all the fears that may exist about national planning of science, each basic researcher tends to have his own personal research plan. He does not flit aimlessly, as idle curiosity's fulfillment might suggest, from unrelated topic to unrelated topic, but instead tries consciously to design project B so that it builds on project A in the same area. One suspects that there was always a bit more of such personal planning than the mythology of basic research implies, but surely the tendency has been given a substantial push by the requirements of federal support.

The significance of this is a matter of speculation, but one would expect it to be in two directions. On the one hand, we probably have a more efficient pursuit of science in the sense that close attention is paid to logical next steps in the development of the knowledge structure. On the other hand, one would expect some net loss in free-wheeling imagination, some tendency to shy away from the high risk projects because future support might be endangered by failure to achieve positive results. I have never heard it suggested that the federal agencies show any great inclination to encourage high risk research. Perhaps some small percentage of each agency's research funds should be explicitly allocated to high risk and off-beat projects, to provide some leeway in the system for the exercise of greater than average imagination.

The social structure of the scientific community may also be undergoing some change as a result of large-scale federal support. For one thing, science becomes necessarily less elitist as the number of practitioners is multiplied over and over again. When basic researchers constituted but a small band of individuals pursuing science despite considerable professional and personal hardship, there must have been little place for the mere time-server, the unimaginative plodder. Today, team research might even be said to *require* some unimaginative plodders—to do much of the necessary but routine experimental work involved in carrying out the ideas of the leaders of science. And every university teacher of science is under strong compulsion to research and publish his results, whether they constitute much of an advance for science or not. Instead of science as such being an elite pursuit, we must now distinguish between the elite and the rank-and-file within the ranks of science.

Secondly, the reward and recognition system of science is probably being skewed by federal support. Earlier, the only possible reward lay in publication of one's findings and respect for those findings by one's colleagues. Now, even before one has any findings, some respect is accorded when one receives a research grant. While it is true that ability to obtain grants is partly an index of the respect in which one's previous work is held and of the quality of one's proposal, it would seem unrealistic to deny that it is also partly an independent prestige factor. And the process is presumably circular: the knowledge that a man has previously been thought worthy of research grants is probably taken as a sign of his value when he applies for another. Furthermore, the high cost of science today puts some premium on the entrepreneur—the scientist who is as good at making proposals as he is in the laboratory. When scientists had no external patrons, such factors could not matter; today they can, and they presumably do.

Vannevar Bush and those who with him pushed for the creation of a science foundation after World War II thought to create a protected enclave for basic research by providing for its funding through an agency largely freed from political control and from the taint of an expectation for applied results. If they had had their way, basic research might today be a thing apart, whether for good or bad. But they did not. By the time NSF attained meaningful budgetary size a quite different tradition was already strongly established, a tradition in which science-using agencies all paid a tithe as it were to basic research. And although an effort is now being made to increase NSF's share of the federal basic research total, it seems most unlikely that it will ever be the source of the majority of such funds.

The scientific community has long since accommodated itself to this state of affairs. Having forgotten that their initial demand was for a foundation that would have a near-exclusive franchise on basic research, the scientists now celebrate the pluralistic quality of the existing system and reject all proposals to centralize research. The bogey of science decisions being made on political criteria has not materialized, and the mission-oriented agencies have not insisted on close relevance to practical missions as a criterion of their support for basic research. Thus the "purity" of basic research has been preserved adequately despite the fact that most of its support comes from agencies whose basic functions are far from pure research.

At the same time, and this constitutes another impact of

government upon science, the agencies have emphasized broad areas of research having ultimate relevance to their respective missions and have thus given a direction to basic research which it would not otherwise have had. Research *has* been tied to areas of utilization, but in such a subtle fashion that the connection has been largely unobjectionable to the scientists. Just what the mixture of fields cultivated and neglected would have been if all support had come from a single basic research agency is impossible to say, but it is a safe bet that it would not have been the same as it has been under the system actually developed. And it seems reasonable to suppose that from society's viewpoint science is more fertile as a source of technology than it would have been if developed more autonomously of agency interests.

The accident of a long dispute over the shape of the proposed science foundation after the war, which permitted the pluralist system to develop to fill a vacuum, may thus have been a happy one by virtue of the fruitful connections made between basic research and the concerns of science-using agencies. It has been proven that support of science and the needs of government need not be kept in separate compartments, that it is feasible to combine practical needs with support of research. And one even suspects that basic research has itself benefited from the mild kind of planning that mission support has constituted. An interesting survey might be developed by examining the ways in which applied problems have led agencies to support certain areas of basic research, and the resultant basic discoveries that emerged in areas that might not otherwise have received the scientific community's attention in the same degree. In any case, it is a major effect of our system that it has brought even the most basic research into touch with the practical needs of government agencies, thus successfully, if paradoxically, amalgamating the general

American tradition of emphasis upon what is useful with the scientific community's tradition of emphasis upon research whose practical consequences cannot be spelled out in advance.

IMPACT ON THE UNIVERSITIES

As we have seen throughout, basic research is in considerable part university research. And research is part of graduate education. So federal funds for basic research have meant in practice, though not in original objective, funds for university and student support. Until very recently, research support was almost the only federal support for higher education. The impact of federal science support upon the universities is therefore an important aspect of the science-government-society partnership. What has that impact been?

It has been rather widely argued that the primary effect of federal research funds has been a deterioration of university teaching, especially of undergraduates. The charge is that the professors teach less, often confine themselves to graduate seminars, and are too busy with their research projects to spend time with students. Undergraduate teaching, it is said, is left too much to teaching assistants, who are graduate students pursuing doctoral degrees. While we all know of instances that fit these charges, I believe they are vastly exaggerated and largely erroneous. Graduate assistants do perform much teaching in the large universities, but the basic reason for this is not federal research funds; rather, it is the explosion in enrollments. If there were no research funds at all, there still would not be enough professors with credentials to perform all of the instruction in the universities. At most, federal research funds are a subsidiary factor, providing some released time for some faculty members. Yet even then the impact is not all in one direction, for the payment of some salaries by federal agencies releases university funds to hire additional faculty, so that the total professorial time available may be as great, but accounted for by a larger number of individuals.

Furthermore, if we consider the qualitative impact rather than just the quantity of time in which professors meet students, the evidence overwhelmingly suggests that the impact of federal research funds has been highly beneficial. It is not the professor actively engaged in research who uses the same lecture notes for ten years. By enabling the faculty to work at the frontiers of knowledge, federal funds have unquestionably enlivened instruction. The best thing a professor can do for his students is to share with them the excitement of learning, but he can't do this very well if he is not learning himself. Meaningful university education today, whether graduate or undergraduate, does not consist of merely passing on what is known; most of that the students can get from their reading. Rather, it consists of showing students *how* to learn, of instilling in them a curiosity for exploring what is unknown, of helping them to realize that education is a life-long process. In doing his own research, the faculty member is preparing himself for an effective role in the classroom, not engaging in something antithetical to teaching. The purported deleterious effect on teaching is, therefore, largely a myth, and such real disadvantages as exist are out-weighed by the stimulation that research adds to teaching.

Less discussed but of greater significance is the problem of universities in part losing control of their own programs because of federal research funds. The project system, as distinguished from institutional support, places emphasis on individual faculty members rather than on institutions, and has with some frequency served to confuse the faculty member's loyalties. Dependent upon a federal agency, he may develop closer ties with the program director in Washington through whom he receives his research support than with the university with which he is affiliated. The availability of federal funds may have more to do with determining the directions of research in a science department than the plans of the institutional leadership.

On the other hand, it might be said that the professors and the agencies together have been filling a vacuum created by the failure of the university administrators to develop campus consensus on directions of development. American universities today are vastly different from before the war and, I believe, vastly better. Challenge and change have largely come from outside however, with federal research funds constituting a major stimulus. The time may now be at hand for some consolidation, for an increase in the proportion of institutional grants that give universities a chance to set their own priorities in greater degree. But it is probably true that such temporary loss of control and skewing of directions as federal research funds have caused have been a necessary price to pay in order to develop the exuberantly healthy research atmosphere that now characterizes the major institutions.

The support of faculty and graduate students afforded by federal funds has enabled the universities to fulfil one of their two essential functions in a way that they would not otherwise have been able to do at all. The university, unlike the college, is charged by society with advancing as well as preserving and disseminating knowledge. In the sciences particularly, the advancement of knowledge would have had to proceed at a drastically slower pace in the absence of federal research funds. And the stimulus has, I believe, spilled over to the social science and humanities departments, too. While it is often alleged that science support has created a science-humanities imbalance, I think it cannot be denied that the example of the sciences has stimulated research in the other academic divisions. They now need greater funds to fulfil their missions, but their very need is in part a function of the stimulus provided by their sister disciplines.

Broadly speaking, the major impact of federal research funds on the universities has been a healthy one. Problems there are, but they are problems of growth, not of decay. Federal research funds have been the vehicle for a new relationship of mutual advancement of interests between the government and the universities. Instead of a national university as in some other nations, we now have a general system of public support for research activities at hundreds of higher education institutions. Government obtains research results important to its own programs, the nation as a whole benefits from the general advancement of knowledge, and the universities are given needed support. It is a partnership that no one planned explicitly, but it is a most successful one in pursuit of the objectives of both parties.

IMPLICATIONS FOR PLURALISM

A major characteristic of American democracy, according to a widely held theory, is the autonomy of social groups and institutions—in particular, their independence of government. Many students of democracy and totalitarianism consider the existence of many independent social groups to be a pivotal factor in providing a buffer zone between government and the individual. This theory of pluralism may be seen, in a sense, as an extension of economic laissez-faire reasoning: the argument that separation of government from business was a prerequisite to individual freedom.

In recent decades, an activist government responding to public demands has taken on a variety of tasks that have brought it into much closer contact with society than in the days when legislation was largely of a negative character, establishing rules outlawing behavior deemed to be anti-social. Now legislation more typically establishes programs by which government acts for and with social groups in pursuit of positive goals. In consequence, the picture of pluralism has had to be modified to recognize a developing partnership between the autonomous social groups and government in pursuit of common goals. This phenomenon in itself represents a considerable change in social structure. But science—in the broad sense of all research and development—has pushed the change much farther. The government-science relationship has in fact brought about a quiet revolution in our social structure by creating a system in which large segments of industry, the universities, and the scientific community have become financially dependent upon government contracts and grants.

In the simple theory of democratic pluralism such financial dependence would spell the end of autonomy and freedom, on the assumption that "he who pays the piper calls the tune." And to have the national government supporting higher education institutions would appear to be the most dangerous incursion of all into the structure of pluralism, for these institutions are the primary fount of free expression of ideas that may challenge government and its policies. Yet there has manifestly not been a stifling of free expression, on the part of university faculties generally or scientific researchers in particular. The scientists, the universities, and the high-technology areospace and defense firms that are dependent on government financing have not become tools of government, have not stopped pursuing their own goals. We have in general let the scientific pipers call the tunes, rather than having them called by the governmental patron. By allowing the scientific and educational communities a large voice in deciding the terms on which government support is given, we have established a hybrid system in which financial dependence may violate the traditional form of pluralism, but has not damaged the substance. Paradoxically, government funds seem to have sustained the autonomy of science and of education by providing them with the means to concentrate on pursuit of their own proper tasks. While financial leverage unquestionably provides a potential base for actions inimical to the social autonomy of science and higher education, it has so far remained largely a potential.

Just how sanguine we should be about the prospects for continuing this benign condition is hard to say. We have noted before a tension between the scientists' desire to pursue knowledge wherever it may lead, for its own sake, and the public-governmental expectation that science will repay its patron by attacking problems to which society seeks solutions. This expectation constitutes a continuing temptation to employ the government's financial leverage to direct science toward utilitarian ends. Certainly some degree of emphasis on utilization is compatible with the essential autonomy of science, yet one cannot deny the existence of a threat. For, if the governmental patron were to push the pay-off expectation to an extreme, basic science would be in deep trouble because it could not conceivably find a substitute source of funds on the same scale as presently provided from Washington. Scientists would then have to work on what government assigned or on nothing. The autonomy of science despite governmental subsidization thus rests importantly on acceptance by government and the public of the notion that patronage means support of what scientists themselves consider worthwhile doing. In a larger sense, this means that the scientific community's autonomy, which can no longer rest on financial independence, now rests on a political ethic of non-interference. And that in turn must depend in the long run on adequate communication and mutual understanding between scientists and their public patrons, which brings us back to the problems stressed in the opening pages of this chapter.

Science and the federal patron have developed a complex and fruitful relationship in the post-war years. It is a relationship that has all the earmarks of permanence, yet its particular forms and characteristics are still undergoing constant change. Science and the polity are partly integrated, yet mutual understanding remains incomplete. It is an uneasy alliance between the political and the scientific estates, one fostered in large part by national security motivations that are remote from the fundamental spirit of science and the natural motivations of scientists. Some tension between science and its governmental patron is both natural and necessary, if each is to be true to its own nature and its own social functions. Yet for that tension to be fruitful it must be informed by greater clarity than we have yet been able to give to the relationship of science and scientists to the larger polity.

The first great burst of activity and institution-building in the government-science relationship may be said to have been completed with the development of OST and the leveling-off of the R&D budget. We are now in a consolidation period, one in which there should be time to assess the workings of what has been brought into being so far and to give thoughtful attention to patterns for the future. A much larger proportion of scientists than heretofore should inform themselves of the characteristics and problems of the patronage relationship, so that science policy does not become too much the private preserve of a small group of activists. In the future, most scientists rather than just a few should concern themselves with the external affairs of science as well as with what they are doing "at the bench." Only by such a broadening of the base of the science affairs community will a healthy relationship be maintained between the federal patron and its beneficiaries.

On its side, government, which depends on science as much as it supports it, has an obligation to contribute to public understanding of the relationship and to review its own policies continually to ensure that the use of science for public purposes is consistent so far as possible with the integrity and healthy functioning of the scientific community. Although it is science's prime financial support—or, rather, exactly because it is—government must do all it can to protect the autonomy of science and avoid its bureaucratization. The worlds of government and of science, no matter how intermeshed and mutually dependent they are, are separate worlds, each with its own distinctive characteristics. It is important that the integrity of both be preserved, if the relationship is to continue to be of maximum mutual benefit.

Appendix

Federal Funds for Science, 1940–68

TABLE I

Total Expenditures on R&D, by Sources
(millions of dollars)

Year	Fed. Gov.	Industry	Universities	Total, all sources
1940	97	?	?	?
1945	1070	430	20	1520
1950	1610	1180	80	2870
1955	3490	2510	190	6270
1960	8720	4510	330	13710
1965 (est)	13070	6530	640	20470
1968 (est)	15560	8330	840	25000

TABLE II

Major Agency Sources of Federal R&D
(millions of dollars; excluding plant)

Year	DOD	Agric.	HEW	AEC	NASA	NSF
1940	26	29	3	0	2**	—
1945	513	34	3	859*	24**	—
1950	652	53	40	221	55**	—
1955	1708	72	70	290	74**	9
1960	5553	121	292	762	330	51
1965	6627	199	681	1241	4555	136
1968 (est)	7605	267	1092	1400	5126	208

* *Manhattan Engineer District: predecessor of AEC*
** *NACA: predecessor of NASA*

TABLE III

Major Agency Sources, Federal Funds for Basic Research
(millions of dollars)

Year	DOD	NASA	AEC	HEW	NSF	Agric.	Total, all agencies
1955	20	14	48	26	20	11	130
1960	181	213	104	103	68	34	741
1965	263	528	258	303	171	90	1690
1968 (est)	288	805	322	412	256	119	2331

Note: *These are obligation figures. Expenditure figures would generally be somewhat lower.*

TABLE IV

University-Performed R&D
(millions of dollars)

Year	Univ. sources	Fed. sources		Total, all sources
		Regular	Contract centers	
1945	20	80	(includes " ")	100
1950	80	240	(" " ")	320
1955	190	170	(180)	410 (+180)
1960	330	410	(360)	830 (+360)
1965	640	1100	(640)	1870 (+640)
1968 (est)	840	1600	(700)	2600 (+700)

TABLE V

University Basic Research
(millions of dollars)

Year	Univ. sources	Fed. sources		Total, all sources
		Regular	Contract centers	
1955	99	103	49	237 (+49)
1960	215	299	97	576 (+97)
1965	473	920	198	1492 (+198)
1966 (est)	530	1063	202	1697 (+202)

TABLE VI

Federal Support of the Social Sciences
(millions of dollars)

Year	Basic and Applied Total	Basic only
1955	25	2.1
1960	35	8
1965	127	37
1967 (est)	222	58

Note 1: *Of the 222 total* HEW 90.8
OEO 35.0
Agric. 27.9
Commerce 18.2
NSF 17.6
DOD 3.9

Note 2: *Of the 58 total* HEW 19.5
NSF 16.8
Agric. 6.4
DOD 1.9
OEO 1.2

Notes

CHAPTER 1

1. A. T. Waterman, "The Changing Environment of Science," *Science* 147 (1 Jan. 65) 13–18.
2. Quoted in Warren O. Hagstrom, *The Scientific Community* (N.Y.: Basic Books, 1965) p. 226.
3. Quoted in Walter Sullivan, *We Are Not Alone* (N.Y.: McGraw-Hill, 1964) p. 88.
4. See G. H. Daniels, "The Pure-Science Ideal and Democratic Culture," *Science* 156 (30 June 67) 1699–1705, and his Book, *American Science in the Age of Jackson* (N.Y.: Columbia U.P., 1967).
5. "Science affairs" is a useful phrase coined by Christopher Wright of Columbia University as a shorthand way of referring to all the relationships between science and society. See Wright's essay in R. Gilpin and C. Wright (Eds.), *Scientists and National Policy-Making* (N.Y.: Columbia U.P., 1964).
6. D. J. deS. Price, *Science Since Babylon* (New Haven: Yale U.P., 1961) pp. 107–108.
7. Statistics from National Science Foundation, *National Patterns of R&D Resources, 1953–68—Funds and Manpower in the United States* (NSF 67-7), pp. 8–9.
8. Quotation from Martha Ornstein, *The Role of Scientific Societies in the Seventeenth Century* (privately published, 1913; re-issued 1963 by Archon Books, London) p. 91.

9. J. G. Crowther, *The Social Relations of Science* (N.Y.: Macmillan, 1942) pp. 600–601.

10. See Ornstein, p. 120, and Crowther, p. 239.

11. Don K. Price, *Government and Science* (N.Y.: N.Y.U. Press, 1954; Galaxy paperback, Oxford U.P., 1963).

12. Caryl P. Haskins, *Report of the President, 1965–66*, the Carnegie Institution of Washington, p. 13.

13. Rachel Carson, *Silent Spring* (Boston: Houghton Mifflin, 1962).

14. Thomas F. Malone, "Weather Modification: Implications of the New Horizons in Research," *Science* 156 (19 May 67) 897–901.

15. National Academy of Sciences-National Research Council Panel on Weather and Climate Modifications, NAS-NRC Publication 1350 (Washington, 1966).

16. "Scientific Statesmanship," *Bulletin of the Atomic Scientists* XIX (Oct., 1963) 6–10.

17. Editorial, "Will Society Be Prepared?" *Science* 157 (11 Aug. 67) 633.

18. James R. Killian, Jr., "Toward a Research-Reliant Society," in Harry Woolf (Ed.), *Science as a Cultural Force* (Baltimore: Johns Hopkins, 1964).

19. Jacques Barzun, *Science: The Glorious Entertainment* (N.Y.: Harper & Row, 1964) p. 16.

20. See House Comm. on Government Operations, Research and Technical Programs Subcommittee, *Hearings, The Federal Research and Development Programs: The Decisionmaking Process*, 89th Cong., 2d Sess., 1966, pp. 6, 15, 57, and 64, and, generally, pp. 1–64.

21. See *Basic Research and National Goals* (1964) and *Applied Science and Technological Progress* (1967), both produced by COSPUP and issued by the House Committee on Science and Astronautics.

22. See Commoner's book, *Science and Survival* (N.Y.: Viking, 1966), for a strong statement of science-society problems.

23. Waterman, *op. cit.*

24. Don K. Price, *The Scientific Estate* (Cambridge: Harvard-Belknap, 1965; Galaxy paperback, Oxford U. P., 1968) p. 97.

25. Don K. Price, "The Scientific Establishment," *Proceedings of*

the American Philosophical Society, 106 (June, 1962) 235. Also available in Gilpin and Wright.

26. Sir Eric Ashby, in Boyd R. Keenan (Ed.), *Science and the University* (N.Y.: Columbia U.P., 1966) p. 195.

CHAPTER 2

1. "Criteria for Scientific Choice," *Minerva* 1 (Winter, 1963) 159–171. Reprinted in Alvin M. Weinberg, *Reflections on Big Science* (Cambridge, Mass.: M.I.T. Press, 1967), pp. 65–84.
2. "Criteria for Scientific Choic II: The Two Cultures," *Minerva* 3 (Autumn, 1964) 3–14. Reprinted in Weinberg, pp. 85–100.
3. Among the most expensive and informative were: House Committee on Science and Astronautics, Subcommittee (Daddario) on Science, Research, and Development, *Hearings, Government and Science,* 88th Cong., 1st Sess., 1963; hereafter cited as Daddario hearings. And House (Elliott) Select Committee on Government Research, *Hearings, Federal Research and Development Programs,* 88th Cong., 1st and 2d Sess., 1963 and 1964. Hereafter cited as Elliott hearings.
4. Daddario hearings, p. 195.
5. Ibid., p. 282.
6. Committee on Science and Public Policy, National Academy of Sciences, *Basic Research and National Goals,* a report to the House Committee on Science and Astronautics. Committee Print, March 1965, pp. 84–85. Cited hereafter as *Basic Research and National Goals.*
7. Ibid., pp. 85–86. Pp. 85–99 contain Brooks's valuable discussion of four justifications.
8. Jeremy Bernstein, *A Comprehensible World: On Modern Science and Its Origins* (New York: Random House, 1967), pp. 4–5.
9. Letter to *Science,* 157 (25 Aug. 67) 873. His book is *Knowledge and Wonder,* a paperback (New York: Doubleday Anchor Books, 1962).
10. Daddario hearings, p. 61.
11. Dale R. Corson, "The Role of the University in Technological Advance," in *Research in the Service of Man: Biomedical*

Knowledge, Development, and Use, A Conference, Senate, Comm. on Government Operations, 90th Cong., 1st Sess., Committee Print, 1967, pp. 13–14.

12. Daddario hearings, pp. 139–140. Contrast, as regards the science-technology interface, John Verhoogen's opinion that although the time-lag between scientific discovery and technological application might be decreased by a greater development effort, yet "on the whole it might increase rather than decrease, for as science becomes more sophisticated, more esoteric, more abstract, and as its ideas become increasingly remote from 'common sense,' it will presumably take them longer to reach the design engineer. The industrial utilization of gravitational energy that keeps 'quasars' going will certainly require much more time than that of nuclear power." (In *Basic Research and National Goals,* p. 270.)

13. Gross, Daddario hearings, p. 139; Lenher, ibid., p. 351: Kaysen, *Basic Research and National Goals,* p. 148.

14. *Basic Research and National Goals,* pp. 89–90.

15. Senate, Comm. on Aeronautical and Space Sciences, *Hearings, Scientists' Testimony on Space Goals,* 88th Cong., 1st Sess., June, 1963, Cited hereafter as *Scientists Testimony.*

16. Elliott hearings, Part 1, p. 69.

17. Quoted in Ivan L. Bennett, Jr., "Application of Biomedical Knowledge: the White House View," in *Research in the Service of Man: Biomedical Knowledge, Development, and Use, a Conference,* Senate, Comm. on Government Operations, 90th Cong., 1st Sess., Committee Print, 1967, pp. 5–6.

18. Ibid., p. 6.

19. President's Science Advisory Committee, *Scientific Progress, the Universities, and the Federal Government* (Washington, 1960), pp. 5, 6, 9, 10, 11.

20. Presidential memo, "Strengthening Academic Capability for Science," in *Science, Technology, and Public Policy During the Eighty-Ninth Congress, A Report,* Subcomm. on Science, Research, and Development, House, Comm. on Science and Astronautics, 90th Cong., 1st Sess., Committee Print, 1967, pp. 169–170.

21. Lee A. duBridge, "University Basic Research," *Science* 157 (11 Aug. 67) 648–650.

22. George Pake, "Basic Research and Financial Crisis in the Universities," *Science* 157 (4 Aug. 67) 517–520.

23. Philip Handler, "Academic Science and the Federal Government," *Science* 157 (8 Sept. 67) 1140–1146.

24. Kenneth S. Pitzer, "How Much Research?" *Science* 157 (18 Aug. 67) 779–781. My italics.

25. L. V. Berkner, *The Scientific Age: The Impact of Science on Society* (New Haven: Yale U.P., 1964) pp. 29–30.

26. *Federal Support of Basic Research in Institutions of Higher Learning* (Washington: National Academy of Sciences, 1964) pp. 12–13.

27. *Basic Research and National Goals*, pp. 268–269.

28. *Federal R and D Programs*, Part 1, p. 57.

29. *Basic Research and National Goals*, p. 136.

30. Ibid., p. 148. See generally, pp. 148–151.

31. Ibid., pp. 55–56.

32. Ibid., p. 271.

33. *Chemistry: Opportunities and Needs, A Report on Basic Research in U.S. Chemistry* (Washington: National Academy of Sciences, 1965) p. 185.

34. Ibid., p. 6.

35. *Plant Sciences: Now and In the Coming Decade* (Washington: National Academy of Sciences, 1966) pp. 4, 7–9.

36. *Ground-Based Astronomy: A Ten-Year Program* (Washington: National Academy of Sciences, 1964) Foreword.

37. G. Feinberg in Luke C. L. Yuan (Ed.), *Nature of Matter* (Washington: Bureau of Standards, Dept. of Commerce, for the Brookhaven National Laboratory, January, 1965) p. 14.

38. Philip Abelson, in Joint Committee on Atomic Energy, *Hearings, High Energy Physics Research*, 89th Cong., 1st Sess., 1965, pp. 209–210.

39. Ibid., p. 216; *Physics: Survey and Outlook* (Washington: National Academy of Sciences, 1966) p. 55; Joint Committee on Atomic Energy, *Hearings, High Energy Physics Research*, p. 214.

40. *Ground-Based Astronomy*, pp. 10–12.

41. This view is supported by a small poll I conducted through the letters column of *Science*. When asked which of the five justifications discussed in this chapter constituted the strongest

argument for federal support, 36 votes went to utilitarian value and 33 to intellectual contribution— but 10 of the 36 said that if they were answering in intellectual rather than political terms they would have opted for the latter value.

CHAPTER 3

1. Harvey Brooks, "Future Needs for the Support of Basic Research," in *Basic Research and National Goals,* p. 99.
2. *Federal Organizaton for Scientific Activities, 1962* (Washington: NSF, 1962), NSF 62-37, pp. 2–3.
3. Donald F. Hornig, "Science and Government" in *Science in Human Affairs, Proceedings* of the Academy of Political Science, Columbia University, XXVIII (April, 1966) 64.
4. Philip Handler, "Federal Science Policy," *Science* 155 (3 March 1967) 1036-66.
5. Paraphrased from *The Office of Science and Technology, A Report* prepared by the Science Policy Research Division of the Legislative Reference Service, issued by the Military Operations Subcommittee, House Committee on Government Operations, 90th Cong., 1st Sess., Committee Print, March, 1967, p. 26. Referred to hereafter as *The Office of Science and Technology.*
6. Quoted in *The Office of Science and Technology,* p. 35. Originally from testimony of Edward Wenk, Subcommittee on Accounts, Committee on House Administration, *Hearings, Establishment of Congressional Science Advisory Staff,* 88th Cong., 1st Sess., 1963, p. 72.
7. From Hornig's testimony, Subcommittee on Independent Offices, House Committee on Appropriations, *Hearings, Independent Offices Appropriations for 1967,* 89th Cong., 2d Sess., 1966, pp. 15–18.
8. For discussion of NIH's use of panels and its general administrative arrangements see the "Wooldridge Report," *Biomedical Science and its Administration* (Washington: The White House, 1965) pp. 91–123, 191–213.
9. *Basic Research and National Goals* (1965) and *Applied Science and Technological Progress* (1967).

10. *Chemistry: Opportunities and Needs* (Washington: NAS, 1965).
11. On COSPUP, see K. Kofmehl, "COSPUP, Congress and Scientific Advice," *Journal of Politics* 28 (Feb., 1966) 100–120.
12. Alvin M. Weinberg, testimony in Research and Technical Programs Subcommittee, House Committee on Government Operations, *Hearings, The Federal Research and Development Programs: The Decisionmaking Process*, 89th Cong., 2d Sess., 1966, p. 37.
13. *Report to the President on Government Contracting for Research and Development* (commonly referred to as "The Bell Report"), April 30, 1962. Available in Sen. Doc. No. 94, 87th Cong., 2d Sess., 1962.
14. L. V. Berkner, *The Scientific Age* (New Haven: Yale U.P., 1964) pp. 75–76.
15. Ibid., p. 77.
16. William D. Carey, "Roles of the Bureau of the Budget," *Science* 156 (14 April 1967) 206–213.
17. This, and the next quotation, are from Harvey Brooks, letter to the editor of *Minerva* 3 (Spring, 1965) 392–397.
18. See ibid., p. 394, for a good brief statement of the extra-scientific qualities needed in OST staff exactly because the decisions they are concerned with are not entirely technical.
19. *Interagency Coordination in Research and Development*, Study No. VIII, House Select Committee on Government Research, House Report No. 1939, 88th Cong., 2d Sess., December 28, 1964, pp. 48–49.
20. See, for example, Senator Gordon Allott's bill (S. 1305), calling for such a committee (90th Cong., 1st Sess., 1967).
21. A good example of SPRD's work is: *The Office of Science and Technology, A Report*, Military Operations Subcommittee, House Committee on Government Operations, 90th Cong., 1st Sess., Committee Print, 1967.
22. See *Government and Science No. 3, Scientific-Technical Advice for Congress*, Staff Study, House, Subcommittee on Science, Research, and Development, Comm. on Science and Astronautics, 88th Cong., 2d Sess, Committee Print, 1964.
23. *The Office of Science and Technology*, pp. 257–259, 291–301.

24. See *16th Annual Report* of the National Science Foundation (Washington: NSF, 1967) NSF 67-1, pp. 135–136.
25. Michael Polanyi, "The Republic of Science: Its Political and Economic Theory," a lecture delivered at Roosevelt University, January 11, 1962.
26. *15th Annual Report of the National Science Foundation for Fiscal 1965,* NSF 66-1, p. xxxii.
27. Donald F. Hornig, "Science and Government," in *Science in Human Affairs,* Proceedings of the Academy of Political Science, Columbia University, XXVIII (April, 1966) 58–59.
28. Ibid., p. 66.
29. Don K. Price, *The Scientific Estate* (Cambridge, Mass.: Harvard-Belknap, 1965) pp. 132–136, 153. See generally, Ch. 5, pp. 120–162.
30. Robert C. Wood, "Scientists and Politics: The Rise of an Apolitical Elite," in Gilpin and Wright, *Scientists and National Policy-Making,* pp. 41–72.
31. Warner R. Schilling, "Scientists, Foreign Policy, and Politics," in ibid., pp. 144–173. An earlier version can be found in *American Political Science Review* LVI (June, 1962).
32. Albert Wohlstetter, "Strategy and the Natural Scientists," in ibid., pp. 174–239.
33. Ibid., pp. 299–300.

CHAPTER 4

1. Wallace S. Sayre, "Scientists and American Science Policy," *Science* 133 (24 March 1961) 859–864.
2. House, Select (Elliott) Committee on Government Research, *Study Number X,* House Report No. 1941, 88th Cong., 2d Sess., December 29, 1964, p. 8.
3. Quoted in *Science* 133 (13 March 1964) 1149–1151.
4. See John W. Gardner, "Government and the Universities," an address given before the American Council on Education, October 1, 1964. Reprinted in Michael D. Reagan (Ed.), *Politics, Economics and the General Welfare* (Chicago: Scott, Foresman, 1965) pp. 108–112.
5. See Don K. Price, *The Scientific Estate,* pp. 233–237, for three tactics of advisory strategy.

6. Ibid., p. 233.
7. James D. Carroll, "The Process Values of University Research," *Science* 158 (24 Nov. 67) 1019–1024.

CHAPTER 5

1. Testimony in Senate Committee on Appropriations, Subcommittee on Independent Offices and Department of HUD, *Hearings*, Part 1, on Fiscal Year 1968, 90th Cong., 1st Sess., 1967.
2. Harvey Brooks, "Science and the Allocation of Resources," a paper read at the annual meeting of the American Political Science Association, New York City, September 6–10, 1966. Reprinted in *American Psychologist* 22 (March, 1967) 187–201.
3. For a description of one effort, see *The Role of the Federal Council for Science and Technology, Report for 1963 and 1964* (Washington: Office of Science and Technology, 1965) pp. 18–22.
4. Ibid., p. 19.
5. Daniel S. Greenberg, *The Politics of Pure Science* (N.Y.: New American Library, 1968) p. 181.
6. Alexander H. Flax, an address given at the dedication of the Francis Bitter National Magnet Laboratory, Cambridge, Massachusetts, November 21, 1967.
7. Caryl Haskins, *Report of the President,* Carnegie Institution of Washington, 1965–66 (Washington: Carnegie Institution, 1967).
8. For the background on that memorandum, and for its initial consequences in agencies' behavior, see *Activities of the Federal Council for Science and Technology,* Report for 1965 and 1966 (Washington: Office of Science and Technology, 1967) pp. 5–6.
9. Senate, Comm. on Government Operations, Subcommittee on Government Research, *Hearings, Equitable Distribution of R&D Funds by Government Agencies,* 89th Cong., 2d Sess., 1966, p. 71.
10. Ibid., pp. 71 and 73.

11. Ibid., p. 37.
12. Ibid., p. 77.

CHAPTER 6

1.   Quoted in Fred R. Harris, "The Case for a National Social Science Foundation," *Science* 157 (4 August 1967) 507–509.
2.   Henry W. Riecken, "Government-Science Relations: The Physical and Social Sciences Compared," *American Psychologist* 22 (March, 1967) 211–218.
3.   Jeremy Bernstein, *A Comprehensible World* (New York: Random House, 1967) p. 194.
4.   Testimony in House, Comm. on Science and Astronautics, Subcomm. on Science, Research, and Development, *Hearings, Government and Science, Review of the National Science Foundation,* 89th Cong., 1st Sess., 1965, pp. 665–666.
5.   Testimony in House, Comm. on Government Operations, Research and Technical Programs Subcommittee, *The Use of Social Research in Federal Domestic Programs,* Staff Study, 90th Cong., 1st Sess., Committee Print, 1967, Part IV, p. 23. Hereafter cited as *Use of Social Research.*
6.   In ibid., Part IV, p. 56.
7.   In ibid., Part IV, pp. 57–58.
8.   In ibid., Part IV, p. 119.
9.   In ibid., Part IV, p. 3.
10. The views reported in this paragraph are found in ibid., Part IV, pp. 26–27, 31, 32, 35 and 50.
11. Quoted in ibid., Part IV, p. 97.
12. Quoted in ibid., Part I, p. 196.
13. See Kingsley Davis's address, "The Perilous Promise of Behavioral Science," as printed in Senate, Comm. on Government Operations, Subcomm. on Government Research, *Research in the Service of Man, A Conference,* 90th Cong., 1st Sess., 1967, pp. 23–32.
14. The primary congressional materials referred to are *Use of Social Research,* previously cited; the Senate (Harris) Subcommittee on Government Research, Comm. on Government Operations, *Federal Support of International Social Science Research;* and the same subcommittee's *Hearings, National*

Foundation for Social Sciences, 90th Cong., 1st Sess., 1967. Cited hereafter as *NFSS Hearings.*

15. *Use of Social Research,* Part III, pp. 8–215.
16. *Use of Social Research,* Part IV, pp. 1–60.
17. *Use of Social Research,* Part III, pp. 98–99.
18. *Use of Social Research,* Part IV, p. 50.
19. Ibid., Part III, p. 183.
20. Herbert A. Simon, in *Use of Social Research,* Part III, p. 193.
21. Philip Handler, in *Use of Social Research,* Part IV, pp. 34–35. See also p. 30.
22. Ibid., pp. 60 (Wiesner) and 46 (Ramo).
23. On a Council of Human Resource Advisers, see Brayfield's testimony in *Use of Social Research,* Part III, p. 47.
24. *Use of Social Research,* Part IV, pp. 40, 27, and 56 respectively for the quotations.
25. Ibid., p. 31.
26. Ibid., p. 25.
27. Ibid., p. 35.
28. Ibid., pp. 38–39.
29. William R. Hewlett, ibid., p. 35. See also Pake, pp. 42–43.
30. H. W. Bode, in ibid., p. 25.
31. K. S. Pitzer, in ibid., p. 46.
32. Sidney D. Drell, in ibid., p. 31.
33. Testimony of Austin Ranney in *NFSS Hearings,* Part 3, p. 658.
34. Ibid., Part 3, p. 797.
35. Ibid., Part 2, p. 263.
36. Ibid., Part 3, p. 662.
37. Ibid., Part 3, p. 620.
38. Testimony in *Use of Social Research,* Part III, p. 63. See similar statements on pp. 81, 102, 104, and 155.
39. In *Federal Support of International Social Science Research,* pp. 249–250.
40. *NFSS Hearings,* Part 3, p. 783.
41. Favoring pluralism, see ibid., Part 3, pp. 703 (Baumol) and 733 (Likert).
42. *Federal Support of International Social Science Research,* p. 214.
43. "Project Camelot: An Autopsy," *The Public Interest,* No. 5 (Fall, 1966) 61.

44. *NFSS Hearings,* Part I, pp. 72, 77.
45. *Use of Social Research,* Part III, p. 201.
46. *NFSS Hearings,* Part 2, pp. 394–395.
47. Ibid., Part 3, p. 645.
48. *Use of Social Research,* Part III, p. 191.
49. *NFSS Hearings,* Part 1, p. 100.
50. *Use of Social Research,* Part III, p. 213.
51. *NFSS Hearings,* Part 1, p. 89.
52. *Ibid.,* Part 2, pp. 272–273.
53. On February 1, 1968, NSF appointed a Special Commission on the Social Sciences to advise on the institutional mechanisms and agency programs needed to maximize the effective development and utilization of the social sciences. It would appear that because of the challenge inherent in Senator Harris's bill to create a National Foundation for the Social Science, NSF is now going to make an effort to strengthen its own programs in this area.

CHAPTER 7

1. Eric A. Walker, "National Science Board; Its Place in National Policy," *Science* 156 (28 April 1967) 474–477.
2. See House, Subcommittee on Science, Research, and Development, Committee on Science and Astronautics, *Hearings, Government and Science: Review of the National Science Foundation,* Vol. I, 89th Cong., 1st Sess., 1965, pp. 90–91.
3. The veto message is reproduced in James L. Penick, Jr., et al. (Eds.), *The Politics of American Science: 1939 to the Present* (Chicago: Rand-McNally, 1965) pp. 87–89.
4. *Second Annual Report of the National Science Foundation, 1951–1952,* p. 4.
5. Philip Handler, "Federal Science Policy," *Science* 155 (3 March 1967) 1063–1066.
6. *First Annual Report of the National Science Foundation, 1950–1951,* p. 16.
7. The draft phrasing is quoted in Nick A. Komons, *Science and the Air Force: A History of the Air Force Office of Scientific Research* (Arlington, Va.: Office of Aerospace Research, 1966) pp. 56–57.

8. House, Subcommittee on Science, Research, and Development, Committee on Science and Astronautics, *Hearings, Government and Science: Review of the National Science Foundation,* Vol. II, 89th Cong., 1st Sess., 1965, pp. 1258, 1372.

9. House, Committee on Science and Astronautics, *Report, The National Science Foundation: Its Present and Future,* House Doc. No. 318, 89th Cong., 2d Sess., February 1, 1966, p. 1.

10. House, Subcommittee on Science, Research, and Development, Committee on Science and Astronautics, *Hearings, Government and Science: Review of the National Science Foundation,* Vol. I, 89th Cong., 1st Sess., 1965, p. 98. See also Vol. II, p. 920.

11. Testimony of Augustus B. Kinzel in ibid., pp. 402–403.

12. Ibid., p. 97.

13. Ibid., p. 152.

14. Ibid., pp. 266, 276.

15. Ibid., p. 655.

16. The writer sent an informal questionnaire on basic research policies to 15 departments and agencies. The comments made here are based on replies from twelve of them.

17. Letter from R. D. O'Neal, Asst. Secretary of the Army (R&D), to author, 19 January 1968.

18. Letter from R. A. Frosch, Asst. Secretary of the Navy (R&D), to author, 16 December 1967.

19. Letter from Erven J. Long, Director, AID Research and Instititutional Grants, to author, 13 December 1967.

20. House, Committee on Science and Astronautics, *Report, The National Science Foundation: Its Present and Future,* House Report No. 1236, 89th Cong., 2d Sess., 1966, p. xvii.

21. House, Subcommittee on Science, Research, and Development, Committee on Science and Astronautics, *Hearings, A Bill to Amend the National Science Foundation Act of 1950,* 89th Cong., 2d Sess., 1966, p. 108.

22. See Eric Walker, "National Science Board," pp. 474–477.

23. Ibid., p. 476.

24. Testimony in House, Subcommittee on Science, Research, and Development, Committee on Science and Astronautics, *Hearings, A Bill to Amend the National Science Foundation Act of 1950,* 89th Cong., 2d Sess., 1965, p. 98.

25. Ibid., p. 102.
26. House, Subcommittee on Science, Research, and Development, Committee on Science and Astronautics, *Hearings, Government and Science: Review of the National Science Foundation*, Vol. I, 89th Cong., 1st Sess., 1965, p. 663.
27. Ibid., Vol. II, p. 1235.
28. Ibid., Vol. II, p. 966.
29. House, Subcommittee on Science, Research, and Development, Committee on Science and Astronautics, *Hearings, A Bill to Amend the National Science Foundation Act of 1950,* 89th Cong., 2d Sess., 1966, p. 83.
30. Walker, "National Science Board," p. 476.
31. Handler, "Federal Science Policy," pp. 1063–1066.
32. House, Subcommittee on Science, Research, and Development, Committee on Science and Astronautics, *Hearings, A Bill to Amend the National Science Foundation Act of 1950,* 89th Cong., 2d Sess., 1966, pp. 35–36 and 65.
33. The Senate version of the Daddario amendments (S. 2598, 90th Cong., 2d Sess.) embodies such a change.

CHAPTER 8

1. Letter from Robert A. Frosch, Asst. Secretary of the Navy (R&D), to author, 16 December 1967.
2. President's Science Advisory Committee, *Scientific Progress, the Universities and the Federal Government,* (Washington: The White House, November 15, 1960), p. 11. Italics in original.

CHAPTER 9

1. House, Committee on Science and Astronautics, Subcommittee on Science, Research, and Development, Report, *Science, Technology, and Public Policy during the Eighty-Ninth Congress,* 90th Cong., 1st Sess., Committee Print, 1967.
2. House, Committee on Science and Astronautics, Subcommittee on Science, Research, and Development, Staff Study, *Government and Science No. 3, Scientific-Technical Advice for Congress,* Committee Print, 88th Cong., 2d Sess., 1964, pp. 77, 81.

3. House, Committee on Science and Astronautics, Subcommittee on Science, Research, and Development, *Hearings, Government and Science,* 88th Cong., 1st Sess., 1963, p. 170.
4. Senator Clinton P. Anderson, "Scientific Advice for Congress," *Science* 144 (3 April 1964) 29–32.
5. Senate, Committee on Government Operations, *Science and Technology Act of 1958, Analysis and Summary,* Sen. Doc. No. 90, 85th Cong., 2d Sess., 1958, pp. 2–3.
6. Hubert H. Humphrey, "The Need for a Department of Science," *Annals* of the American Academy of Political and Social Science, 327 (January, 1960) 30.
7. Senate, Committee on Government Operations, Subcommittee on Reorganization, *Hearings, Create a Department of Science and Technology,* 86th Cong., 1st Sess., 1959, Part 2, pp. 127, 129.
8. Lloyd V. Berkner, "Government Support of Scientific Research," *Science* 129 (27 March 1959) 817–821.
9. Dael Wolfle, "Government Organization of Science," *Science* 131 (13 May 1960) 1407–1417.
10. Testimony of William F. Finan, Senate, Committee on Government Organization, Subcommittee on Reorganization, *Hearings, Create a Department of Science and Technology,* 86th Cong., 1st Sess., 1959, Part 2, pp. 180–181.
11. Testimony of Alan T. Waterman, ibid., p. 124.
12. Don K. Price, "Organization of Science Here and Abroad," *Science* 129 (20 March 1959) 759–765.
13. A. Hunter Dupree in Senate, Committee on Government Operations, Subcommittee on Reorganization, *Hearings, Create a Department of Science and Technology,* 86th Cong., 1st Sess., 1959, Part 1, p. 87.
14. See House, Committee on Government Operations, Military Operations Subcommittee, *Report, The Office of Science and Technology,* 90th Cong., 1st Sess., Committee Print, 1967, pp. 35–36, 146.
15. Senate, Committee on Government Operations, Subcommittee on Reorganization, *Hearings, Science and Technology Act of 1958,* 85th Cong., 2d Sess., 1958, Part 2, pp. 306–307. Italics added.

CHAPTER 10

1. Reported in Philip M. Boffey, "American Science Policy: OECD Publishes a Massive Critique," *Science* 159 (12 January 1968) 176–178.

2. In National Academy of Sciences, *Science, Government, and the Universities* (Seattle: U. of Washington, 1966) p. 63.

3. For a generally similar viewpoint, see Stephen Toulmin, "The Complexity of Scientific Choice: A Stocktaking," *Minerva* II (Spring, 1964).

4. For a case study involving the NAS survey of chemistry, see Daniel S. Greenberg, *The Politics of Pure Science* (New York: New American Library, 1967) pp. 151–169.

5. Stephen Toulmin, "The Allocation of Federal Support for Scientific Research," unpublished paper for the National Science Foundation, April, 1965.

6. A statement prepared by NSF, printed in House, Committee on Government Operations, *Conflicts Between the Federal Research Programs and the Nation's Goals for Higher Education,* House Report No. 1158, 89th Cong., 1st Sess., 1965, p. 59.

7. For useful discussions of a number of approaches to an overall allocations formula, see *Basic Research and National Goals,* especially the essays by Brooks, Kaysen, Kistiakowsky, Verhoogen, and Weinberg.

8. In *Basic Research and National Goals,* pp. 160–161.

CHAPTER 11

1. Senate, Committee on Government Operations, Subcommittee on Intergovernmental Relations, *Hearings, Establish a Select Senate Committee on Technology and the Human Environment,* 90th Cong., 1st Sess., 1967, p. 122.

2. On major trends of values and action patterns within the scientific community, see Norman Storer, *The Social System of Science* (New York: Holt, Rinehart and Winston, 1966), and Warren Hagstrom, *The Scientific Community* (New York: Basic Books, 1965).

Glossary of Abbreviations

AEC   Atomic Energy Commission
BOB   Bureau of the Budget
CEA   Council of Economic Advisers
COSPUP   Committee on Science and Public Policy
DOD   Department of Defense
FCST   Federal Council for Science and Technology
HEW   Department of Health, Education, and Welfare
HUD   Department of Housing and Urban Development
JCAE   Joint Committee on Atomic Energy
JCST   Joint Committee on Science and Technology (hypothetical)
JEC   Joint Economic Committee
NAS   National Academy of Sciences
NACA   National Advisory Committee on Aeronautics
NASA   National Aeronautics and Space Administration
NASC   National Aeronautics and Space Council
NFAH   National Foundation on the Arts and the Humanities
NFSS   National Foundation for the Social Sciences (hypothetical)
NIH   National Institutes of Health
NSB   National Science Board
NRC   National Research Council
NSF   National Science Foundation
OE   Office of Education
OEO   Office of Economic Opportunity
ONR   Office of Naval Research
OSRD   Office of Scientific Research and Development
OST   Office of Science and Technology
PSAC   President's Science Advisory Committee
SPRD   Science Policy Research Division

Index

343